NEW EDITIONS

The Northwest's newspapers, as they were, are, and will be

Seattle Post-Intelligencer building, with the globe on top. (photo/Joe Mabel)

NEW EDITIONS

The Northwest's newspapers as they were, are, and will be

Steve Bagwell
Randy Stapilus

Ridenbaugh Press
2013

Library of Congress Cataloging in Publication Data

Steve Bagwell, Randy Stapilus.

NEW EDITIONS: The Northwest's Newspapers as they were, are, and will be

Bibliography

1. Northwest. 2. Journalism. 3. Northwest-History.

I. Bagwell, Steve. II. Stapilus, Randy. III. Title.

ISBN 978-0-945648-10-9 (softbound)

Cover design by Randy Stapilus.
Front cover photo by Yeko Photo Studio.
Back cover photo by Linda Watkins.

Ridenbaugh Press
P.O. Box 834, Carlton OR 97111
Phone (503) 852-0010
www.ridenbaugh.com

Contents

From a century-old edition of the *Washington Newspaper*:

"The good old times when it was thought that a man who had failed at all else could still keep a hotel and edit a newspaper have passed away. Editors have actually to be educated to their work and to work for their living." – Henry Watterson

Frame of reference

Before getting started, the authors have to note up front that they are not disinterested in the subject at hand.

Both have worked for a number of newspapers around the Northwest over a period of decades, and their views about newspaper journalism in the region aren't ... dispassionate.

Few people have stronger opinions about newspapers than those who have worked for them.

Here's the background.

After earning a degree in history at Stanford University, Steve Bagwell got his introduction to journalism in the graduate program at the University of Oregon. He served as a sportswriter for the *Coos Bay World*, then as a reporter and photographer for the *Springfield News*, during grad school. He also freelanced for a variety of papers, including the Seattle *Post-Intelligencer* and Spokane *Spokesman-Review*.

After three years as a reporter and photographer at *The Daily Astorian*, he moved to the Salem *Statesman Journal*. He served as a reporter, copy editor, and assistant city editor in the early years, then went on to supervise coverage of politics and government and help oversee editorial policy.

During the later half of the 1980s, he served first as city editor, then as editorial page editor, at *The Idaho Statesman* in Boise. He served as managing editor of *The Bulletin* in Bend from 1991 to 1997, then assumed his current position as managing editor of the *News-Register* in McMinnville.

On the side, he has taught journalism at Oregon State University since 1999 and Linfield College since 2000.

Randy Stapilus started newspaper writing at the University of Idaho student newspaper the *Argonaut*, and contributed some articles to the local Moscow *Idahonian* (now the *Daily News*) while there. His first full-time newspaper job was covering county, courts, and schools at the Caldwell *News-Tribune* (since merged with the Nampa *Idaho Free Press* into the current *Idaho Press Tribune* at Nampa). He also covered legislative sessions for the *Coeur d'Alene Press*.

In 1978 he joined the *Idaho State Journal* at Pocatello as political reporter and columnist, and became editorial page editor in 1983. In mid-1984 he moved to the *Idaho Statesman* as local government reporter, later becoming political editor and often working on the editorial page.

In 1990 he left newspapering but continued writing a column picked up by a number of Idaho newspapers, and in 2001 covered the Idaho Legislature for the Lewiston *Tribune*. Currently, he's again writing a column run by Idaho newspapers including the Twin Falls *Times News* and the *Idaho Press Tribune*. (He may hold the record for writing for more Idaho newspapers than any other journalist.)

From the beginning

Two centuries ago, many communities in the United States had newspapers, but none were in the Pacific Northwest territories of Washington, Oregon, and Idaho. One century ago the number of newspapers in the region might easily have topped 750. Today, depending on how you count, the number is somewhere south of a third as many.

As in most industries, the less stable publications didn't last long, or merged with stronger competitors. Most newspapers that ever have published in the Northwest lasted only a few years – no more than five. A relative handful still publish.

Still, the talk about newspapers in the new millennium has become notably dire. As we mention working on this book to people in the business, a common refrain has been: "You're not saying, let's do this before the newspapers are all gone ... are you?"

Well, no. That would be a long wait. Some newspapers in fact are in tough shape, but by no means all. Some have remained quite stable. Some even have expanded. Little noted but true: The Northwest has in this new century seen the launching of some new titles.

Change really has been the constant.

Early history — launching

The very first lasting and stable settlement in the Northwest, at what is now Astoria (founded in 1811), didn't quickly generate a newspaper. The economy wouldn't support it, since for decades after its founding Astoria was a one-shop stop, a single-company operation (under first American, then British, then American control again). Its first post office (a prerequisite for newspapering) was set up in 1847, but it was a couple more decades before a newspaper appeared there.

By then, newspapers had opened at other new settlements to the west, near Oregon City, the first permanent settlement by Euro-Americans inland in the Northwest (reaching back to 1829), and the first city west of the Rocky Mountains to be incorporated (in 1844). Four years later, it became the capital of Oregon Territory. Government, shipping, timber production, and other commerce provided an ample base for a newspaper: Subscribers and, especially, advertisers.

The first regular paper there, or anywhere west of the Missouri River, seems to have been the *Oregon Spectator*, launched in February 1846 and lasting nine years, under the slogan "Westward the Star of Empire takes its way." It was a tabloid appearing at first twice a month and later more frequently, published by a seven-man group called the Oregon Printing Association. They seem to have decided early on against aligning with either the Democratic or Whig American parties, but instead settled for advocating United States merchant interests over those of the British Hudson's Bay Company, which had a commercial presence at Oregon City. That did not mean its management was stable. The president of the group, and the paper's first editor, was William Green T'Vault, a pro-slavery Democrat and later speaker of the Oregon Territorial House, who lasted only five editions. He blamed politics for his firing by Publisher George Abernethy (who was also territorial governor, and a Whig), while others cited his poor spelling. T'Vault would eventually found another paper, in Jackson County, called the *Table Rock Sentinel*. His replacement at the *Spectator*, Henry A.G. Lee, lasted for nine editions. In the paper's nine years, it was led by eight different editor-publishers, under four different sets of owners.

As that paper became clearly pro-Whig, local Democrats moved in 1851 to found their own, the *Oregon Statesman*. When Salem took over as territorial capital two years later, the *Statesman* and its benefactors moved there too. Its descendant, the Salem *Statesman Journal*, is still in print, giving it some claim to being Oregon's oldest newspaper.

It's not quite the oldest continuously published newspaper in the Northwest, however. Months earlier, in December 1850, some of the earliest settlers of a tract of muddy land just north of Oregon City had attracted enough business to try establishing a newspaper. William Chapman, an attorney and a territorial legislator who also had made money in the California gold rush, bought a California newspaper called the *Gold Hunter*, stripped its assets, and sent them north to the new settlement of Portland. Recruiting first a business partner (Stephen Coffin) and then an editor (Thomas Jefferson Dryer, who brought a small hand press with him from the San Francisco Bay area), Chapman christened the new paper the *Weekly Oregonian*, and Coffin appears to have set the paper's Republican orientation in stone but Dryer reportedly "ran the paper as his personal fief."

As communities multiplied around the Northwest, similar patterns emerged: As soon as a small, even prospectively viable, commercial base, and a significant number of subscribers, settled anywhere, one paper appeared, quickly followed by more.

In 1850, the only Northwest newspapers were in Oregon City and neighboring Milwaukee. By 1860, Oregon had papers in Portland, Oregon City, The Dalles, Salem, Albany, Corvallis, Eugene, Roseburg, and Jacksonville. The new Washington Territory had papers that year in Olympia, Port Townsend, and Steilacoom. Idaho's first would come in 1862, at Lewiston.

The era of many papers

On the basis of sheer numbers, the late 19th century and the first decade of the 20th was a wonderland of American newspapering.

Seattle from 1880 to 1910 was home to the *Daily Bulletin, Daily Call, Daily Chronicle, Daily News, Daily Press, Daily Record, Daily Times, Post-Intelligencer, Press, Press-Times, Republican, Star, Telegraph, Times,* and the *Union Record* – to name just the general-interest and city-wide publications.

But this wasn't a phenomenon only of large cities. From 1886 to 1907, Lewiston, Idaho, had six newspapers, and nearby Grangeville was home to seven. Small, remote Salmon had six in that period. In fact, around the dawn of the 20th century, most small towns had at least two papers, if not more. That was the norm for any town large enough to support more than a couple of blocks of Main Street businesses.

These ballooning numbers happened for various related reasons. The 1880s and 1890s were a time of boom towns and rapid growth in much of the western part of the country, especially in the Northwest. Newspaper sizes and print runs were still small enough that relatively small and inexpensive presses could be used to print them, and – with the rapid growth of the timber industry, again notably in the Northwest – paper prices plunged. When they dropped to three cents per pound, and then two cents, in the 90s, the economics of newspapering improved, and the barriers to entry lowered.

These were, however, very much newspapers of another era. Most of them ran in large paper size (broadsheet), but contained only a few pages. Small-town papers often ran four to eight pages or so, larger city papers typically 12 or 16. An August 1897 copy of the Seattle *Daily Times* proudly proclaimed itself a "Sixteen page edition."

Compared to papers a century and more later, they were gray with type, not just because any dollop of color (most often used in such cases as an illustration of the United States flag on patriotic occasions) was rare and expensive, and not just because photos also were rare, but also because type was small with little white space allowed, and because advertising was scarce. Most newspaper ads, until well into the 20th century, ran only one or two columns and occupied little space. Advertising generated income for newspapers, but in those days it was a relatively small portion of a newspaper's total income.

Unlike today's newspapers, most of the revenue came from subscriptions and single-copy sales. Two approaches to newspaper finance developed in the late 19th century, one that relied mostly on subscribers, the other – the model newspapers have used since then – relying much more on advertising.

The old model involved higher subscription and single-copy prices, which often amounted to about five cents per copy. That was the single-copy price, for example, of the Klamath Falls *Evening Herald* or the *East Oregonian* in Pendleton. Subscription prices would vary according to whether delivery was by mail, by carrier, or some other approach, and by length of the subscription period. And there were other inducements. The Pendleton paper said in March 1888 that, "Patrons of the Daily or Semi-Weekly East Oregonian can freely make use of the East Oregonian library whenever they so desire. … Seventy-five cents in money or stamps will pay for the semi-weekly East Oregonian from now until after the June elections." It was available for $2 by mail. Weekly newspapers actually were sometimes as expensive or more so; the *Bohemia Nugget* (in Cottage Grove), a new weekly, in 1899 advertised subscriptions for $1.50 a year.

Late in the century, however, the nickel paper was being challenged in larger communities by the penny press. Starting with the New York *Sun* in 1833, big-city papers around the country experimented with a new approach, slashing subscription and single copy prices to drive up circulation, then charging more for advertising, and building up advertising by making the case that the big-circulation paper would reach far more people than before.

These approaches were very much business model experiments, and they didn't always work. In his Minneapolis newspapering days before coming to Seattle, publisher Alden Blethen in 1895 tried launching a one-cent-per-copy local "working class" newspaper called *The Penny Press*. It crashed. When he took over the Seattle *Daily Times*, he positioned it as a populist upstart paper priced at three cents a copy, against the more expensive establishment *Post Intelligencer*. (His newspaper hero was William Randolph Hearst, who used a similar strategy in building his newspaper chain, which–several decades later bought the P-I.)

Smaller city papers were cutting sales prices as well. The Salem *Capital Journal* advertised itself (on August 20, 1895) as the "Cheapest and best daily and weekly paper in Oregon. The $1 Weekly and one cent daily."

From the trade publication *Washington Newspaper*, in 1918:

Sixty five years have passed since the first newspaper appeared on Puget Sound. Owing to the lack of banks, exchanges, markets, bonds, money and commercial paper in general, most persons of that time had been forced upon the primitive basis of barter few outside the mills the shipping interests and the government escaping this arrangement. This state of affairs would have been enough to perplex any editor but it was augmented as far as he was concerned by the fact that the newspaper was hardly a business unless the booming of a town and the heckling of rival political parties could be called a business.

While the early editor always circulated the slogan that "it pays to advertise," the average merchant had his doubts and although he patronized he could seldom be induced to part with much hard cash for a charity ad.

Nevertheless the editor in a matter of fact way announced that his paper was $5 or so a year by mail or taken at the office and his advertisements $5 or so for three insertions of 12 lines yet he knew as did his public that the dollar sign was a mere blind. He must make such individual arrangements as he could.

The basis of the editor's success lay in his ability to barter. As long as he could get his living from those who would part with no cash and save the cash from those who would he was able to survive, perchance to grow rich. The ingenious editor utilized every source and kind of income to his advantage which fact in large part explains the longevity of so many ventures in a wilderness.

And how would the barter system meet approval with a newspaper's distant corporate owners? Well, there weren't any. Most newspapers in the 19th century were locally owned, as well as individually owned. There were cases of joint ownership of newspapers going back before Revolutionary days in America; in fact, Ben Franklin could, arguably, be considered founder of the first newspaper chain in the country. There were some cases of people or groups owning two papers in a single community, sometimes to put out both a morning and evening edition of a daily.

But such "chains" were small and uncommon, and the large corporate model so familiar in more recent decades didn't really start until around 1895, with the founding of the Scripps-McRae League around Ohio and Kentucky. Still, until well into the 20th century, Northwest newspapers mostly rose or fell individually. And there were a lot of them.

Consolidations

The number of newspapers in the United States reached a peak just after the turn of the 20th century at more than 2,000 daily newspapers and about 14,500 weeklies. The number has been in steady decline ever since, and the Northwest experience mirrors that.

Factors contributing to the decline have shifted and evolved over time, but most of them have been economic in nature. Especially in the early decades, newspaper production costs grew, and more money was to be made by consolidating operations. World War I, when newspaper supplies, including paper and ink, were in short supply, was a time of massive consolidation. (There was even a specific federal policy advising businesses that consolidation, not competition, was more aligned with the national interest.) But the war and federal policy weren't the impetus for consolidation. It had started before that.

In 1918, the Washington Newspaper Publishers Association trade publication, *Washington Newspaper*, analyzed the trend as it was playing out in the Evergreen State. It noted the number of one-newspaper communities in Washington (as opposed to communities with no newspaper) had increased from 164 in 1880 to 427 in 1910. That meant consolidation had already affected about 250 communities in that state alone.

The article continued:

The gain in the number of these one paper towns was proportionally much greater than in the number of papers, showing both the trend toward concentration and toward the pushing out into unoccupied territory. This trend toward concentration is shown by various tests such as the pounds of paper used, average circulation, value of products, etc. These tests all prove conclusively that the newspaper industry is being concentrated into fewer and larger establishments.

The opinion seems to be that the increased cost of getting out a paper is responsible for this movement. That more papers do not succumb and die outright, instead of being absorbed by a rival the common form of consolidation, is due to the value of the good will and subscription list. This costs much to build up and is worth something to a rival publication, so that few papers of any consequence really suspend.

As an example of what is meant here take the Chicago Herald. The Chicago Herald was established in 1881. In 1895, the Times was merged with it as the Times Herald. In 1901 the Record was consolidated with it as the Record Herald, and in 1914, the old Inter Ocean was merged with the Record Herald and we have the Herald once more.

In this country, we have been taught to fear the general tendency toward consolidation, and it has its dangers, of course. But in the case of newspapers, it has its advantages as well. The subscriber gets a bigger better newspaper for the same outlay without duplication of news. The advertisers certainly can buy as much publicity for less money as the duplication of subscribers is abolished. And last but not least, the publisher gets a better living."

Close to a century later economic considerations remain the biggest reasons behind consolidations – and how they are executed. But, as this article suggests, the concerns about loss of newspapers are not new, they're a century old.

We can see how some of those consolidations many decades ago played out at the time, because some of them were written about at length. Here's another article from the *Washington Newspaper*, in early 1918, describing the uneasy merger of two newspapers at Kent, Washington, southeast of Seattle.

Now is the time for the editor to talk with his competitor regarding purchase consolidation or some other method of eliminating one of the two newspapers In the town If the two of them cannot get together in war times they probably never will in of peace The number of weeklies in Washington Is decreasing It has been slowly smaller for several years It will get much smaller yet For comment on the change at Kent see editorial pages of this Issue of the Newspaper.

The town of Kent Wash is about 22 miles from Seattle on interurban and steam railways that run between Seattle and Tacoma. Its population is about 2,300. It is not a county seat of course. In the valley between Seattle and Tacoma are several newspapers two at Puyallup one at Sumner one at Auburn two at Renton and at Kent. Formerly there were still more. The two at Kent are the Journal and the Advertiser. The is an eight page six column paper mostly home print. Its editor is Timothy Brownhill. The Advertiser is an eight page six column paper. Its editor is AA Risedorph.

The reason this story is written is as follows. First Kent is not adequate field for two weekly newspapers and hereafter there is to but one; second, a good many other fields in Washington that are supporting two newspapers are large enough only for one, and the example set by the editors at Kent is a good example for other pairs of competitors to consider.

Even if Seattle were not 16 miles distant on one side and Tacoma 31 miles away on the other and even if there were no weeklies in towns in the valley Kent would still be a smallish field for two papers. There would be a substantial business there for one, but only one. A big trouble with the country weekly business in the state is that two papers are barely existing where one might prosper mightily; but certainly all Washington Newspaper readers know that.

Kent has long tried to maintain two newspapers. One has been operated 30 years and the other about eight. The income tax has never worried the various proprietors. The Journal finally purchased a linotype; the Advertiser used hand composition, outside linotype composition and plate.

A conviction finally came to Mr Brownhill "that it is the duty" to quote his own words "of the two editors in any town like Kent to try to get together as a war economy." Accordingly he made in substance the following statement to his competitor.

"The government has called upon the citizens to reduce overhead in plants and communities to cut the cost of living to strike out luxuries and unnecessary commodities and to conserve all possible resources for the war. If the Journal and the Advertiser were merged the business men of Kent would be saved $2,500 to $3,000 a year. Instead paying you fifteen cents an inch and me fifteen cents, they could pay twenty cents to one and all parties would he ahead. Kent cannot support two papers right. I'll either buy you out at so many dollars or sell to you at so many."

The two editors discussed the offer off and on for days. At first they were $2,500 apart. This great discrepancy is mentioned although perhaps it is only the business of the two editors to show how possible it is for men who are in earnest to get together. On January 22 they were $1,250 apart and two members of the faculty of the department of journalism were sent for to appraise the plants and the businesses. When they departed one of the editors had decided to make a concession that he believed would assure completion of the deal. The appraisals were accepted.

The final papers were closed early in February, Mr. Risedorph becoming owner of the Journal. His Advertiser plant, a comparatively small one, was turned over to Mr Brownhill who will move it from Kent Mr Risedorph will move to the Journal building and will publish from the Journal plant. His purchase included plant with linotype."

Of course, not all newspapers closing in that period fell into this pattern.

Here's another example, again from the *Washington Newspaper*: "Exchanges state that the *Washtucna Enterprise* has discontinued because of loss of subscribers. The loss is attributed by these exchanges to the refusal of the editor AS Honer to donate bills for a Red Cross auction or rather to an unpleasant attitude which he took toward the matter. Mr Honer has been asked to give his version of the matter to The Washington Newspaper but has not done so."

Broad-based journalism

As newspapers went through all these changes, what impact did it have on journalism?

Newspaper journalism as Americans have known it for most of the last century was very different from the century before. Through most of the 1800s (and back to Revolutionary times), most newspapers were strictly partisan organizations, explicitly backing sides and candidates much as many political blogs have done in the new millennium. They often self-identified, typically, as a Republican or Democratic newspaper, and remnants of that persist in modern newspapers. Lists of newspapers from decades back often included those partisan designations alongside a newspaper's publishing schedule and name of publisher. Some of these practices persisted well into the new century. A 1934 Idaho state almanac, for example, listed 52 Idaho newspapers as Republican, 29 as Democratic, and 27 as independent; about a half-dozen declined to list. In those circumstances, the logic of a small town with two papers becomes clearer: A reader could pick up the Democratic and the Republican views by collecting the papers identified with each.

The consolidations that began in earnest around 1900, however, changed journalism. No longer could a reporter write or an editor edit simply for a single-party audience. A newspaper whose income was dependent on advertising sold on the basis of reaching a whole community had to write and edit in a way that would reach most readers, not just a single segment of the population. The industry's shift to reliance on advertising for the bulk of a newspaper's income created the need to appeal to greater portion of the subscribers in its circulation area. Thais had many effects. One big subject of industry discussion around the dawn of the 20th century, for example, concerned department stores, which became big advertisers in newspapers, and which aimed their message primarily at women. This created the need to make newspapers more appealing, both in content and appearance, to women than they had been.

Advertising, however, wasn't the only influencing factor in the newspapers' move toward political neutrality. As daily newspapers became increasingly reliant on wire services, starting with the Associated Press (and later United Press International and others), they and the services had to write about the news in a manner that would work for a wide range of communities and interests. A new style of news writing emerged; sometimes described as "objective" (in intent at least), it was intended to be neutral – an approach not required, or expected of the earlier news-writing styles.

Purchase by chains

When the 20th century began, nearly all of the newspapers in the Northwest were owned by local business people, and nearly all were independent. When the century ended, the bulk of the dailies and most of the weeklies were owned by large media companies, in "groups" or "chains," and few remained in individual of family ownership.

It was a gradual process.

In understanding the acquisition of newspapers, a few points have to be borne in mind.

First, even today not all newspapers are group-owned. Some of the largest newspapers in the Northwest are still locally owned, generally operating as family businesses. That includes, at present, the largest newspaper in the Northwest, the *Seattle Times*, which as it has for many decades is run by the Blethen family (though about 49% of its corporation is held by the McClatchy Company). Other papers still controlled by local families include the dailies in Spokane, Eugene, Vancouver, Idaho Falls, Bend, Lewiston, Grants Pass, and Wenatchee. Quite a few weeklies are still under local ownership.

Second, many significant newspaper ownership buyouts have been intra-region. Oregon has some of the most striking examples. Elmo Smith, starting with a mimeographed weekly in Ontario, began buying other small weeklies in central Oregon in the 1940s, as well as founding papers of his own. The Forrester family of Astoria, which long has owned the *Astorian* there, took over the East Oregonian Publishing Company at Pendleton in 1973. Robert Chandler at Bend started buying other newspaper properties soon after taking over in 1953; he bought the *La Grande Observer* and *Baker City Herald* not long after that.

Third, the large national newspaper organizations which sprang up around the opening of the 20th century, such as Hearst and Pulitzer, founded as many or more papers as they bought. The tendency, up until World War I, was to just start a new publication as often as try to buy someone else's.

The story of newspaper ownership consolidation in America really starts with the Scripps family, especially founder Edward Wyllis Scripps, as cantankerous a 19th-century newspaper publisher as lived. A study of the Scripps family by author Jack Casserly, *Scripps: The Divided Dynasty*, which sometimes reads like an episode of the television show *Arrested Development*, said that, "He drank more whiskey, cavorted with more women and smoked more bad cigars than Hearst, Pulitzer, and most of their contemporaries put together. Scripps raised more business and family hell than any of the media giants in their wildest moments of rage or elation. ... Scripps got along with almost nobody. He cut off his beloved eldest son, Jim, who had served him well, and cast him adrift. He turned over his empire to his son, Robert, who had long been a idler, a drunk and inept."

The family has had divisions ever since, as pieces of the newspaper empire scattered among them. Their battles had important effects on newspapers in the Northwest. The Scripps League of Newspapers owned papers nationally, but in 1978 a group in the Northwest spun off (for reasons having much to do with Scripps family politics) into what became Pioneer Newspapers. The rest of its properties were sold in 1996 (generally, and over time) to Lee Enterprises. Another company, Scripps-Howard Newspapers (which owned the Twin Falls *Times News*), also was sold to Lee. The E.W. Scripps Company, which is different, still owns a large batch of newspapers around the country, including several in Texas, and one in the Northwest, the *Kitsap Sun* at Bremerton.

Scripps' early efforts in the region turned out to be peripheral. Like most of his contemporaries, E.W. Scripps founded more papers than he bought. Frank Luther Mott's book *American Journalism* described Scripps' method: "He would choose a city (usually of 50,000 to 100,000 in population), advance a sum of cash (usually around $25,000) and pick a man from his organization to start the paper. This man would receive a salary of $25 a week until the money was gone or the paper showed a profit; but if an operating profit was reached before the money was gone, the manager received a large block of the stock." The Scripps family became ownership partners with a number of other people in this way.

Scripps also was an early founder of United Press International, and most Scripps papers for many years used the UPI wire service rather than Associated Press.

While living in California in the early 20th century, E.W. became interested enough in the Northwest to found a string of papers there: The *Seattle Star*, the *Spokane Press*, the *Tacoma Times*, the *Portland News* – all later bought out or folded.

When Scripps entered the region again after that, it did so in a more modest but long-lasting way, buying ownership interest in, or buying outright, mostly mid-sized papers in mid-sized communities. The first may have been in Pocatello. The dominant newspaper there was the *Pocatello Tribune*, founded and owned by the Ifft family. At some point in the 1940s the Scripps League of Newspapers became involved, which may have been occasioned by – but certainly happened by the time of – the *Tribune*'s buyout of the other daily in town, the *Pocatello Post*. The new paper, renamed the *Idaho State Journal* (still its name today), was reported as owned by G. Nicholas Ifft, his sister Catherine Kirchhof, and the Scripps League of Newspapers. Over time the owning company became known as Scripps-Ifft Newspapers, which also bought several small papers in Montana, Oregon, and Minnesota.

In 1954 Scripps returned to Idaho, this time to buy a paper outright: The Nampa *Idaho Free Press*. That was followed by the purchase of the Caldwell *News-Tribune* two years later. (Those two papers later merged.) In 1963, Scripps League bought the *Klamath Falls Herald and News*. These papers, and eventually Pocatello's, were among those in the group spun off by Scripps into Seattle-based Pioneer Newspapers, still mainly run by Scripps interests, and one of the major newspaper organizations in the Northwest.

The Scripps activities were no doubt noticed by the industry observers, but the regional thunderclap came in December 1950 when the S.I. Newhouse group bought the Portland *Oregonian* for $5.6 million, reported as the largest purchase price up to then for a single newspaper. It also would buy the *Oregonian*'s Portland rival, the *Oregon Journal*, in 1961, and later merge the papers.

The University of Oregon's newspaper history web page (by Richard Heinzkill) recounts that, "The sale of the *Oregonian* (Portland) to S.I. Newhouse in 1950 was a significant event in American journalism. Up until that time the Newhouse Group had concentrated on acquiring newspapers on the East Coast and several in the Midwest. The jump to the West Coast launched the Newhouse Group on a series of acquisitions throughout the country, until today they are one of the largest media owners in the United States."

Sales to national companies continued and accelerated in the 1960s. The Boise *Idaho Statesman*, owned by the local Cobb family for most of a century, was sold to the small Federated Newspapers organization of Michigan in 1963. Federated quickly developed an appetite for the Northwest, buying the *Bellingham Herald* and the *Olympian* at Olympia in 1967. Federated in turn was swallowed by Gannett Company in 1971.

Lee Newspapers, which later would own many of the Scripps papers, bought the *Corvallis Gazette Times* in 1969 and the neighboring *Albany Democrat Herald* soon after.

The wires

In the newsroom of any daily newspaper one of the obvious centerpieces of daily effort is the wire.

The first newspaper wire service in the United States was the New York Associated Press, started during the Mexican War by five New York newspapers wanting to share the cost of war coverage. Other regional wire services developed over time, and the modern AP got its real start in Chicago during the Civil War; it later moved to New York, and its reach became international by 1900.

Despite its origins the AP, which is a not for profit cooperative rather than a for-profit company, developed a practice of serving just one newspaper per community, and a local paper with an AP link had a valuable commodity and a significant sales point – one often mentioned in promotions – over in-town rivals.

Those rivals developed their own answer to the problem: Alternative wire services. The for-profit United Press (later United Press International), founded in 1907 by E.W. Scripps, was the largest of these, competing closely with the AP in many places, and at times serving more broadcast clients than the AP. More limited wire services based around newspapers or newspaper groups, like the *New York Times* and the Gannett Company bureaus, also became available by the mid-20th century.

Daily newspapers interacted with the wire services in several ways. First, they would take the never-ending stream of news items from the services and use them to provide national and international, and often regional, news coverage.

Second, and especially at the AP, member papers were required to contribute to the service as well, sending to the wire service any local articles which might be of broader interest. These copies of local stories (by the 80s called "electronic carbons," after carbon paper) might run regionally or, if they caught enough attention, internationally.

The use of the wire services led to a standardization of news style. The AP (and UPI) had and have specific writing and editing styles, designed for use by newspapers anywhere (at least in the United States). Because their product was so widely used across the pages of local newspapers, they also influenced how local newspaper stories were written – a style usually intended to match up, partly also because "electronic carbons" sent elsewhere would be used only if they also generally comported to AP standards.

That's one reason American daily newspapers, for most of a century, have been written to a single broad-based standard. The style, approach, and standards of AP and UPI generally were a close match.

Dailies in the Northwest were deeply split between the services. Some of the larger papers (at Seattle, Portland, Spokane, and Boise) occasionally used both AP and UPI, pitting the local offices against each other, though because the news reports usually covered similar subject matter, not many papers did this for long.

Expansion times

With hindsight, much of the later 20th century was a good time for newspapers. The 70s were a period when books and movies like "All the President's Men" (which was both) contributed to a more favorable public view of newspapers. But so did much of the work of newspapers themselves. Investigative reporting became more widely practiced – even expected – in the 70s than before; news staffs also tended to increase, and papers drew more attention to their efforts at investigative journalism.

Business was good too. For many papers, print circulation reached all-time highs during that period. Newspapers became increasingly profitable, and financial leaders began to take notice. Before the 1980s, newspapers were widely regarded as stable but unexciting financial investments. Come the 80s, they became an increasingly hot property. The activities of Gannett's long-time leader, Al Neuharth, were widely noted. And among the papers the Gannett Company owned in the Northwest – which for about a quarter-century included the dailies in Boise, Salem, Olympia and Bellingham – the effects would be directly felt. The feel and style of those papers changed substantially through the 80s and 90s, moving closer to that of the corporation's national startup paper, *USA Today*.

During the 80s and 90s, the consolidation of newspapers into groups not only continued – sweeping up many of the remaining independents – but those decades also saw the merger of groups into fewer and larger organizations.

The Internet era

When commercial radio became widespread in the 1920s, and focused initially heavily on the spoken word, many people warned that newspapers' days might be numbered. Again in the 1950s and 1960s when television moved into nearly all American homes, the death of the newspaper was widely proclaimed. Neither of those developments seem to have presaged any major shift in the newspaper industry, which prospered through both.

The Internet has proven a more difficult situation. When the World Wide Web emerged in the first half of the 1990s, newspapers only gradually moved into it, and in many cases, grudgingly. There seemed to be little way to make much money from the net, and that observation has held firm ever since, as many newspapers approach two decades of maintaining their own web sites.

Newspapers have been developing a wide range of responses, as you'll see as we survey the newspapers of the three-state region.

In the region

Idaho is home to 47 paid-distribution, general-circulation newspapers, plus a free-distribution alternative paper included because of its reach and influence – *Boise Weekly*. The mix includes 11 dailies, 35 weeklies, one twice-weekly and one tri-weekly.

Six of the dailies publish seven days a week, the rest six. Twenty of the weeklies publish Wednesday, 14 Thursday and one Monday.

Six papers, all weeklies, maintain no web presence. The other 42 are split evenly between paid and unpaid sites. The paid group includes five dailies and 16 weeklies, the unpaid group six dailies and 15 weeklies.

Oregon boasts 82 paid-distribution, general-circulation newspapers, plus two major free-distribution counterparts – the Portland *Tribune* and *Willamette Week*. The roster features 16 dailies, 56 weeklies, 10 twice-weeklies and two tri-weeklies.

Seven of the dailies publish seven days a week and the rest are split between five and six. Thirty-five of the weeklies publish Wednesday, 16 Thursday and five Friday.

Eleven papers, all weeklies, lack any online presence. The other 73 run 33 paid and 40 unpaid. The paid group features 12 dailies and 21 weeklies, the unpaid group four dailies and 36 weeklies.

Washington hosts 97 paid-distribution, general circulation newspapers, plus three major free-distribution alternatives – *Seattle Weekly*, *The Stranger* (Seattle) and *Tacoma Weekly*. The complement consists of 19 dailies, 77 weeklies, three twice-weeklies and one tri-weekly.

Thirteen of the dailies publish all seven days, the rest five or six. Forty-one of the weeklies publish Wednesday, 24 Thursday, eight Friday, three Tuesday and one Monday.

Seven papers, all weeklies, have no web presence. The other 93 run 21 paid to 72 unpaid – a much more lopsided split than either Oregon or Idaho.

The paid component consists of seven dailies and 14 weeklies, the unpaid component 12 dailies and 60 weeklies. The number of weeklies maintaining unrestricted websites is greatly influenced by Sound Publishing's free-access stance.

The **Northwest** as a whole claims 226 paid-distribution, general-circulation newspapers, bolstered by six large and influential free-distribution counterparts. The tally encompasses 46 dailies, 168 weeklies, 14 twice-weeklies and four tri-weeklies.

Twenty-six of the dailies publish all seven days, 14 six days and the rest five days. Ninety-six weeklies publish Wednesday, 54 Thursday, 13 Friday, three Tuesday and two Monday.

Twenty-four papers, all weeklies, lack websites. The other 207 split 75 paid to 133 unpaid, reflecting Washington's strong tilt toward unpaid.

More dailies charge for online access than don't these days, the count running 24 to 22. However, weeklies that charge are outnumbered 110 to 51. The free-access orientation of Washington's Sound Publishing has a lot to do with that, as does that of Oregon's Pamplin Media to a somewhat lesser extent.

The groups

By company, in alphabetical order.

Country Media

Headquarters: Tillamook, Oregon
Ownership: Privately owned by Steve and Carol Hungerford, who also have significant newspaper holdings in the Midwest
Phone: 503-842-7535
URL: www.tillamookheadlightherald.com
Oregon holdings: *News-Guard*, Lincoln City; *North Coast Citizen*, Manzanita; *Chronicle*, St. Helens; *Headlight-Herald*, Tillamook

A relatively new group, Country Media was established in Tillamook County in 2000 by Steve and Carol Hungerford. It has focused on buying and running coastal weekly and twice-weekly newspapers in Oregon, though it also owns papers in Montana and the Dakotas.

Country Media had been printing its papers at a commercial plant in McMinnville, but moved its printing business to Astoria when the Forrester family purchased a used press from the Chicago *Sun Times* and installed in there to serve *The Daily Astorian*. Early in 2013, it went on to sell three of its publications to the Forresters, including the weekly *Seaside Signal*.

Before beginning to buy up papers in the Midwest, Steve Hungerford held an executive position for several years in the early 1980s with the Salem *Statesman Journal*. That gave him contacts and insights in Oregon newspapering that proved valuable when he began establishing his network of papers on the Oregon coast.

Dow Jones Local Media Group

(formerly Ottaway Newspapers Inc.)
Headquarters: Middletown, New York
Ownership: Newcastle Investment Corp., subsidiary of Fortress Investment Group
Phone: 845-341-1100
URL: www.dowjoneslmg.com
Oregon holdings: *Daily Tidings*, Ashland; *Mail Tribune*, Medford

Dow Jones Local Media is a group of eight dailies and 15 weeklies assembled largely by James Ottaway Sr., now deceased, and managed for many years by son James Ottaway Jr., now retired. The chain was once significantly larger, but has shed 13 dailies and four weeklies in recent years. The remaining papers lie mostly along the Eastern Seaboard, but include the dailies serving Medford and Ashland in Southern Oregon. The flagship is the 87,000-circulation *Times Herald Record* in upstate New York.

The elder Ottaway got his start in 1936 with purchase of the *Bulletin* in Endicott, N.Y., home of the fledgling International Business Machines Corp. The nation was still in the grip of the Great Depression, but he promptly converted it from a twice-weekly to a six-day daily. After completing his World War II service, he proceeded to add the Oneonta (N.Y.) *Star*, Salem (Mass.) *Evening News* and other papers in the Northeast. His son took over as CEO upon sale of the group to Dow Jones in 1970. He went on to become chairman of the board of the independently operated subsidiary in 1979.

In 2007, Rupert Murdoch's News Corp. purchased Dow Jones, whose principal asset was the *Wall Street Journal*, for $5 billion. Ottaway fiercely opposed the sale, feeling the British press baron would not sufficiently respect his group's standards, traditions and independence. Murdoch contracted with the New York investment bank Waller Capital in the spring of 2013 to explore sale of the group. In early September, he found a taker at a selling price of $87 million – Newcastle Investment Corp., a wholly owned subsidiary of the Fortress Investment Group.

Fortress also owns GateHouse Media, a newspaper chain based in Rochester, N.Y. GateHouse's holdings include 78 dailies in 21 states, along with 235 weeklies and 91 shoppers. GateHouse is staggering under a debt load of more than $1.2 billion, but Newcastle has bought up more than half of it, at deeply discounted rates, in preparation for reorganization under Chapter 11 bankruptcy protection. According to Fortress, it plans to bring GateHouse back out of bankruptcy and merge it with Dow Jones Local Media under the New Media banner.

Eagle Newspapers

Headquarters: Salem, Oregon
Ownership: Denny and Deanna Smith
Phone: 503-393-1774
URL: www.eaglenewspapers.com
Idaho holdings: *Idaho County Free Press*, Grangeville
Oregon holdings: *Polk County Itemizer-Observer*, Dallas; *News*, Hood River; *Chronicle*, The Dalles
Washington holdings: *Camas-Washougal Post-Record*, Camas; *Daily Sun News*, Sunnyside; *Okanogan County Chronicle*, Omak; *The Enterprise*, White Salmon

Early in 2013, Eagle sold six Oregon weeklies – the *Canby Herald*, *Madras Pioneer*, *Molalla Pioneer*, *Newberg Graphic*, *Wilsonville Spokesman*, and *Woodburn Independent* – to the Portland-based Pamplin Media Group. It followed up mid-year by selling the twice-weekly Prineville *Central Oregonian* to Pamplin as well.

However, Eagle still owns two dailies, four weeklies, a twice-weekly, nine specialty publications, four printing plants and a mailing service serving all three Northwest states. And thanks to its printing capacity, it prints a wide array of newspapers for other Northwest publishers.

Eagle continues to print all seven of the papers it sold to Pamplin, as well as Pamplin's flagship *Portland Tribune*, at a plant in Salem.

Eagle got off to an unusually humble start two generations back, in 1933, when future Oregon governor Elmo Smith and and his wife, Dorothy, borrowed $25 to start a mimeographed weekly in Ontario.

Smith later sold his Ontario operation, moved to John Day and bought the *Blue Mountain Eagle*. Then he teamed up with a partner to buy the *Madras Pioneer* and found the Blue Mountain Eagle chain. The company shortened its name to Eagle some years later, after selling its namesake paper.

Under the leadership of son Denny, who served five terms in Congress (representing Oregon's second congressional district) before opting to devote his full attention to the family firm, the company went on to amass a stable of 25 publications in the Northwest and develop a major commercial printing operation in Salem.

Eagle has become a major contract printer for private businesses and public agencies in the Northwest, offering a wide variety of web offset printing services.

EO Media Group

(formerly East Oregonian Publishing Company)
Headquarters: Salem, Oregon
Ownership: Privately owned by the Forrester family
Phone: 503-364-4431
URL: www.eomediagroup.org
Oregon holdings: *Daily Astorian*, Astoria; *Gazette*, Cannon Beach; *Wallowa Chieftain*, Enterprise; *Blue Mountain Eagle*, John Day; *Herald*, Hermiston; *East Oregonian*, Pendleton; *Capital Press*, Salem; *Signal*, Seaside
Washington holdings: *Chinook Observer*, Long Beach

Astoria is the oldest continuously existing community on the West Coast of the United States, and the newspaper there is among Oregon's oldest. Founded in 1873 by DeWitt Clinton Ireland as the *Tri-Weekly Astorian* (it became a daily within the year), it went through a series of owners and name changes in the next few decades. But has been controlled by the Aldrich-Forrester family for more than 80 years.

The family, which came into ownership of the East Oregonian Publishing Company in 1908, used that as the corporate mantle for all of its holdings for several decades. After undergoing a burst of expansion in recent years, however, it opted in early 2013 to change its name to the EO Media Group. The new name is designed to better reflect the diversity of its holdings.

One of its major publications is the Salem-based *Capital Press*. While it is very much a news publication, it is not a general-circulation newspaper, but a specialty publication that tracks agricultural news in a five-state region.

Except for the *Cannon Beach Gazette*, recently picked up from Country Media in a package deal with the *Seaside Signal*, all of the rest of the company's papers are paid-distribution, general-interest weeklies.

The Forresters got their start with newspaper holdings inherited from the Aldrich family after J.W. "Bud" Forrester married Eleanor Aldrich. The company is now being run by Bud's sons, Mike and Steve. They recently installed a used press from the Chicago *Sun Times* in Astoria. They use it to print *The Daily Astorian*, the *Chinook Observer*, the coastal papers in Steve Hungerford's Country Media group, and the *Seaside Signal* and *Cannon Beach Gazette*, which they acquired from Hungerford in early 2013.

They contract with *The Oregonian* for the printing of their Salem-based ag weekly. They print their group of Eastern Oregon papers on the *East Oregonian* press in Pendleton.

Gannett Co. Inc.

Headquarters: McLean, Virginia
Ownership: Publicly traded (GCI)
Phone: 703-854-6000
URL: www.gannett.com
Oregon holdings: *Statesman Journal*, Salem; *Appeal Tribune*, Silverton; *Mail*, Stayton

A couple of decades back the national Gannett newspaper chain cast a much larger shadow in the Northwest. At the time, it's coast-to-coast roster of more than 100 daily newspapers included the dailies serving all three state capitals – Boise, Olympia, and Salem.

Gannett remains the nation's largest newspaper chain by most measures. However, it traded the bulk of its Northwest holdings to Knight-Ridder for other assets. In the region, that left it with only the Salem *Statesman Journal* and two associated weeklies, serving neighboring communities. McClatchy later bought out Knight-Ridder. It already had a major presence in the region, with ownerships in Tacoma and the Tri-Cities, and the Knight-Ridder purchase in 2006 expanded that presence exponentially. Virtually overnight, McClatchy effectively became king of the realm.

Gannett, best known for the national newspaper it launched in the 1980s, *USA Today*, had been printing its Oregon papers on a big Goss double-wide serving the *Statesman Journal*. It was also printing other papers there under contract, including the Forrester family's Salem-based *Capital Press*, a multi-state ag weekly.

However, it recently shut its Salem press down and diverted all of its printing business, both in-house and contract, to *The Oregonian* in Portland.

Hagadone Newspapers

Headquarters: Coeur d'Alene, Idaho
Ownership: Privately held (Duane Hagadone)
Phone: 208-667-3431
URL: www.hagadone.com
Idaho holdings: *Herald*, Bonners Ferry; *Press*, Coeur d'Alene; *Shoshone News Press*, Kellogg; *Press*, Post Falls; *Times*, Priest River; *Bonner County Daily Bee*, Sandpoint
Washington holdings: *Columbia Basin Herald*, Moses Lake

Duane Hagadone began his newspaper career at the *Coeur d'Alene Press* as a paperboy at the age of 11. He was following in the footsteps of his father, Burl. E.W. Scripps Company promoted Burl from ad director to publisher at the *North Idaho* daily in 1936 and went on to sell him a half-interest in 1946. After graduating from high school, Duane Hagadone enrolled at the University of Idaho. But he was so anxious to rejoin his father at the paper, he dropped out mid-way through his freshman year and took a job in the circulation department. When his father died in 1959, he was named publisher. At the age of at 26, he had just assumed command – and half ownership – of his first newspaper.

That was the beginning of what became a substantial accumulation. Now he owns every Idaho paper north of St. Maries, including the *Press*, along with several Montana papers, Washington's *Columbia Basin Herald*, a golf course resort, a $30 million estate in California and other interests. The city's main newspaper aside, Hagadone is a major figure in Coeur d'Alene and in northern Idaho.

Interestingly, Hagadone owns more papers these days than Scripps, which got its start in 1922. He's at 20, Scripps at 13. However, Scripps also owns 19 television stations.

Horizon Publications

Headquarters: Marion, Illinois
Ownership: Privately held
Phone: 618-993-1711
URL: www.horizonpublicationsinc.com
Idaho holdings: *Morning News*, Blackfoot
Washington holdings: *Statesman-Examiner*, Colville; *Tribune*, Deer Park

Created in 1999 by a group of Canadian investors headed by Canadian press lord Conrad Black, Horizon went on a North American buying binge that swelled its ranks to 75 papers at one point. It has far fewer now, but still claims ownership of papers in 16 U.S. states and two Canadian provinces.

In the Northwest, its holdings consist of a small daily in Idaho and two community weeklies in Washington, typical of the publications it has traditionally targeted.

In addition to paid dailies and weeklies, it publishes an array of free-distribution publications on both weekly and monthly cycles. It concentrates on markets where it is the dominant source of news and advertising, if not the sole source.

Lee Enterprises

Headquarters: Davenport, Iowa
Ownership: Publicly traded (LEE)
Phone: 563-383-2100
URL: www.lee.net
Idaho holdings: *Times-News*, Twin Falls
Oregon holdings: *Western World*, Bandon; *Democrat-Herald*, Albany; *World*, Coos Bay; *Gazette-Times*, Corvallis; *Express*, Lebanon
Washington holdings: *Daily News*, Longview

Lee was founded in 1890, in Ottumwa, Iowa, by the eponymous A.W. Lee. It likes to note the roster of midwesterners working for it at some point or another includes Mark Twain, Thornton Wilder, and Willa Cather.

For many years, Lee was a mid-sized group based around its Iowa and central Illinois home base. But it acquired a major western operations in 1959 with the purchase from the Anaconda copper company of a string of Montana dailies – at Billings, Butte, Helena, Missoula, and Hamilton, missing among the state's larger communities only Great Falls.

Lee picked up Oregon's daily *Corvallis Gazette-Times* in 1969, and later added a group of Oregon papers headed by the daily *Albany Democrat-Herald*. These had been assembled by second-generation family newspaperman Glenn Jackson, then sold to Capital Cities Communications. Cap Cities swallowed ABC in 1985, the Walt Disney Company swallowed Cap Cities-ABC in 1996 and Disney sold the papers to Lee in 1998.

The big 1998 buy was the first in a series by Lee. The one most noteworthy in the Northwest was its 2002 acquisition of Howard Publications, whose stable of 16 papers included Idaho's Twin Falls *Times News* and Washington's *Longview Daily News*.

In the years following, Lee bought nearly all of the other newspapers in Idaho's Magic Valley, including those in Burley, Rupert, Shoshone, Gooding, Jerome, and Hailey. But it ultimately closed the whole bunch, opting to concentrate its resources on the *Times News*.

Lee has been, as the "Enterprises" element of its name suggests, a company diversified among various interests, not just newspapers. But it has focused more on newspapers in recent years, having sold off its television stations in 2000. It now publishes 54 daily newspapers, and a number of non-dailies, in states as far east as Pennsylvania and west as Hawaii.

McClatchy Company

Headquarters: Sacramento, California
Ownership: Publicly traded (MNI)
Phone: 916-321-1855
URL: www.mcclatchy.com
Iaho holdings: *Idaho Statesman*, Boise
Washington holdings: *Herald*, Bellingham; *Tri-City Herald*, Kennewick; *Olympian*, Olympia; *News Tribune*, Tacoma. *Herald*, Puyallup; *Peninsula Gateway*, Gig Harbor

McClatchy is the third-largest newspaper group in the country, and casts one of the largest media footprints in the Northwest.

During much of its 155 years, it was strictly a California company. Starting with the *Sacramento Bee* in 1857, it went on to add the *Fresno Bee* and *Modesto Bee*, lying to the south in California's Central Valley. The company first reached outside California when it bought Alaska's *Anchorage Daily News* in 1979. It followed in the 1980s and '90s by moving swiftly and aggressively into new territory around the country, its acquisitions including Puget Sound's Tacoma *News Tribune* in 1986.

It's biggest acquisition yet, and one of the largest in the history of newspapering, came when it paid $4 billion in cash and stock, and assumed $2 billion in debt, to acquire the national Knight-Ridder chain in 2006. McClatchy already owned the Tacoma *News Tribune* and *Tri-City Herald* by then, and the Knight-Ridder deal added three former Gannett papers from the region – *The Idaho Statesman, The Olympian,* and *The Bellingham Herald*.

However, McClatchy is still suffering from a severe case of financial indigestion from the transaction, which came just before the online boom and housing market crash destroyed newspaper economics and value. Presently, it owns and operates 30 daily newspapers, 11 in the Northwest and the rest in arcs running from northeastern Texas and eastern Kansas southeast to Florida and northeast to Pennsylvania.

Its annual revenues exceed $1 billion. Unfortunately, it is saddled with a heavy debt load and heavy operational costs on the other side of the ledger.

The company casts a large shadow in Puget Sound, with major dailies in the northernmost, southernmost and second-largest of the region's substantial cities. Its circulation in the region is competitive with that of the Seattle *Times*, and it holds a minority interest in that big metro as well, acquired in the big Knight-Ridder deal.

And, though we're not covering Alaska in this guide, we should note that McClatchy has owned the *Anchorage Daily News*, Alaska's largest newspaper, since 1979.

News Media Corporation

Headquarters: Rochelle, Illinois
Ownership: Sole proprietorship (John C. Tompkins)
Phone: 815-561-2136
URL: www.newsmediacorporation.com
Oregon holdings: *News-Times*, Newport; *Siuslaw News*, Florence; *Sentinel*, Cottage Grove; *South Lincoln County News*, Waldport

NMC owns more than 75 publications in nine states, including Oregon. Founded in 1975 by John C. Tompkins, it operates in Arizona, California, Colorado, Illinois, Nebraska, Oregon, South Dakota, West Virginia, and Wyoming. All of its papers are located in cities of less than 50,000 population.

It also owns and operates 10 printing presses, including a press in Newport, on the central Oregon Coast, where it prints its Oregon papers.

Pamplin Media Group

Headquarters: Portland, Oregon
Ownership: Privately owned by Robert Pamplin Jr.
Phone: 503-684-0360
URL: www.pamplinmedia.com
Oregon holdings: *Beaverton Valley Times*, Beaverton; *Herald*, Canby; *Review*, Clackamas; *News*, Estacada; *News-Times*, Forest Grove; *Outlook*, Gresham; *Regal Courier*, King City; *Review*, Lake Oswego; *Southwest Community Connection*, Lake Oswego; *Pioneer*, Madras; *Pioneer*, Molalla; *Graphic*, Newberg; *News*, Oregon City; *Tribune*, Portland; *Central Oregonian*, Prineville; *Post*, Sandy; *South County Spotlight*, Scappoose; *Bee*, Sellwood; *Gazette*, Sherwood; *Tigard-Tualatin Times*, Tigard; *Tidings*, West Linn; *Spokesman*, Wilsonville; *Independent*, Woodburn

A business mogul who doubles as an ordained minister, Robert Pamplin Jr. is the son of a long-time executive with the Georgia-Pacific wood products conglomerate, Robert Pamplin Sr. *Forbes* magazine pegged the elder Pamplin's fortune at $560 million in 1998. Pamplin Jr. is reputed to be the third-wealthiest man in Oregon in his own right. His holdings include Ross Island Sand & Gravel and Mount Vernon Mills in addition to a wide array of media holdings. They used to include the Nashville-based Pamplin Music, a Christian music company, as well.

He began his foray into newspapering in the 1990s, amassing a batch of suburban weeklies, many once grouped under the Community Newspapers mantle. He followed up in 2001 by launching his flagship Portland *Tribune* from scratch.

In addition to an array of community weeklies and specialty publications, Pamplin Media Group includes six radio stations. The flagship of the radio group is Portland's KPAM, whose call letters echo the corporate name.

Community Newspapers, based in Tigard, is now operated as a division of the Pamplin Media Group. It includes 25 newspapers, all but two within an hour's drive of downtown Portland. Together, they cover Portland and its suburbs like a blanket.

Like Sound, its closest counterpart, Pamplin publishes mostly weekly, general-interest newspapers on a paid or voluntary paid basis. And like Sound, it publishes a few papers on a strictly free-distribution basis and/or a less-frequent cycle.

Pamplin founded the *Tribune* as a twice-weekly. The intent was apparently to challenge the *Oregonian* head-on. However, the paper debuted in a weak advertising environment and increasingly competitive news environment, with electronic sources cutting deeply into historic print dominance. Over time, the company reduced its staffing and frequency. Unlike most of Pamplin's Portland-area weeklies, and twice-weekly in Gresham, where many of its papers are printed, the *Tribune* is a free-distribution publication.

None of the Pamplin papers is home-delivered. Distribution is mainly accomplished through the USPS and secondarily through newsracks, the latter being a particularly important component for the *Tribune*.

Eagle Newspapers prints the *Tribune* and seven of Pamplin's weeklies at a large, modern, and well-equipped commercial plant in Salem. Pamplin prints the rest of its stable of papers on the *Gresham Outlook* press in eastern Multnomah County.

Early in 2013, the company launched a free-distribution, total-market paper in Hillsboro to to compete with the paid-circulation, twice-weekly *Argus*. The *Hillsboro Tribune* launched as a semi-weekly, but was soon converted to a weekly. John Schrag, publisher of Pamplin's *Forest Grove News-Times*, is overseeing the Hillsboro *Tribune*'s business operations. He is being assisted by Advertising Director Harvey Berkey, formerly of the *Argus*. Schrag justified the move by saying, "Many major metropolitan dailies are still really struggling. But smaller weekly papers that have retained their community focus are doing fine. We plan to provide top-quality journalism in Hillsboro."

The *Argus* is owned by the Newhouse family's Advance Publications. Advance also owns *The Oregonian*, which allows the *Argus* to piggyback on its big brother's robust web operation.

The *Oregonian* countered almost immediately by launching the weekly, free-distribution, total-market *Forest Grove Leader* to challenge Pamplin's paid-distribution *News-Times* on its home turf. It followed up a few weeks later by announcing plans to launch free-distribution weeklies on a major scale in Beaverton and Hillsboro, modeled after the *Leader*. Among them, the three weeklies, all publishing on Wednesday, will reach 138,000 homes in Washington County, according to *The Oregonian*.

With both the Pamplin forces and *Oregonian*/Newhouse forces having very deep pockets, this has the earmarks of a classic newspaper war the likes of which Oregon hasn't seen for many decades.

Pioneer News Group (Pioneer Newspapers)

Headquarters: Seattle, Washington
Ownership: Privately held by members of the Scripps and Wood families
Phone: 206-284-4424
URL: www.pioneernewspapers.com
Idaho holdings: *Teton Valley News*, Driggs; *Messenger-Index*, Emmett; *News-Examiner*, Montpelier; *Idaho Press-Tribune*, Nampa; *Idaho State Journal*, Pocatello; *Citizen*, Preston; *Standard Journal*, Rexburg
Oregon holdings: *Herald and News*, Klamath Falls; *Lake County Examiner*, Lakeview
Washington holdings: *American*, Anacortes; *Skagit Valley Herald*, Mount Vernon; *Argus*, Burlington; *Courier Times*, Sedro-Woolley; *Daily Record*, Ellensburg; *Stanwood/Camano News*, Stanwood (minority partner)

The largest newspaper group based in the Northwest, Pioneer's holdings include daily newspapers in many of the region's mid-sized markets and one in Idaho's growing Boise metro area. It has not reached much outside the region, but it does own papers in neighboring Montana.

Pioneer was formed in 1974 by members of the Scripps family, which spent about a decade building the group into something approaching its present configuration. It has had a role in the declining numbers of printing presses at newspapers. In 2000, it set up a new press operation at Preston, Idaho, and the dailies at Pocatello and Logan, Utah, which had printed in their own buildings, now had the work done at that site about midway between them.

Not long after, the situation worked in another direction in Nampa, where the company's *Idaho Press-Tribune* began providing daily printing services for the Idaho *Statesman*.

Skagit Publishing, founded by the Wood family, has come to hold a majority interest in Pioneer. Based in Mount Vernon, it prints and manages all of Pioneer's Washington papers except the Ellensburg *Daily Record*.

Post Company

Headquarters: Idaho Falls, Idaho
Ownership: Privately held (Brady family and Employee Stock Ownership Plan)
Phone: 208-522-1800
URL: www.postregister.com (subscription-based news site; does not maintain separate corporate site)
Idaho holdings: *Messenger*, Challis; *Post Register*, Idaho Falls; *Jefferson Star*, Rigby; *Pioneer*, Shelley

For the most part, the Idaho Falls *Post Register* is the Post Company, and vice versa. But in recent years, the company has added three Eastern Idaho weeklies to its stable.

The company's flagship is the product of the 1931 merger of *The Daily Post* with the *Times-Register*. And the Brady family has been associated with it almost from the outset. Jim Brady came on board in 1933. His brother, Robb, followed in 1941. Eventually, Jim's son, Jerry, signed on as well. Robb ascended to publisher 1977. He was succeeded by Jerry in 1988.

In 1998, several members of the family cashed out interests in the company by selling to an Employee Stock Ownership Trust. However, other members retained stakes large enough to ensure continued family control.

In 2002, Jerry Brady temporarily relinquished the post of publisher to longtime general manager (and former editor) Roger Plothow, freeing him to run for governor. After losing to Dirk Kempthorne, he decided to retire, putting the paper – and company – in Plothow's hands. (Brady ran again, again unsuccessfully, for governor in 2006, and continues to write a column for the *Post Register*.)

RIM Publications

Headquarters: Bellevue, Washington
Ownership: Partnership headed by Stephan Routh
Phone: 425-247-2000
URL: www.rimpublications.com
Idaho holdings: *Kuna-Melba News*, Kuna
Washington holdings: *Dispatch*, Eatonville; *Monitor & Valley News*, Monroe; *Capitol Hill Times*, Seattle

The newest of the Northwest groups was founded primarily to exploit a new and rather novel line of business – the publication of foreclosure notices as paid legal advertising. It's public face is co-founder Stephen Routh, CEO of Northwest Trustee Services Inc., which handles foreclosure actions for mortgage-holders.

In a January 2012 article, *The Oregonian* said the company's "one-stop shopping business model has made it the largest foreclosure trustee in the region." It said: "Owning newspapers will reduce costs for Northwest Trustee's lender clients and could make foreclosures more profitable for Routh's firm. Oregon and most other states require that lenders or their trustees run a series of legal notices in the local newspaper before they auction off a foreclosed home. These legal ads, which generally cost $500-$2,000, are one of the largest expenses of the foreclosure process."

Routh's solution to controlling that cost was purchase of newspapers where foreclosure notices could be published in both printed and online form. In addition to four traditional weeklies that intersperse legals with news, holdings include the Washington and Oregon *Legal Journal* publications, which have a more limited scope, strictly commercial in nature.

If that sounds maybe a little un-journalistic, remember that newspapers have been founded for many reasons of no great nobility, including – through much of American history – serving as an adjunct to a print shop. While regional publishers have cried foul over loss of legals business to the upstarts, the greatest threats to its future appear to be a housing market turnaround and a move to put foreclosures on a judicial track with limited notice requirements.

Robinson Newspapers

Headquarters: Seattle, Washington
Ownership: Privately held by Robinson family
Phone: 206-783-1244
URL: www.robinsonnews.com
Wshington holdings: *News*, Des Moines; *News*, Federal Way; *Times*, Highline; *News*, White Center; *News-Tribune*, Ballard (Seattle); *Herald*, West Seattle (Seattle)

This string of Seattle-area weeklies got its start in the early 1950s, when Jerry Robinson, then about 30, bought the *White Center News*, a small community weekly serving an unincorporated area bumped up against southwest Seattle. Following up, he bought more papers in Federal Way, Highline, and West Seattle, and founded a paper in Des Moines. The papers, tightly connected, each cover a small slice of the area on the western and southern fringes of Seattle.

Robinson sold them to American Community Newspapers in 1989, and American sold them to the Seattle Times Company two years later. But in 1997, he came out of retirement and, in a rare move, bought them back. Now in his 90s, he has since turned day-to-day operations over to sons Ken and Tim, though he continues to write a weekly column published in all of the papers. Sons Patrick and Scott have joined the operation as well.

The company is credited with establishing the first rotary web offset publishing operation west of the Mississippi in 1956, a time when the vast majority of papers, large and small, were printed on letterpresses. It went on to become one of the biggest web press operators in the region.

Seattle Times Company

Headquarters: Seattle, Washington.
Ownership: Blethen family, 51%; and McClatchy Company, 49%
Phone: 206-464-2111
URL: www.seattletimescompany.com
Washington holdings: *Press*, Issaquah; *News*, Newcastle; *Review*, Sammamish; *Times*, Seattle; *SnoValley Star*, North Bend; *Union Bulletin*, Walla Walla; *Herald-Republic*, Yakima

The Blethen family has owned a controlling interest in the Seattle *Times* and its parent Seattle Times Company since 1896. That's the year family patriarch Alden J. Blethen bought the 3,000-circulation *Seattle Press-Times*, renamed it the *Seattle Daily Times* and embarked on an expansion campaign that would push its circulation to 70,000 by the time of his death in 1915.

Over the years, the company went on to acquire the *Walla Walla Union-Bulletin* daily in 1971, the *Yakima Herald-Republic* daily in 1991 and the Pacific Media Group weeklies in 1995.

Alden Blethen was a native of Maine, making the company's 1998 purchase of Maine's Guy Gannett Communications group something of a return to its roots. However, the $213 million purchase never proved profitable, and the Times Company sold the papers to private investors in 2009 at a substantial loss. Now operating as Maine Today Media, the group includes the *Portland Press Herald*, *Maine Sunday Telegram*, *Kennebec Journal*, *Kennebec Morning Sentinel*, and several weeklies.

The Blethen family enjoyed full ownership of the company until the stock market crash of 1929 and profligate spending by current CEO Frank Blethen's grandfather, Col. Clarance Brettun "C.B." Blethen, brought it to the brink of bankruptcy. Bernard Ridder, scion of a newspaper family that went on to team up with a like family to create the Knight-Ridder newspaper chain, came to the rescue with an infusion of $1.5 million in cash, according to a 2003 Harvard University study. In exchange, according to the study, he was awarded 49.5% of the stock. After spending decades trying unsuccessfully to wrest control of the Seattle Times Company and its crown jewel from the Blethens, Knight-

Ridder ran aground itself. The McClatchy Company picked up the pieces for $4.5 billion in 2006, and suffered no little indigestion as a result.

McClatchy professes to have no designs on its Seattle partner.

Sound Publishing

Headquarters: Everett, Washington (as of October 2013)
Ownership: Black Press, based in Canada, where it has extensive holdings
Phone: 360-394-5800
URL: www.soundpublishing.com
Wshington holdings: *Times*, Arlington; *Reporter*, Auburn; *Review*, Bainbridge Island; *Reporter*, Bellevue; *Courier-Herald*, Bonney Lake/Sumner; *Patriot*, Bremerton; *Reporter*, Bothell/Kenmore; *Whidbey Examiner and South Whidbey Record*, Coupeville; *Courier-Herald*, Enumclaw; *The Daily Herald*, Everett; *Mirror*, Federal Way; *Forum*, Forks; *Journal of the San Juans*, Friday Harbor; *Reporter*, Issaquah/Sammamish; *Reporter*, Kent; *Community News*, Kingston; *Reporter*, Kirkland; *Reporter*, Maple Valley; *Globe*, Marysville; *Reporter*, Mercer Island; *Whidbey News-Times*, Oak Harbor; *Valley Gazette-Tribune*, Okanogan; *Islands Sounder*, Orcas Island; *Peninsula Daily News*, Port Angeles; *Independent*, Port Orchard; *North Kitsap Herald*, Poulsbo; *Reporter*, Redmond; *Reporter*, Renton; *Seattle Weekly*, Seattle; *Gazette*, Sequim; *Central Kitsap Reporter*, Silverdale; *Record*, Snoqualmie Valley; *Reporter*, Tukwila; *Beachcomber*, Vashon-Maury Island; and a broad array of specialty publications, including 14 Little Nickel classified advertising publications

Sound Publishing isn't terribly well known. That's partly because its parent company is based in Canada and partly because it only publishes two dailies, one of them small and remote, the other new to its ownership. But it has a good case for the claim it makes on its website – "Washington's largest newspaper publisher."

In addition to a whole network of specialty publications – military, business, legal, ethnic, classified and so forth – Sound publishes more than 30 general-interest newspapers. That's more than any other company has in the three Northwest states combined. Together, those papers boast more than 800,000 circulation. That's more than Washington's four largest newspapers – the *Seattle Times*, *Tacoma News Tribune*, the *Spokane Spokesman-Review* and the Vancouver *Columbian* – combined.

Sound also boasts, "Today, more people read Sound Publishing's community newspapers than traditional dailies in the Pacific Northwest markets we cover." And it's true.

Sound is not a stand-alone, however. It is a division of the Black Press, based in Victoria, B.C., Canada and largely owned by Canadian newspaper mogul David Holmes Black. In addition to its network of more than 40 papers in Canada, and its Sound Publishing subsidiary in Washington, Black owns large dailies in Honolulu, Hawaii, and Akron, Ohio.

Most of Sound's community publications publish general-interest news on a paid or voluntary paid basis and weekly cycle, meeting the criteria for inclusion in this guide. A few, however, publish on a strictly free-distribution basis and/or a less-frequent cycle.

Western Communications

Headquarters: Bend, Oregon
Ownership: The eight children of the late Robert W. Chandler
Phone: 541-382-1811
URL: www.bendbulletin.com
Oregon holdings: *Herald*, Baker City; *Bulletin*, Bend; *Curry Coastal Pilot*, Brookings; *Observer*, La Grande; *Spokesman*, Redmond

Robert W. "Bob" Chandler was one of the larger-than-life figures in Oregon journalism, and a journalist by trade. He worked as a reporter for a small California weekly and for large dailies like the *San Francisco Chronicle* and the *Denver Post*, and for United Press International. When the longtime owner of the Bend *Bulletin* wanted to retire and sell, Chandler bought, having to make only a $6,000 down payment.

He served as the paper's editor and publisher for the next 43 years. In the process he bought several other papers, including a daily in La Grande and then-daily in Baker City. When he died in 1996, his youngest daughter, Betsy McCool, assumed command as chairman of the board. She has seven siblings, but only one has been actively involved in the operation and most live out of the area. The family brought in Gordon Black as publisher prior to Bob Chandler's death and he has overseen day-to-day operations since.

The company used to own two other Oregon weeklies, the *Hermiston Herald* and *Burns Times-Herald*, but sold them to other interests. It still owns a pair of small California dailies, the *Union Democrat* in Sonora publishing Monday through Friday, and *Del Norte Triplicate* in Crescent City, a tri-weekly.

Western Communications prints its Bend and Redmond papers in Bend, its LaGrande and Baker papers in LaGrande and its Crescent City and Brookings papers at a joint printing plant located between the two cities.

Idaho Newspapers

By city, in alphabetical order.

The Times   Aberdeen

Owner: Crompton Publishing
Address: 31 S. Main St., Aberdeen, ID 83210
Phone: 208-397-4440
URL: www.press-times.com (unrestricted, joint with Power County)
Established: 1912
Published: Wednesday
Market: Aberdeen-Springfield area in Bingham County
Circulation: 1,000
Publisher: Brett Crompton, press1@press-times.com
Editor: Vicki Gamble, times1@dcdi.net
Deadline: Monday

Bingham County was created in 1885. Blackfoot is the largest city and county seat; Aberdeen is much smaller, with about 2,000 people.

The first newspaper in town was the *Gazette*, a weekly established by the Aberdeen Townsite Co. and operated on its behalf by Dewitt Foster. It was initially printed in Salt Lake City, a goodly distance to the south, and later in American Falls, just up the way in Power County. As E.L. Davis recalls in historical memories published on the city website, Jasper "Jap" Toner, a man with big city reporting experience, moved to Aberdeen in 1908 and decided to start a paper. He tried and failed to acquire the *Aberdeen Gazette* name, so launched his paper in 1912 as the *Aberdeen Times*, setting up shop in a corner of the T.J. Wedel Lumber Co.

He was succeeded at the helm in 1920 by Lee Jenkins. Over the ensuing decades, the paper was published in turn by Milo Enderson, John Heer, Harry Nims, and Robert Hammes.

The Crompton family came into ownership of the neighboring *Power County Press*, based in the larger American Falls (population about 4,500), in 1959. The following year, the Cromptons acquired the *Times* of Aberdeen (population about 2,000). They have run the papers ever since as a family enterprise, but kept them distinct and separate, as they serve distinct and separate audiences despite their close proximity in southeastern Idaho.

Power County Press   American Falls

Owner: Crompton Publishing
Address: 174 Idaho St., American Falls, ID 83211
Phone: 208-226-5295
URL: www.press-times.com (unrestricted, joint with Aberdeen)
Established: 1898
Published: Wednesday
Market: Power County
Circulation: 2,000
Editor & Publisher: Brett Crompton, press1@press-times.com
Deadline: Monday

American Falls, the Power County seat of government, was named for a series of sharp drops on the Snake River that early explorers like John C. Fremont found treacherous to navigate. The falls are long gone now. Thanks to the massive American Falls Dam, erected in 1927 and replaced downstream in 1978 to avert an imminent failure, they have given way to the 56,000-acre American Falls Reservoir. In fact, the original townsite lies at the bottom of the reservoir today. In 1925, American Falls became the first town in the United States, but by no means the last, moved completely to make way for a power and irrigation project. American Falls is dominated by farm, farm supply, and food-processing industries, but its location less than half an hour west of Pocatello on Interstate 86 has begun to introduce a bedroom community component as well.

The Press was created via merger of the *American Falls Press* and *Power County Booster*. It has been run by the Crompton family since November 1959 and by Brett Crompton since July 1980. The family assumed control of the neighboring *Aberdeen Times* in 1960. It once owned papers in Gooding and Shoshone as well. The family has a long history in the printing business in southeastern Idaho and continues to print the *Idaho Mountain Express* of Ketchum and *Herald* of Buhl on a web press it owns in Burley.

Brett Compton, current head of the family company, is a 1972 graduate of American Falls High School and 1977 graduate of the Idaho State University School of Journalism. He took over as publisher of the two family papers in July 1980. In a publisher's statement, he says: "The mission of *The Power County Press* and *The Aberdeen Times* is to inform the community. Our allegiance is to the reader. Our commitment is to the truth. Our job is to question. Our ambition is to provide a forum through which this area becomes a better place to live."

Crompton said his operation seems to be adapting to the age of the Internet. "Circulation has held up pretty well," he said, "and we're starting to get a pretty good following on Facebook."

Advertiser Arco

Owner: Cammack family
Address: 146 S. Front St., Arco ID 83213
Phone: 208-527-3038
URL: Once had site at arcoadvertiser.com, but no longer maintains online presence
Established: 1909
Published: Thursday
Market: Butte and southern Custer counties
Circulation: 1,900
Publisher: Don Cammack, arcoadv@aol.com
Editor: Chuck Cammack, arcoadv@aol.com
Deadline: Noon Monday

The small, high plains community of Arco, seat of Butte County, is named for a German pioneer in radio technology (an improvement from its original moniker of Root Hog). It is best known for being the first city powered by nuclear energy, supplied by the nearby National Reactor Testing Station, later known as the Idaho National Energy Laboratory and now simply as the Idaho National Laboratory.

If you're expecting a gentrified place bristling with high-tech wonders, though, prepare for some disappointment. Despite the proximity, this town of 900-odd souls has only limited ties to the federal research site and its scientific community. Arco is a rugged little farm and ranch community. As a supplement, it gets a bit of tourist traffic from the Craters of the Moon National Monument to the west.

It is the only substantial community in about an hour's drive in any direction, barely big enough to sustain a viable economic base. Arco supports one of Idaho's smallest and most idiosyncratic general news weeklies – one founded shortly after the town.

The Advertiser was founded by a North Dakota publisher who sent a 19-year-old apprentice out west to run it. The apprentice, Clarence Bottolfsen, bought the paper and ran it until he retired in 1949. During that time, he was twice elected governor of Idaho, in 1938 and 1942.

In more recent decades, the Cammack family has owned and operated the paper. Early in 2013, 93-year-old Don Cammack was still listed as publisher, but Chuck Cammack was actually overseeing day-to-day operations.

Very much locally focused, the paper has retained the look and feel of decades past. The *Advertiser* tried running a website for a while, but felt it was draining off subscribers. When it shut the site down, the Cammacks said, circulation rebounded.

They said they might return to the web at some point, but see no reason to get in a hurry. "The whole area is just kind of quiet," Chuck Cammack said. "Real quiet."

Morning News   **Blackfoot**

Owner: Horizon Publications (Marion, Illinois)
Address: 34 N. Ash St., Blackfoot, ID 83221
Phone: 208-785-1100
URL: www.am-news.com (unrestricted, but e-edition requires subscription)
Established: 1904 (1887 in some accounts)
Published: Monday through Saturday AM
Market: Bingham County
Circulation: 4,000
Publisher: Leonard Martin, publisher@cableone.net
Editor: Bob Hudson, mnews@cableone.net

Blackfoot was one of Idaho's major communities in territorial days, but it suffered the misfortune of being situated about halfway between Pocatello and Idaho Falls, and got squeezed between the two larger marketplaces. Mainly oriented around food processing and farm supply services, Blackfoot has a significant population. However, many of its people and organizations conduct much of its business in one of the larger cities, each less than a half hour away by interstate.

The Morning News always has had some difficulty operating successfully in that environment. Its role was clearer and more distinctive during the second half of the 20th century, when the papers in Pocatello and Idaho Falls both published on the PM cycle, leaving it alone in the morning field. During those years, it heavily played up the "Morning" part of its name on its front page flag. But today, all three daily papers are distributed in the morning.

The *News* was locally owned until the early 1980s, operating for decades under the management of Drury Brown. But it has gone through a dizzying series of owners and managers since. It is currently owned by Horizon Publications, a national chain based in Illinois. Oddly, the Pocatello and Idaho Falls dailies don't seem to have ever made a very serious play for it.

The Idaho Statesman building in Boise, about 1990. (photo/Randy Stapilus)

Idaho Statesman   **Boise**

Owner: McClatchy Company
Address: 1200 N. Curtis Road, Boise, ID 83706
Phone: 208-377-6200
URL: www.idahostatesman.com (unrestricted)
Established: 1864
Published: Monday through Sunday AM
Market: Southwestern Idaho, principally Ada and Canyon counties
Circulation: 46,521 weekday, 49,461 Saturday, 68,108 Sunday (ABC)
Publisher: Mike Jung, publisher@idahostatesman.com
Editor: Vicki Gowler, vgowler@idahostatesman.com

The *Idaho Statesman* is not quite Idaho's oldest newspaper: Small weeklies in Lewiston and Idaho City preceded it. But almost from its beginnings in 1864 it has played a central role in Idaho journalism.

Boise, founded near one of the offshoots of the Oregon Trail, started as a service center for the more prosperous and heavily populated mining country to the north, around Idaho City. It was under the watch of the Fort Boise military compound, elements of which still exist. It quickly evolved into a governmental and commercial center, so that in July 1864 three men who had arrived planning to set up a rival newspaper in Idaho City, decided to launch one in unserved Boise instead.

The *Idaho Tri-Weekly Statesman* got its start in a little log cabin where Boise City Hall now sits. And for more than a century, its offices would remain within two or three blocks of that location. It was a true pioneer operation. In a description in the 1962 *Idaho Almanac*, a former employee was quoted as saying, "In getting out the paper on time, we worked nearly all night, and frequently the Boise Basin Stage would pull out ahead of us, and we would have to send Dick Reynolds to overtake it on a horse with the mail packages for the different mining camps." Reynolds and his two partners, both of which shared his last name, charged $20 a year or $1 an issue – So much for the penny press.

Judge Milton Kelly later acquired the paper from the Reynolds group. He took it daily and sold it in 1888 to the Cobb family. Calvin Cobb, who had far-flung business interests, and was active in Republican politics on both the state and national levels, served as publisher for many years. He was succeeded by his daughter, Margaret Cobb Ailshie. The Cobb family ran the operation for about 70 years in all. And during that period, it became a fixture in the Idaho business and political community.

Unlike most papers in rapidly urbanizing western locales, the *Statesman* faced only limited competition. Its most enduring challenger was the *Capitol News*, which published from 1901 to 1942. The *Statesman* leaned Republican and published in the morning, the *News* Democratic and published in the afternoon.

However, the *News* faced a major constraint: Cobb and some of his Republican allies were able to acquire a significant stake in it early on. In 1942, with newsprint scarce at the outset of World War II, it was shuttered, and Boise has been a one-daily-newspaper town since.

The Statesman was acquired by Federated Publications, a national newspaper group based in Battle Creek, Michigan, in 1963. It was one of six papers in the Federated stable. Eight years later, Gannett Co. Inc., already on its way to becoming the largest aggregator of newspapers in the country, scooped up Federated. Gannett continued to own and operate the *Statesman* until 2005, when it included the *Statesman* in a swap with Knight-Ridder for papers that better fit its holdings.

The following year, the McClatchy Company, based in Sacramento, acquired Knight-Ridder in a blockbuster $6 billion deal. And the *Statesman* has remained with McClatchy, which has extensive Northwest holdings, ever since.

The paper abandoned its strategic location in the city's downtown core, near Boise City Hall, the Ada County Courthouse and the Idaho State Capitol, in 1972. It moved out to a freeway interchange property on Boise's west side, which facilitated distribution of the paper into the far northern and eastern reaches of the state.

In the new millennium, however, the value of ready freeway access for circulation trucks began to diminish. Like other regional dailies around the country, the *Statesman* began to find distant circulation no longer paid its own way and began to pull back. As a consequence, it came to concentrate more and more on Ada and Canyon counties.

The *Statesman* is no longer printed at its Curtis Road site in Boise in any event. In 2009, it shut down its presses and began contracting with the *Idaho Press Tribune* in Nampa for printing services. The move to contract with its smaller Canyon County neighbor may have been influenced by a fire that badly damaged the *Statesman* pressroom in March 2004. The papers signed a 20-year contract. The *Statesman* goes on the press first, leaving the *Press-Tribune* the more desirable late run.

Like many dailies with a statewide reach, the *Statesman* maintained an extensive network of regional correspondents for several decades. It also manned bureaus in Nampa, Payette, Twin Falls and other strategic locations too distant to staff effectively from the home office in Boise.

The paper began to scale back in the 1980s, and ramped up its retrenchment as the economics of newspapering became ever more problematical in the age of the Internet. It began to suffer erosion in its circulation base about the same time, for the same reasons.

In 1963, its weekday circulation stood at 46,613. Over the next three decades, it rose to more than 70,000. But by 2012, it was back down below its 1963 level. It is hardly alone in that, of course. The pattern has been repeating itself all around the region and, indeed, nation. To see it playing out on an even larger level, one need look only take a look at Portland's *Oregonian*.

Weekly   Boise

Owner: Sally Freeman through Bar Bar Inc.
Address: 523 Broad St., Boise, ID 83702
Phone: 208-344-2055
URL: www.boiseweekly.com (unrestricted)
Established: 1992
Published: Wednesday
Market: Ada County
Circulation: 32,000 (free-distribution)
Owner & Publisher: Sally Freeman, publisher@boiseweekly.com
Editor: Rachael Daigle, editor@boiseweekly.com

Boise has been served by – and often entertained by – a variety of alternative newspapers through the years. The most renowned surely was the *Intermountain Observer*, created via the 1966 merger of Perry Swisher's Pocatello *Intemountain* and the *Boise Bench Observer*, which had a history in southern Boise reaching back to the 40s. Its mix of political analysis and often pungent investigative reporting was widely admired, but did not prove very profitable. It locked its doors in 1974.

The *Boise Weekly* is the most substantial alternative weekly to emerge in Idaho in the years since. Founded in 1992 by Larry Regan, and Andy and Debi Hedden-Nicely, it has been more oriented toward arts and culture than politics and government, though it has salted that with political fare, in keeping with alternative weeklies around the country.

The paper has gone through a number of owners.

The City of Roses Newspaper Company, then owner and operator of highly regarded alt weeklies in Portland (*Willamette Week*) and Santa Fe (the *Reporter*), picked it up in 2000. The honeymoon was brief. The next year, City of Roses sold it off to a local couple, Mark and Sally Barnes.

In 2007, Mark "Bingo" Barnes left both the relationship and the state, settling in Alaska. Sally reverted to her former name of Freeman and stayed on as owner and publisher.

Herald   Bonners Ferry

Owner: Hagadone Newspapers
Address: 7183 Main St., Bonners Ferry, ID 83805
Phone: 208-267-5521
URL: www.bonnersferryherald.com (unrestricted)
Established: 1891
Published: Thursday
Market: Boundary County
Circulation: 3,000
Publisher: David Keyes, dkeyes@bonnercountybee.com (with Bonner County)
Editor: Laura Roady, lroady@bonnersferryherald.com
Deadline: Monday

Bonners Ferry is the northernmost substantial community – and economic market – in Idaho, about mid-point from a pair of Canadian border crossings, each half an hour away. It was little more than a remote Kootenai River crossing point until well into the 1900s, when railroad tracks were laid and timber companies began to set up shop, intent on cutting stands of white pine.

As soon as the little town began to take root on the riverfront, it developed a pair of competing papers, the *Kootenai Valley Daily Sentinel*, a Democratic-leaning daily, and *Bonners Ferry Herald*, a Republican-leaning weekly published on Thursdays. They long predated the logging boom ushered in by the laying of rail lines. The advertising base proved unable to support a daily operation; it was the *Herald* that survived.

It was eventually acquired by Duane Hagadone and made part of his Hagadone Newspapers chain.

A series of weekly newspapers have given it a go in Bonners Ferry, trying to supplant Hagadone's *Herald*, but none have lasted more than a few years.

Herald   Buhl

Owner: Sandra Wisecaver
Address: 126 Broadway Ave. S, Buhl, ID 83316
Phone: 208-543-4335
URL: No online presence
Established: 1906
Published: Wednesday
Market: Western Twin Falls County
Circulation: 2,638
Editor, Publisher & Owner: Sandra Wisecaver, buhlherald@cableone.net
Deadline: Monday

The area around Twin Falls went from desert landscape to irrigated farmland with stunning speed, just after the advent of the 20th century. Buhl, some miles west of Twin Falls, benefited greatly from that, quickly developing into a farm supply and service center for a rich farming district. Buhl was founded in 1905, its downtown platted in 1906, and its weekly newspaper set up shop the same year.

The *Herald* originated in nearby Filer. Its owners moved it to Buhl about 18 months later, correctly sensing Buhl had a brighter future. The *Citizen Record* sprang up in Filer, but the *Herald* bought it out.

After many decades under the ownership and direction of the Bailey family, it was sold in 2005 to long-time employee Sandra Wisecaver. She focuses on happenings in Buhl, Filer, and Castleford. "It's a seven-day-a-week job if you own it," she says.

"Business is a little slower, but we have advertisements every week and people read them. It's probably because you're not going to find the stories that we print somewhere else. The daily is not going to carry the applause for somebody who's done something good in the community, or been a great volunteer," she said. "I think its important to have the kids in."

And the Internet? Like several other small and relatively remote Idaho weeklies, the *Buhl Herald* isn't online. And it has no plans to go online; you won't find a Facebook page for it.

Weekly News Journal   **Burley**

Owner: Former South Idaho Press employees led by Jay Lenkersdorfer
Address: 221 West Main St., Burley, ID 83318
Phone: 208-678-6643
URL: www.minicassia.com (unrestricted)
Established: 2008
Published: Thursday
Market: Cassia and Minidoka counties
Circulation: 2,347
Publisher: Jay Lenkersdorfer, jay@minicassia.com

Cassia County was created in 1879. Originally, the focal point of its economy was cattle ranching in its central and southern mountains. But its first substantial town and original county seat, Albion, never developed a newspaper with staying power. Repeated attempts in the 1890s all went on the rocks in short order. It managed to support a college from 1893 to 1953, but not a newspaper.

And no newspaper surfaced elsewhere in Cassia County until the magic of irrigation led Burley and Heyburn to burst forth on the northern, Cassia side of the Snake River, and Rupert and Paul to shoot up in like fashion on the southern, Minidoka side. When that did happen, Burley had a pair of newspapers vying for its favor. As was often the case in that era, one, the *Herald*, leaned Democratic, and the other, the *Bulletin*, leaned Republican. In the 1930s, the *Bulletin* was published by Henry Dworshak, who used it to help him win election first to the U.S. House and later the U.S. Senate. He served through the '40s, '50s and '60s – as a Republican, of course.

The papers eventually joined forces and went daily, first as the *Herald Bulletin* and later, as its ambitions escalated, the *South Idaho Press*.

Ownership remain rooted in Burley for decades. Then the *Press* got scooped up by New York-based Liberty Group Publishing, which acquired hundreds of small newspapers in the 1990s, but ran into financial trouble and began unloading them by the score early in the new century.

In one of Liberty's many reorganizational deals, it traded the *South Idaho Press* and several other Idaho papers to Lee Enterprises in January 2004, in exchange for papers Lee owned in Illinois and New York. Packaged with the *Press* were the *Minidoka County News* at Rupert, the *Wood River Journal* at Hailey, the *County Leader* at Gooding, the *Northside News* at Jerome and *Lincoln County Journal* at Shoshone.

Within four years, Lee, facing financial challenges that would ultimately lead it to seek bankruptcy protection, had shut them all down.

That was not the final chapter, though. A group of former *South Idaho Press* employees revived newspapering in Burley in 2008 with the launching of the *Weekly News Journal*. Its website proclaims: "Founded in 2008, the *Weekly News Journal* fills a void that was left when the *South Idaho Press* was closed by its parent corporation. Our staff includes its former publisher, advertising director and several reporters. We are Mini-Cassia's newspaper for the next 100 years."

In 2011, the *Journal* became official newspaper of record in Rupert, across the river in Minidoka County, where Lee had also closed the local paper. It displaced Lee's daily *Twin Falls Times-News*, which the city had been using for three years. That gave the *Journal* access to another lucrative stream of legal advertising. State law makes a newspaper eligible when it has published for 78 straight weeks and achieved paid circulation of at least 200. In its most recent publisher's statement, the paper reports paid circulation of 2,347.

Messenger   Challis

Owner: Post Company
Address: 310 E. Main Ave., Challis, ID 83226
Phone: 208-879-4445
URL: www.challismessenger.com (subscription required for full access)
Established: 1881
Published: Thursday
Market: Custer County
Circulation: 1,800
Editor: Anna Means, info@challismessenger.com

Perched high in the Sawtooths, Challis anchors Idaho's remote and rugged interior. From there, it takes several hours to reach any community with a population of even 5,000. From its founding in 1878 it has had only two main reasons to exist, ranching and mining.

The *Idaho Messenger* arrived in Challis' third year of existence. Published every Wednesday until recent years, when it switched to Thursday, it was Republican in orientation.

In more recent years, the paper was owned and operated by local resident Peggy Parks for decades. But in 2004, she sold it to the Post Company of Idaho Falls.

Press   **Coeur d'Alene**

Owner: Hagadone Newspapers
Address: 201 N. Second St., Coeur d'Alene, ID 83814
Phone: 208-664-8176
URL: www.cdapress.com (unrestricted, including e-edition)
Established: 1892
Published: Monday-Saturday AM, joint Sunday AM as *North Idaho Sunday*
Market: Kootenai County
Circulation: 17,303
Publisher: Jim Thompson, jthompson@cdapress.com
Editor: Mike Patrick, mpatrick@cdapress.com

The first weekly newspaper at Coeur d'Alene, which abuts the vast and natural Lake Coeur d'Alene, was the *Lake Side Leader*. Founded in 1882, it later became the *Kootenai County Leader*, then the *Coeur d'Alene Leader*.

In the 1880s, hardly anything existed on the north shore of the lake except an army post established by General William Tecumseh Sherman. There aren't many vestiges of Sherman left, but the main downtown roadway is named for him. Enjoying access to North Idaho's vast reserves of white pine, Coeur d'Alene soon came to be dominated by the timber industry. And it prospered mightily as a result.

In 1889, a second weekly emerged, the *Coeur d'Alene Times*. By the 1930s, the papers had expanded, the *Leader* into a Tuesday-Friday twice-weekly and the *Times* into the six-day *Coeur d'Alene Press*. Along the way, the *Press* came into the hands of the expansionist E.W. Scripps Company, which eventually picked up the *Leader* as well and folded it into the *Press*.

In 1936, Scripps promoted a young executive named Burl Hagadone from advertising manager to publisher. And 10 years later, it agreed to sell him a half-interest in the paper, later to become a full interest. That would have important implications for the future of Idaho newspapering, as Burl had a son, Duane, who exhibited fierce drive and ambition early on. And Duane would go on to establish a newspaper empire in the region.

Duane Hagadone got his start as a paperboy at the age of 11. Seven years later, he dropped out of the University of Idaho his freshman year to get a jump on his newspaper career. At the age of 26, he succeeded his dad as publisher, and he would soon first supervise a string of papers for Scripps, later cutting a deal to purchase them. He went on to acquire every Idaho paper north of St. Maries, and make inroads in neighboring Washington to the west and Montana to the east.

He has also become a major figure in real estate development, both downtown and along the waterfront. His showpiece is the nationally renowned Resort on the Lake.

Chronicle   Cottonwood

Owner: Wherry Publishing
Address: 503 King St., Cottonwood, ID 83522
Phone: 208-962-3851
URL: www.cottonwoodchronicle.com (unrestricted)
Established: 1917 (predecessor in 1901)
Published: Thursday
Market: Northwest Idaho County
Circulation: 800
Editor & Publisher: Greg Wherry, editor@cottonwoodchronicle.com or cotchron@qwestoffice.net
Deadline: Monday

Geographically, Idaho county is the largest in the state. So perhaps it's not surprising that it has spawned newspapers at many of its far-flung outposts, including Grangeville (the *Free Press*), Ferdinand (the *Enterprise*), Denver (the *Progress*), Elk City (the *Bugle* and the *Mining News*), Florence (the *Miner*) and Kooskia (the *Clearwater Valley Review*). Oddly, the relatively remote commercial center of Riggins has never laid claim to one.

The longest-running by far has been the *Cottonwood Chronicle*. Founded in 1917, it was the successor to an even earlier publication, the *Camas Prairie Chronicle*, founded in 1901.

The *Chronicle* is owned by Wherry Publishing. It also operates a similar sister weekly in the nearby community of Nezperce, across the line in Lewis County. The Chronicle's motto, carried proudly on its flag, is "Voice of the Camas Prairie."

Adams County Record   Council

Owner: Timothy J. Blevins
Address: 108 Illinois Ave., Council, ID 83612
Phone: 208-253-6961
URL: www.theadamscountyrecord.com (unrestricted, but no news posted)
Established: 1993 (predecessor in 1908)
Published: Thursday
Market: Adams County
Circulation: 1,100
Publisher: Lyle Sall, record@ctcweb.net

Editor: Dale Fisk, editor@theadamscountyrecord.com
Deadline: Monday

Council was founded as a farm service center just after the turn of the 20th century, and fortified for a time by the Seven Devils mining boom to the northwest. Council never managed to get much past 1,000 in population, borderline for a newspaper venture. However, it saw the launch of the *Adams County Leader* in 1908. For decades, local residents Bert and Shirley Rogers published the *Leader* every Thursday. Council's remoteness allowed it to establish just enough of an economic base to support the venture.

Improbable as it might seem, a competitor emerged in the 1980s in the form of the *Council Record*. It held its own until the 1990s, when a mill closure devastated the local economy.

In fact, both papers succumbed initially. But in 1993, they were resurrected in merged form as the *Adams County Record*, which remains locally owned.

Editor Dale Fisk, who took the reins early in 2012, said he's trying to find ways to make peace with an increasingly electronic world. While it has a website now, its main Internet presence comes via Facebook. "We have a more active Facebook face," he says.

The paper is printed a couple of hours away, on the *Owyhee Avalanche* press in Homedale.

Teton Valley News   Driggs

Owner: Pioneer Newspapers
Address: 75 N. Main St., Driggs, ID 83422
Phone: 208-354-8101
URL: www.tetonvalleynews.net (subscription required for e-edition, full access)
Established: 1909
Published: Thursday
Market: Teton County.
Circulation: 2,700
Publisher: Scott Anderson, sanderson@tetonvalleynews.net
Managing Editor: Rachael Horne, editor@tetonvalleynews.net
Deadline: Monday

Some of Idaho's earliest recorded history played out in the Teton Valley. As far back as the 1830s, before settlers started streaming West on the Oregon Trail, mountain men often rendezvoused there. Settlers began showing up from the East in the 1860s, but never in great numbers. The rugged valley, just across the majestic Teton Range from the Wyoming resort community of Jackson, remained stubbornly rural for decades. Mormon pioneers founded Driggs in the 1890s. But it wasn't until 1909 that *The Teton Valley News* debuted.

The *News* passed through a series of owners, mostly local, over the course of the ensuing decades. Among them, the paper's website lists Vern Craver and Fred and Elizabeth McCabe.

The Grand Teton News group acquired the paper in the 1990s and shepherded it into the new century. The inner circle included three Wyoming couples – Gary and Sue Stevenson, Robb and Jen Hicks, and Tom and Annie Mullen. In 1996, Seattle-based Pioneer Newspapers bought out the locals and added the *News* to its growing collection of eastern Idaho publications.

Driggs' growing role as a high-end recreational and second-home destination like Jackson has swelled the local commercial base and fostered periodic attempts to make a go of it with an alternative weekly. None has firmly established itself for very long.

Valley Times   Eagle

Owner: Valley Times LLC (Frank Thomason)
Address: P.O. Box 1790, Eagle, ID 83616
Phone: 208-407-5224 or 208-381-0160
URL: www.valleytimesidaho.com (no news is posted online, but an e-edition can be downloaded in a PDF format at no charge)
Established: August 2000
Published: Monday
Market: Suburban communities of Meridian, Eagle, and Star in western Ada County
Circulation: 3,500
Editor, Publisher & Owner: Frank Thomason, editor@valleytimesidaho.com

The *Valley Times* has been publishing in western Ada County, with an interruption, since August 2000. Based in Eagle, it also circulates around the Meridian and Star areas. Published on Mondays – unusual among weeklies in the Northwest – it is available by subscription for $38 a year to locals and $45 a year to out-of-staters; current editions are available in pdf format online. Alternatively, it can be picked up on newsstands for 50 cents a copy.

In January 13, the *Valley Times* got a competitor when the Seattle-based Pioneer News Group, which owns a string of weeklies and small dailies in Idaho, Utah and Washington, announced at a Meridian chamber meeting the launch of the weekly *Meridian Press*. Available free or bundled with the Nampa *Idaho Press-Tribune* (see that entry), it arrived with a substantial web operation and a set of mobile apps for Apple and Android phones and tablets.

According to Pioneer, it decided to enter the field after conducting a survey in which "71 percent said they would read a new publication covering just Meridian, 68 percent said they want to know more about what's happening in Meridian and 53 percent said they felt that current media does not do a very good job covering Meridian." It's too early to tell how the competition between the well-heeled Seattle firm and well-entrenched local individual will play out.

Messenger-Index   Emmett

Owner: Pioneer Newspapers
Address: 120 N. Washington St., Emmett, ID 83617
Phone: 208-365-6066
URL: www.messenger-index.com (subscription required for e-edition, full access)
Established: 1893
Published: Wednesday
Market: Gem County
Circulation: 7,500
General Manager: Tonja Hyder, thyder@messenger-index.com
Managing Editor: Diana Baird, dbaird@messenger-index.com
Deadline: 9 a.m. Monday

Emmett, half an hour's drive northwest of Boise, started as an orchard farming community. Early on, it anchored many acres of trees, producing apples and other types of orchard fruits. Later, logging and ranching emerged as well, giving it a more diversified economy. However, all three went into long, slow fades during the second half of the 20th century. In the process, Emmett began to become more and more of a bedroom community for Boise.

The *Emmett Index* and an associated printing business were founded in 1893. The *Index* faced competition from the *Examiner* from 1910 to 1925 and *Messenger* from 1934 to 1957. But it has owned the field since 1957, when it absorbed the *Messenger* and became the *Messenger-Index*.

For several decades, under then Editor and Publisher Lewis Hower, it was one of the few Idaho papers offering a relatively liberal, Democratically oriented editorial perspective. It was, during that time, also one of the larger, more successful of the state's weeklies.

The paper is currently owned by the Pioneer News Group.

While several of Idaho's weeklies don't even maintain a web presence, the *Messenger-Index* boasts a thriving home page, Facebook, and e-edition offshoots, and apps designed to deliver news content via iPhones, Droid phones and tablets.

The Courier News Fairfield

Owner: Edward Reagan via Sammac Visual Arts
Address: A113 Willow Ave. East, Fairfield, ID 83327
Phone: 208-764-3322
URL: www.couriernews.webs.com (online news limited to paid e-edition)
Established: 2012
Published: Wednesday
Market: Camas, Gooding, and Lincoln counties
Circulation: Unlisted
Publisher: Edward Reagan, news4u@gmx.com

Camas County, carved out of Blaine in 1917, only counted 1,117 residents in the 2010 census. Only 416 of them lived in Fairfield, the county seat and largest community.

Though among Idaho's smallest distinct marketplaces, Fairfield and Camas County have supported newspapers for decades. The first was the *Fairfield Sun*, which published from 1911 to 1913 before flaming out. It also published the allied *New Soldier Sun*, aimed at the enclave of Soldier, which persisted despite the snub it suffered at the hands of the railroad. The *Camas County Courier* enjoyed a much longer run, publishing from 1914 to 1968, albeit with occasional interruptions. For a couple of years early on, the community of Hill City, west of Fairfield, also supported a newspaper.

Aside from occasional manifestations of the high school paper, the *Snowshoe*, that was it. After all, there's not a lot of advertising to be had in a county barely claiming a thousand residents.

In March 2012, however, another newspaper emerged – the *Courier News*. It set out initially to cover Gooding and Lincoln counties as well, but soon narrowed its focus to Camas. It has launched a subscription-only website with the note, "I've been resisting the whole website thing for a long time, but I guess all good things must come to an end. It's very simple. No time for anything else."

The operation is based in Fairfield. It originally had some space in Gooding as well, which it shared with a food bank.

The new Idaho County Free Press building at Grangeville. (photo/Randy Stapilus)

Idaho County Free Press   Grangeville

Owner: Eagle Newspapers
Address: 900 W. Main St., Grangeville, ID 83530
Phone: 208-983-1070
URL: www.idahocountyfreepress.com (unrestricted)
Established: 1886
Published: Wednesday
Market: Idaho County
Circulation: 3,684
Publisher: Andy McNab, amcnab@idahocountyfreepress.com
Editor: David Rauzi, drauzi@idahocountyfreepress.com or freepressnews@idahocountyfreepress.com

The *Idaho County Free Press* has been the main weekly newspaper at Grangeville, making it the largest newspaper (though not the only one) in the state's largest county, consistently since its founding in 1886.

Grangeville was only then beginning to coalesce, but the paper's founding turned out to be a considerable event.

In his book *Idaho for the Curious*, Cort Conley recounted: "Aaron Parker arrived in Grangeville in 1886, packing a hand press to begin publication of the *Idaho County Free Press*. Parker was a native of England and had been a sailor for six years before he jumped ship in San Francisco and swallowed the anchor in Idaho. The first copy of the paper was auctioned for $50, and the rest of the copies of the first issue brought $5 each as collector's items. Before long, A.F. Parker had established himself as Idaho's only active volcano. In addition, he was one of the signers of the state constitution and among the first regents of the University of Idaho."

After the turn of the century, growth in Grangeville drew a tribe of other papers – the *Globe*, the *Daily Reminder*, the *News*, the *Standard*, the *Standard-News* and others. But none lasted more than a year or two.

By the 1920s, the *Free Press* stood alone in its large but lightly populated county, and has had the field to itself ever since. For many years, the *Free Press* was produced from an office on the east edge of downtown. With the turning of the millennium, it moved to newly built quarters on the west side, just across Highway 95 from town.

There have been a few other print operations here as well over the years.

For a time in the '90s, a paper called the *Grangeville Gazette* published articles on politics, regional issues and other topics. Shortly into the new millennium, local residents acquired the paper and turned it into the *Central Idaho Post*, a forum for exchanges on conservative politics on the regional and national level. Editor Dorothy Walker said the paper it has developed a steady audience, but has not yet established a web presence.

Owyhee Avalanche   Homedale

Owner: Owyhee Publishing Company
Address: 19 E. Idaho Ave., Homedale, ID 83628
Phone: 208-337-4681
URL: www.owyheepublishing.com (subscription required for e-edition, full access)
Established: 1865
Published: Wednesday
Market: Western Owyhee County and portions of southern Canyon County
Circulation: 1,600
Publisher: Joe Aman, joe@owyheeavalanche.com
Managing Editor: Jon P. Brown, jon@owyheepublishing.com
Deadline: Monday

The *Avalanche* has its roots – and a gnarly tangle they are – in the early days of mining in the Owyhee Mountains. In August 1865, it became the first daily newspaper launched in Idaho, serving the first county created in Idaho.

Like the current weekly, it was called the *Owyhee Avalanche*, a name reflecting its origins in rough and tumble mining country. It was founded in Ruby City, the original county seat. When the mining industry's local center of gravity began to shift to Silver City, another mountainous mining town, both the county seat and local paper followed.

During its silver-producing heyday – Silver City is now little more than a picturesque ghost town, getting by on tourism – a series of rival papers came and went as well. The newcomers included the *Tidal Wave, Bullion, Leader,* and *Nugget.* But when the silver played out, Silver City faded fast. In 1934, it lost its county seat status. And from then on, local newspapering was limited to the occasional special edition.

It migrated downhill, to the Snake River Valley farming towns of Homedale, Marsing, and Bruneau, along the county's northern border. These places had better staying power.

A weekly launched at Bruneau didn't last long, but a pair of stable, regularly published papers had emerged by the middle of the 20th century – the *Owyhee Nugget* in Marsing, edited and published for decades by Rodney Hawes, and the *Owyhee Chronicle* in nearby Homedale. The competition became so intense that each publisher introduced an edition designed to serve the other's home town – even though the two towns were only eight miles apart.

In 1984, Joe Aman, who intermittently had been publishing the *Chronicle* for some years, acquired both papers and united them. He dubbed the product of the merger, based at Homedale, the *Owyhee Avalanche,* and in 1985 managed to reclaim the original *Avalanche* nameplate.

The Aman family has been publishing the paper since. It focuses mainly on the western side of Owyhee County. The family also owns and operates a print shop. It not only prints its own paper there, but several others as well.

Idaho World   Idaho City

Owner: The Hart family
Address: P.O. Box 50248, Boise, ID 83705
Phone: 208-429-1606
URL: www.idahoworld.com (unrestricted, but displays only most recent front page)
Established: 1863
Published: Wednesday
Market: Boise County
Circulation: Unlisted
Publisher: Wayne Hart, editor@idahoworld.com
Editor: Theresa Hart, editor@idahoworld.com
Deadline: 5 p.m. Friday

The *Idaho World* can trace its ancestry to 1863, farther back than any other paper in southern Idaho, when Idaho City was one of the great mining boom towns of the West – a time when newspaper people were commonly active in politics, mining, and even the occasional bout of fisticuffs or gunfire. From that point, it published consistently until 1918, then fell into a long slumber, punctuated by occasional brief revivals.

Idaho City remains the seat of Boise County, which has proven one of Idaho's more problematic jurisdictions. The county is mountainous, lightly populated, and hard to navigate. It is so deeply divided that travel from the eastern Boise River basin side to the western Payette River basin side, where Horseshoe Bend, Banks, and Garden Valley are located, can be a challenging endeavor – particularly in winter. Most often, people just drive the highways outside the county and go to one side from the other by way of Boise city.

None of the Payette Basin communities on the west side has ever supported a newspaper. Idaho City has actually supported two. *The Idaho Mountaineer* was published there from 1941 to 1958. The *Mountaineer*'s demise left the county without any kind of sustained news coverage again.

That changed in 1991, when a partnership bought the rights to the *World* and revived the paper in its original quarters, or at least what remained of them. And they began covering the problematic county on a relatively ambitious scale.

Wayne and Theresa Hart, two of the partners in that purchase, still run the paper. However, they have more of a physical presence in Boise and the Boise suburb of Garden City than they do in Idaho City. It seems everything in Boise County requires an asterisk, including its local newspaper.

Post Register   Idaho Falls

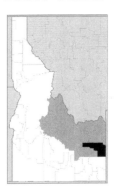

Owner: Post Company
Address: 333 Northgate Mile, Idaho Falls, ID 83401
Phone: 208-522-1800
URL: www.postregister.com (subscription required)
Established: 1880 (in Blackfoot)
Published: Tuesday through Sunday AM
Market: Eastern Idaho, Salmon-Challis south to Blackfoot
Circulation: 22,000
Editor & Publisher: Roger Plothow, rplothow@postregister.com
Managing Editor: Rob Thornberry, rthornberry@postregister.com

Center of one of two metro areas in eastern Idaho, Idaho Falls grew up around a toll bridge where the Montana Trail crossed the Snake River. It was originally known as Eagle Rock. It started out as a transportation center, a place where road, rail, and river traffic all converged. And that enabled it to eventually become a farm and ranch supply center. As the story goes, the night before Bingham County was carved out in 1885, a group of Blackfoot men bribed a clerk to replace Eagle Rock as the designated county seat with Blackfoot. And the change stuck.

Naturally, then, Idaho Falls' early newspaper history is intertwined with Blackfoot's. It begins with establishment of the *Blackfoot Register* in 1880, the year after the city acquired its name and first downtown buildings. It appears the owners soon changed their bets. By decade's end, they were publishing out of Idaho Falls.

The *Register* faced competition from the Idaho Falls *Times* until 1920, when they joined forces as the *Times-Register*. The *Times-Register* faced competition from *The Daily Post* until 1931, when another merger created the paper that endures today – the *Post Register*.

The Brady family's involvement began in 1925, when J. Robb Brady, grandfather of current company president Jerry Brady, moved out West from Kansas to purchase *The Post*. Back in the Midwest, he had co-founded Oklahoma's *Tulsa World* and gone on to publish newspapers in the Kansas communities of Galena and Salina, so he came equipped with sterling credentials. However, he died in 1926, and was succeeded as publisher by E.F. McDermott.

J. Robb's eldest son, Jim, returned to join the family business in 1933, after getting his education at the University of Notre Dame, Boston College, and Harvard University. Younger son Robb followed in 1941, after earning a degree at Notre Dame. McDermott continued to serve as publisher until his death in 1977, when Robb took over. The mantle subsequently fell to Jerry Brady.

The Post Company has been eyed with interest by other media companies, but the Bradys have spurned all suitors and kept it local. One mechanism helping ensure that was Jerry's creation of an Employee Stock Ownership Plan, in which employees got a piece of the company, but the Bradys retained operational control.

The family also boasts some substantial involvement in Idaho politics. James H. Brady, a Republican businessman from Pocatello, was elected governor in 1908 and U.S. senator in 1912. In 2002 and 2006, grandson Jerry twice ran for governor – unsuccessfully, it turned out – as a Democrat.

When he announced his first candidacy in March 2002, he turned the publisher's chair over to Roger Plothow, a former *Post Register* editor then serving as the paper's general manager, on an interim basis. Eventually, the appointment was made permanent.

Plothow has become one of the central figures in Idaho newspapering in recent years. One of his key accomplishments came when he helped organize the Newspaper Association of Idaho, bringing together daily and weekly newspaper publishers who had stubbornly resisted all such efforts previously, preferring to maintain separate organizations sometimes operating at cross-purposes. He has been active, too, in exploring avenues for newspapers to cope with their new economic environment.

The *Post Register* once published seven days a week, but has cut back to six, eliminating its Monday edition. It maintains an aggressive web operation behind a tight paywall.

Plothow describes the juxtaposition this way: "The *Post Register* is a seven-day news operation that posts regularly online all week, including Monday. Online access requires a subscription, just like the traditional print product, and that's the only way quality can be maintained."

The budget pressures are significant, as elsewhere in the industry. By 2012, the paper's newsroom was down about one-quarter from its 2006 peak, also mirroring the industry at large, where cuts have been the order of the day in recent years.

But Plothow thinks it's been overstated, at least with respect to small dailies and community weeklies. "There's a perception of gloom," he says, "and some of it is self-inflicted. We have written stories that focus first on the large newspapers, and the small handful that have gone out of business, and second on the bad news."

But he says, "The smaller you are, the more connected you are to your community, the more you're woven into your community, the more successful you are in this environment." Plothow said the Post Company has honored that connection at weeklies it has acquired in Challis, Rigby, and Shelley, leaving them to maintain their operations mostly as they have historically for a century and more, the main change being consolidation of printing and web publishing operations in Idaho Falls.

Clearwater Progress   Kamiah

Owner: The Bennett family
Address: 417 Main St., Kamiah, ID 83536
Phone: 208-935-0838
URL: www.clearwaterprogress.com (subscription required for full access)
Established: 1905 (1953 in its present incarnation)
Published: Thursday
Market: Lewis County and part of northern Idaho County
Circulation: 4,325
Co-Publishers: John and Susan Bennett, progress@clearwaterprogress.com
Editor: Ben Jorgensen, bjorgensen@clearwaterprogress.com
Deadline: Noon Monday

The Kamiah paper dates back to 1905, about the time the townsite was being established. Founder Charles Hofstetter launched it in Stites, but soon shifted his operation to Kamiah, feeling the new town's more central location might prove advantageous. It was.

During its first decade, the paper had a series of owners. And every time it got a new owner, it seemed, it also got a new location. In 1908, Hofstetter sold the paper to W.A. Dissmore, who moved it to the IOOF Hall. The next year, Dissmore sold it to local ferry operator J.M. Shaw, who set up at the corner of 6th and Main. In 1910, Dissmore bought the paper back and moved it to yet another location. In 1912, Jesse Hurley and J.M. Shaw bought the *Progress* and moved it to a building where they sold insurance, real estate, and pianos in addition to publishing a paper.

Other owners and part-owners followed in rapid succession, including Paul Blake, E.L. Grinnell, and C.H. Martin. Then Ralph Prescott came along in 1918, and stabilized the operation. According to a history posted on the paper's website, he only took three vacations in nearly a quarter of a century at the helm, missing only 10 printing runs out of 2,352. He also owned and operated the Stites *Enterprise* and Kooskia *Mountaineer* in nearby communities. When Prescott's run came to an end on June 24, 1942, so did the paper's. The subscription list was transferred to the *Nezperce Herald*, which tried to pick up the slack in local coverage. The advent of war virtually emptied the town of its male citizens, at least those of fighting age.

In his final issue, Prescott said: "All this represents a lot of work, but there has been much pleasure mixed in, for there is a fascination about newspaper making and printing in general which gives to one who loves the profession an unusual amount of job, which offsets a vast amount of grief which is bound to go along with it. We have tried at all times to hold close to the motto carried with the paper's heading, 'Always Working for Kamiah's Progress,' and believe we have hit the mark pretty much of the time. Anyway we've surely published a lot of good things about this wonderful valley, and will continue to spread the word of its beauty and resources without the help of printer's ink."

With that, the web history tells us, he retired to Florida.

Bruce Wilkinson revived the paper in December 1953 under a grander name, reflecting his larger ambitions: the *Clearwater Progress*. By then, the Stites and Kooskia papers had folded. According to the web history, he sold the newspaper and printing plant to Thomas Campbell of Lewiston in 1958. Campbell in turn sold to Larry McIntosh in 1960 and McIntosh sold in turn to Larry and Karon Schlieper in 1963. After 20 years at the helm, the Schliepers sold to John and Cloan McNall. Owners again came and went in rapid succession for a time, the paper passing in turn to Scott and Cheryl Anderson, Barney and Wilma Mowrey, Bill and Shirley Glenn and, finally, current owners John and Susan Bennett on July 1, 2001.

The *Progress* adopted a free-distribution model in 2008, but has since returned to the paid-distribution fold. It offers home delivery of the print paper for $25 to $37 a year, selling copies from stores and racks.

Shoshone News Press   Kellogg

Owner: Hagadone Newspapers
Address: 401 S. Main St., Kellogg, ID 83837
Phone: 208-752-1121.
URL: www.shoshonenewspress.com (unrestricted)
Established: Late 1800s
Published: Tuesday through Saturday AM and joint Sunday AM as *North Idaho Sunday*
Market: Shoshone County and part of neighboring Kootenai County
Circulation: 3,900
Publisher: Dan Drewry, ddrewry@hagadone.com or ddrewry@shoshonenewspress.com

The Silver Valley is not as heavily populated now as in its mining heyday, when it peaked at 23,000 or so around 1950. But it has a lot of communities, many of them incorporated, and most of these communities have clear and distinct identities. As a result, it has had a lot of newspapers.

The first four in what is now Shoshone County, and the sixth as well, all were located in Eagle City, the first mining town in the Coeur d'Alene Basin, over a pass from the Silver Valley. It was a boisterous place where Wyatt Earp once ran a saloon, but now marked by nothing more than a few obscure gravesites. Murray, a few miles up the road, had the fifth, seventh, and ninth papers in the basin. Only then did the *Wardner News* and the *Wallace Free Press* bring newspapering to the Silver Valley proper, some miles to the south.

Most of the Silver Valley communities there had papers of their own at one point or another in the ensuing years. Even trying to count them all accurately would be problematic.

But by the 1940s, only the seven-day *Kellogg Evening News*, weekly *Kellogg-Wardner News* and six-day *Wallace Press Times* remained. The Kellogg papers merged in the 1960s. However, both Wallace, the county seat, and Kellogg, the largest city, retained dailies up to the 1980s – when the Silver Valley mining economy, and its population, crashed.

Duane Hagadone, who had owned the *Press Times*, in 1985 picked up the *Kellogg Evening News* as well and merged it with the *Press Times* to create the daily *Shoshone News Press*, based in Kellogg.

Like the other Hagadone papers in the North Idaho Panhandle, the *News Press*' operations are closely coordinated with those of his flagship paper in Coeur d'Alene. The papers share both look and content.

Wayne Kinney, now living at Bend, Oregon, recalled his days in Silver Valley journalism in the 80s. Here's his recollection.

I was editor of the *Kellogg Evening News* in early 1985 when I started hearing rumors that Harry Magnuson, the owner of the *North Idaho Press* in Wallace, was going to buy our paper.

The KEN and the NIP had a fierce rivalry. The KEN was the older paper, had better circulation, and was doing better financially. The NIP was losing money. It was seen by some as Magnuson's hobby, and there were areas of Shoshone County where it wasn't welcome. It was an anti-labor paper in an area that was heavily unionized, and Magnuson was not a popular fellow.

There wasn't room for two daily newspapers in a county that was then 19,000 people and dropping, but we slugged along anyway. But we were upset with the idea of Magnuson buying the KEN. If it hadn't been for his deep pockets, the NIP would have folded long ago.

We had been asking the owners of the KEN, Gary and Cricket Corbeill, for an explanation. For a while, they wouldn't talk, but in February of 1985, they called an employee meeting and announced that Magnuson had an option to buy the KEN for $1 million. The Corbeills said they didn't expect Magnuson would want to pay that much, and that he would not follow through.

I wasn't sure. For one thing, the NIP editor had twice talked to me about coming over to work there. For another, the Corbeills seemed to be tired of running a newspaper. Actually, we were all tired – it was a very stressful time. There was lots of yelling, a good deal of it by me.

One of the members of the staff and I talked about starting a weekly newspaper if the KEN were sold to the NIP. I left the paper in March, and started to work with some people in Wallace on starting a weekly. There was a fair amount of angst over the thought of Magnuson owning both papers, and it seemed as if we weren't going to have much trouble raising funds for equipment and start-up costs.

I called the *Coeur d'Alene Press* to set up a meeting to discuss it printing the weekly.

The publisher of the *CdA Press* was friendly. I had worked for the paper as a stringer, and he knew me. We set a day for a meeting. Two days later, the meeting was canceled.

Very shortly after, Hagadone announced that he had purchased the KEN and the NIP. He had already bought the papers in Bonner and Boundary counties, and might have bought the weekly in Post Falls by then. Hagadone had every paper in the five North Idaho counties but the paper in St. Maries, and he tried to get that.

The Corbeills were furious, and refused to run the announcement in the KEN. Magnuson hadn't told them that he was thinking of selling the option to Hagadone. But ... there was a clause in the option that would have prohibited Magnuson from transferring the option to someone else. The Corbeills agreed to waive that option in return for keeping a van that was owned by the KEN. They weren't being disingenuous – they never expected Magnuson would go to Hagadone.

Idaho Mountain Express   Ketchum

Owner: Express Publishing
Address: 591 First Ave. N, Ketchum, ID 83340
Phone: 208-726-8060
URL: www.mtexpress.com (unrestricted)
Established: 1974
Published: Wednesday and Friday
Market: Blaine County
Circulation: 11,000
Publisher: Pam Morris, pmorris@mtexpress.com
Editor: Greg Foley, gfoley@mtexpress.com
Deadline: 5 p.m. Friday for Wednesday edition, 5 p.m. Tuesday for Friday edition

One of the largest non-dailies in Idaho, the *Mountain Express* has enjoyed the advantage, since the closure of the *Wood River Journal* at Hailey, of being the only newspaper serving the trendy, affluent, and recreation-oriented Wood River Valley. That gives it a very high-end advertising base, compared to most of its Idaho counterparts.

The Wood River Valley, like many others in rugged, highly mountainous Idaho, got its start as a mining district. Now home to the world-renowned Sun Valley, things wouldn't begin to change until snow was discovered – or at least the marketability of snow on steep and picturesque mountain slopes.

The valley had a rash of newspaper launchings in the early days, the first being the *News-Miner* at Hailey in 1879. More papers in Hailey, Ketchum, and Bellevue soon followed, but the Great Depression felled all but one of them – the weekly *Hailey Times*, which mutated into the *Wood River Journal* in 1969.

Blaine County is one of the few places in the Northwest that gained rather than lost newspapers in the fourth quarter of the 20th century. By the 1970s, the Sun Valley-Ketchum-Hailey area had begun to boom with resort and recreational development, built around skiing. That created a thriving retail advertising market centered more in Ketchum than Hailey.

A group of local business people formed Express Publishing in 1974 to launch the *Idaho Mountain Express* at Ketchum. The move partly represented a revolt against the absence of a local paper on their side of the valley and partly simply a desire for an alternative to the *Journal*.

The *Express* quickly became one of Idaho's most successful weeklies. It soon spawned various special editions in addition to its standard weekly.

In the mid-1980s, Clint Stennett sold the *Express'* arch-rival *Wood River Journal* to Lee Enterprises, making him that paper's final local owner. The Iowa-based chain was snapping up Idaho papers willy nilly at the time, its acquisitions including most of those serving the Magic Valley, including the daily *Twin Falls Times-News*. In April 2008, Lee sold the *Journal* to a limited liability company managed by the Post Company of Idaho Falls. The LLC ceased publication a few months later, and sold the remnants of the operation to the *Idaho Mountain Express*.

When the *Journal* closed, the *Express* became the direct successor, as it acquired all of the Hailey paper's assets, including the archived issues. In the process, the *Express* became the paper of record for Blaine County, giving it first crack at a rich vein of legal advertising.

Kuna Melba News   **Kuna**

Owner: RIM Publications
Address: 326 Avenue D, Kuna, ID 83634
Phone: 208-922-3008.
URL: www.kunamelba.com (subscription required for full access)
Established: 1982
Published: Wednesday
Market: Parts of Ada and Canyon counties
Circulation: 2,200
Editor: Laura Colvin, editor@kunamelba.com
Deadline: 5 p.m. Friday

The Kuna-Melba area may be Idaho's newest significant newspaper market. As recently as 1980, Kuna was home to fewer than 1,800 people, and the larger Kuna-Melba area probably had no more than twice that many.

That's not enough people to sustain the businesses necessary to sustain a newspaper. But Kuna in the 90s and since then has turned into a boomtown, a sprawling suburban area north of the Snake River Birds of Prey area. The *Kuna-Melba News* was launched in 1982 to capitalize on that development. It was run for a time by Marjorie Ruth Moon, a former state treasurer. By 2012, Kuna's population was about 16,000, with the nearby area supporting several thousand more. But that wasn't the reason RIM publications of Bellevue, Washington, bought the paper in December 2011.

RIM specializes in publication of legal notices, particularly those stemming from foreclosure actions. And the Kuna-Melba News was positioned to qualify as a legal newspaper of record in both Ada and Canyon counties, taking in the cities of Boise, Nampa, and Caldwell.

It continues to cover news of the region as well, and maintains a newsier, more active website than many Idaho weeklies.

Tribune   Lewiston

Owner: TPC Holdings (Tribune Company)
Address: 505 Capital Street, Lewiston, ID 83501
Phone: 208-743-941
URL: www.lmtribune.com (subscription required for e-edition, full access)
Established: 1892
Published: Monday through Sunday AM
Market: Latah, Nez Perce, Lewis, Clearwater, and Idaho counties in central and northern Idaho, plus Asotin, Whitman, and Garfield counties in southeastern Washington
Circulation: 23,421
Editor & Publisher: Nate Alford, alford@lmtribune.com
Managing Editor: Doug Bauer, dbauer@lmtribune.com

The first newspaper on record in Idaho was *The Golden Age*. Launched on August 2, 1862, it published on Saturdays, and it was based in Idaho's original capital of Lewiston, one of the state's oldest communities. It advertised, "...liquors, provisions, saddles, harnesses, inns, and placer mining tools," reflecting Lewiston's early role as a service town for the mining district up the Clearwater River around Pierce and Orofino.

The Golden Age did not last long, printing only a couple of years. It folded around the time the territorial capital was moved to Boise, and Lewiston took a subsequent nose dive. One of its co-owners, former Portland newsman Alonzo Leland, went on to found or acquire several other papers that followed in Lewiston's rough early days, including the *Teller* and the *Journal*.

Amid that uncertain journalistic stew, brothers Eugene and Albert Alford arrived in Lewiston in 1892 and started a new weekly, the *Tribune*. At the time, the only other paper in the field was the weekly *Teller*. Within a decade, the *Tribune* would move about the downtown area five times, each time to larger digs, a sign that it was rapidly catching on. It went daily in May 1898, initially publishing in the afternoon. In 1906, the *Teller* went under, eliminating its only serious competitor.

The *Tribune* started as a family newspaper – that family being the Alfords – and it is today. But the Alfords' hold turned tenuous at times.

In 1981, A.L. "Butch" Alford sold the Tribune Company, whose properties included the daily serving the neighboring college towns of Moscow and Pullman, to the Kerns-Tribune Corporation, whose flagship was the *Salt Lake Tribune*. Alford remained as publisher at Lewiston as part of the deal. But corporate issues developed in Salt Lake, and Alford launched an almost unprecedented buyback effort that eventually succeeded. He managed to regain control of the *Moscow-Pullman Daily News* as well, and set up an employee stock ownership program.

The *Tribune* was the first Idaho newspaper to reach the web and one of the first to establish a paywall.

Idaho Enterprise   Malad City

Owner: Kris Smith
Address: 100 E. 90 S, Malad City, ID 83252
Phone: 208-766-4773
URL: www.idahoenterprise.com (unrestricted, but extremely limited)
Established: 1879
Published: Thursday
Market: Oneida County
Circulation: 1,400
Editor, Publisher & Owner: Kris Smith, idahoenterprise@atcnet.net or publisher@idahoenterprise.com

Remote from the rest of Idaho in the extreme south, nearly on the Utah border, Malad City has remained a locally close-knit farm and ranch town ever since its founding in 1864.

Aside from a weekly briefly appearing in the early 1920s, the *Oneida County News*, the *Enterprise* is the only newspaper Malad City has ever had. That's also true for the Malad Valley and the rest of lightly populated Oneida County. It was founded in June 1879. There have been some interruptions in its run, but it continues to publish regularly in print and periodically online.

The paper is owned by Melissa Krishel (Kris) Nieffenegger Smith. She is a Malad High grad with deep local roots.

Star-News　　　　　　　　　　　　　　　　　　McCall

Owner: Central Idaho Publishing
Address: 1000 First St., McCall, ID 83638
Phone: 208-634-2123
URL: www.mccallstarnews.com (subscription required for e-edition, full access)
Established: 1967
Published: Thursday
Market: Valley County and part of Adams
Circulation: 4,500
Publisher: Tom and Tomi Grote, starnews@frontier.com
Editor: Tom Grote, starnews@frontier.com
Deadline: Monday

Long before it became a vacation and second-home hot spot, the shore of Payette Lake attracted the attention of timber processors. They set up shop there around the dawn of the 20th century. The *Payette Lake Star* began publication in 1918, just as McCall was emerging in its original form as a timber town. Now publishing as the *Star-News*, it has managed to make the transition from timber to tourism along with its home town.

It has been owned and operated since 1985 by Tom and Tomi Grote, formerly reporters at *The Idaho Statesman*, with partner A.L. "Butch" Alford, long-time owner and operator of the *Lewiston Tribune*. Fittingly, the *Star-News* prints on the *Lewiston Tribune* press.

Today, it is the only paper serving the Long Valley. Cascade supported a paper called the *News* from 1915 to 1967. In 1993, former Associated Press newsman Dan Gallagher launched the *Long Valley Advocate* in Cascade, but its finances were never flush and it eventually folded, lasting less than a decade.

Valley County is notable for many tiny towns that once sported their own weekly newspapers, including Roseberry (the original *Advocate*, published not far from Cascade), Roosevelt (the *Thunder Mountain News*), Stibnite (the *Miner*), Van Wyck (the *Times*) and Yellow Pine (the *Gazette*, in the early 70s). The towns as well as the newspaper mostly are long-departed today.

The Grotes continue to make a go of it in McCall.

"After five years of revenue decline, following the boom-boom, as we call it, our revenues have finally flattened out and begun an uptick again," Tom Grote says. "We are still 30% below our peak revenues, but closer to normal revenues that existed prior to the craziness that kicked in around 2003-04. When the real estate market crashed, then so did the construction industry, and all the related business (furnishings, paint, hardware), and by extension the service industries that supported them (banking, restaurants, bars, et cetra). So, there was a general funk around here between 2008-10. Then, in 2011, green shoots of recovery came poking up."

News-Examiner   Montpelier

Owner: Pioneer News Group
Address: 847 Washington St., Montpelier, ID 83254
Phone: 208-847-0552
URL: www.news-examiner.net (unrestricted)
Established: 1896
Published: Wednesday
Market: Bear Lake County
Circulation: 1,800
Editor & General Manager: Sherry Brown, newseditor@news-examiner.net
Deadline: Noon Friday

The town of Paris, the Bear Lake County seat of government, produced three newspapers before its larger neighbor, Montpelier, got its first.

They were the *Paris Post* (1880), the *Bear Lake Democrat* (1881) and the *Southern Idaho Independent* (1885). Montpelier got its first paper, the *Examiner*, in 1896. By then the town was already well on its way to becoming the county's commercial center. The *News* later entered the field. Competition continued until 1937, when the rival papers merged to create the *News-Examiner*.

The *News-Examiner* has historically been operated in conjunction with a print shop and LDS bookstore. By virtue of its *Examiner* heritage, it boasts on its website of being the oldest surviving business in Montpelier.

The paper was owned until the 1990s by members of a local family that also owned and operated the nearby *Preston Citizen*. They sold both papers to the Seattle-based Pioneer Media Group, with extensive holdings in Idaho and Utah, including the dailies serving Pocatello and Logan.

The last of the Paris papers was the *Post*, which folded in 1966. So the *News-Examiner* now has southeastern Idaho's remote Bear Lake County all to itself.

Moscow–Pullman Daily News   Moscow

Owner: TPC Holdings (Tribune Company)
Address: 409 S. Jackson Street, Moscow, ID 83843
Phone: 208-882-5561
URL: www.dnews.com (subscription required for e-edition, full access)
Established: 1911
Published: Monday through Saturday AM
Market: Latah County in Idaho and Whitman County in Washington
Circulation: 6,615
Publisher: Nate Alford, alford@dnews.com
Managing Editor: Lee Rozen, lrozen@dnews.com

Latah County has had a lot of newspapers over the years. Maybe the out-sized local presence of the University of Idaho has something to do with that.

The small town of Troy, just eight miles from Moscow, had a string of them through the 20th century, from the *Weekly News* and *County Press* and *Vedette* (when it was briefly called Vollmer) to the more recent *Latah-Whitman Republic*. Earlier, Genesee had the *Advertiser*, the *News* and the *Recorder*, Deary the *Enterprise* and the *Talk of the Town*, and Bovill the *Herald* and *Record*. And that's not to mention five different papers emanating from Juliaetta, the long-running *Gazette* coming out of Kendrick or the *Latah Eagle* publishing from Potlatch.

Moscow has been Latah's most prolific source of newspaper titles however, ranking second only to Boise in the state as a whole. It even produced a short-lived paper, in 1968, called the *Eunuch*.

But Moscow newspapering has long been dominated by a pair of papers enjoying common ownership for almost 40 years – the *Lewiston Tribune*, which maintains a bureau in Latah County and circulates heavily there, and the city's smaller home-grown daily, now known as the *Daily News*. The Moscow paper was known for many years as the *Idahonian*, which, as any proper Idahoan will tell you, is not the proper demonym for residents of the state.

It grew out of the 1939 merger of the *Star-Mirror*, founded in September 1911, and the *News Review*, whose reporting staff once employed future Oregon Governor Tom McCall. Published in the afternoon, it was owned for decades by the Marineau family.

In 1967, William Marineau responded to a takeover attempt by a national chain by selling a 40% stake to the Tribune Company, owner of the Lewiston *Tribune* 30 miles south. That company was owned by the Alfords, who eventually bought out the rest of the Marineaus' stake.

In 1984, the Tribune Company began publishing a paper designed to serve the city of Pullman, Washington, home of Washington State University. Actually printed in Moscow, it was called the *Palouse Empire News*. In 1991, the Tribune Company merged the two college-town papers into the *Moscow-Pullman Daily News*. Like its parent Lewiston Tribune, the *Daily News* was a pioneer in launching its own website and subsequently in putting that site on a subscription basis.

News   Mountain Home

Owner: Rust Communications
Address: 195 S.E Third St., Mountain Home, ID 83647
Phone: 208-587-3331
URL: www.mountainhomenews.com (unrestricted)
Established: 1888
Published: Wednesday
Market: Elmore County and eastern Owyhee County
Circulation: 4,000
Publisher: Coleen Swenson, cswenson@mountainhomenews.com
Editor: Kelly Everitt, keveritt@mountainhomenews.com
Deadline: 1 p.m. Monday

Idaho's lone military-base community, Mountain Home, has an unusual history with its local newspapers.

The first paper in Mountain Home, which originally was known as Rattlesnake Junction, was said to have been called the *Range and Valley*. That's "said to" because no copies are known to have survived from its founding in 1883 or brief existence thereafter.

A paper with more staying power, the *Mountain Home Bulletin*, emerged in 1888. After a series of name changes, it became the *News* in 1947. From 1960 to 1986, the *News* was owned by the local Waters family. It came under corporate ownership in the 1980s, and ended up after a series of sales with Rust Communications, which still owns it.

Rust is based in Cape Girardeau, Missouri. But its local management – including Publisher Coleen Swenson, a member of the Waters family, and Managing Editor Kelly Everitt – have been in place for about a generation. It also is one of a minority of Idaho weeklies still maintaining its own print shop.

The paper changed its publication day from Thursday to Wednesday many years ago, adopting a schedule preferred by local grocers, who remain substantial advertisers, Everitt said; and circulation has been holding steady, pleasing both the advertising base and management team.

Several other Elmore County communities have had newspapers, including Rocky Bar (in the 1800s), remote Atlanta (briefly, in 1885) and, more recently and tellingly, Glenns Ferry (the *Gazette* from 1908 to 1971 and the *Pilot* from 1974 to 1995). In 1996, the *Gazette* was revived as an adjunct to the *Mountain Home News*. Published on Mondays, with Friday deadlines, it is produced on the dining table of Editor Mel Brown, who e-mails its weekly editions to the *News* shop in Mountain Home for printing.

The *News* also produces an adjunct called the *Patriot*, which serves the Mountain Home Air Force Base. Everitt subscribes to The Associated Press wire for the *Patriot*, because the base's airmen hail from all over the country and harbor significant interest in international news.

Many airmen stay on or return after completing their tour of duty. As a result, more than half of Mountain Home residents have military backgrounds. "We've managed to maintain penetration," Everitt says. "I believe the last newspapers to exist will be community newspapers."

Idaho Press-Tribune   **Nampa**

Owner: Pioneer Newspapers
Address: 1618 N. Midland Blvd., Nampa, ID 83651
Phone: 208-467-9251
URL: www.idahopress.com (subscription required for e-edition, full access)
Established: 1883
Published: Monday through Sunday AM
Market: Canyon County
Circulation: 19,900
Publisher: Matt Davison, mdavison@idahopress.com
Managing Editor: Vickie Holbrook, vholbrook@idahopress.com

Nampa first came to the fore as a stop along the Oregon Short Line Railroad, which eventually became part of Union Pacific. It lies in the heart of an expanse of rich farmland, to which canals and irrigation lines were just then being extended. Caldwell, situated to the northwest, got an earlier start and thus was named Canyon County seat. It was eventually outpaced by Nampa, which lies closer to Boise.

Despite their close proximity, the two towns have long maintained distinct identities.

Caldwell had the earlier and livelier newspaper environment. Several papers emerged in the early 1880s, and they competed fiercely. The two emerging from the fray were the *Caldwell Tribune* and the *Caldwell News*. The *Tribune* was edited and published by Frank Steunenberg, a future Idaho governor who would be assassinated, famously, less than a mile from its downtown office. It merged with the *News* in 1928 to create the *News Tribune*.

Nampa papers emerged later, but they grew numerous. For years, it seemed each new launch would prompt yet another in response. According to the *Press-Tribune* website:

"The first newspaper, The *Nampa Progress*, was printed June 23, 1888. The *Nampa Leader* was first published on April 3, 1891; *The Nampa Times*, August 1902; *The Nampa Leader Herald*, Dec. 23, 1904; and *The Nampa Evening Leader*, April 1, 1907. Populists and Socialists played heavy roles in Nampa's newspaper development. The *Leader-Herald* was a strong Republican paper, and that prompted the birth of the *Idaho Free Press* on April 9, 1919."

In 1946, Bernard Mainwaring bought both the *Idaho Free Press* and its remaining competitor, the *Leader-Herald*, and folded the *Leader-Herald*.

In 1954, the *Free Press* became one of the first Idaho newspapers picked up by a national newspaper chain. In this case, it was the Scripps League, one of several groups involving members of the Scripps family. Scripps acquired the *Caldwell News Tribune* a couple of years later and set about merging their operations, one piece at a time. Eventually, the Caldwell paper became effectively a zoned edition of the Nampa paper.

In the 70s, Scripps sold its Canyon County operation to another Scripps family enterprise, Pioneer League Newspapers. The Seattle-based company later became Pioneer Newspapers, then Pioneer Media Group. Pioneer, which owns an array of daily and weekly newspapers in Washington, Idaho, and Utah, killed off the separate nameplates in 1980 to create the *Idaho Press-Tribune* and established new quarters in Nampa.

The paper's current publisher, Matt Davison, transferred in out of Pioneer's *Ellensburg Daily Record*.

Both before and after the merger, all editions were published in the afternoon. But Pioneer moved the *Press-Tribune* to the morning cycle in 1999, putting it in head-to-head competition with the *Idaho Statesman*, published half an hour away in Boise.

Eventually, the *Statesman*, Idaho's largest and widest-circulating daily, shut down its press and begun printing under contract at the the *Press-Tribune* plant in Nampa. By then, the *Statesman* had drawn its circulation area in significantly, making the move more feasible. Each night, the *Statesman* rolls off the press first, followed by the *Press Tribune*.

Lewis County Herald   Nezperce

Owner: Wherry Publishing
Address: 517 Oak St., Nezperce ID 83543-0159
Phone: 208-962-3851.
URL: No web presence, but sister paper 20 miles away, *Cottonwood Chronicle*, carries news at www.cottonwoodchronicle.com (unrestricted)
Established: 1917 (predecessor in 1901)
Published: Thursday
Market: Western Lewis County
Circulation: 800
Co-Publishers: Greg Wherry, cotchron@qwestoffice.net, and Steve Wherry, cotchron@camasnet.com
Editor: Steve Wherry, cotchron@camasnet.com or editor@cottonwoodchronicle.com
Deadline: Monday

Lewis County is small in size and population, but not cohesive. It harbors two distinct populations, the river people concentrated around Kamiah, the county's largest city, and the prairie people, concentrated in the Camas Prairie communities of Craigmont, Winchester, and Nezperce, the latter serving as county seat. Winchester and Craigmont were barely communities a century back. Both had their own newspapers then, but the dominant local print voice has long been the *Lewis County Herald* at Nezperce.

In a detailed history of Nezperce posted on the city website, early newspaper history is recounted this way:

"The first newspaper, the *Nezperce News* was established in 1896, just a few short months after the opening of the reservation, and probably disappeared soon after opening. The second newspaper was the *Record*, which later became the *Nezperce Herald*, with the subscription rate being $1.00. The newspaper was sold to W. P. Conger in 1909.

"Most newspapers were very political in the early years, with Nezperce being very Democratic. Conger did his best to keep political fires fanned, writing tidbits during World War I such as: 'One serious defect is noticeable in the selective draft law; it should have included food speculators and the idle rich,' and, 'Congress shouldn't worry; the mentally deficient are exempted from the draft.'"

The newspaper remained under the ownership of W.P. and his son, Ernest Conger, for more than 30 years. It is now owned by Wherry Publishing, which also owns and operates a sister weekly in Cottonwood, about 20 minutes' drive to the southwest.

Clearwater Tribune   Orofino

Owner: Clearwater Tribune Publishing
Address: 161 Main St., Orofino, ID 83544
Phone: 208-476-4571
URL: www.clearwatertribune.com (subscription required for e-edition, full access)
Established: 1912
Published: Thursday
Market: Clearwater County
Circulation: 5,000
Co-Publishers: Cloann McNall and Marcie Stanton, cleartrib@cebridge.net
Managing Editor: Marcie Stanton, cleartrib@cebridge.net
Deadline: 5 p.m. Monday

The Clearwater River country, uphill from Orofino, was the scene of a mining boom in 1862. It is considered Idaho's first, even though the area was actually part of Washington Territory at the time. The mining town of Pierce briefly supported a weekly newspaper. When the mines began to play out, attention turned to timber. By the early 1900s, the area was supporting extensive logging and log processing, with the Clearwater River providing a convenient source of transportation.

Clearwater County had just been carved out of neighboring Nez Perce County in 1911, with Orofino, its budding commercial center, winning designation as the county seat. That gave Orofino the edge over Pierce, Elk River, Weippe, Ahsahka, Cavendish, and Greer for a weekly newspaper enterprise, and several entrepreneurs had a go at it, both before and after the county's founding.

The *Clearwater Tribune*, product of the *Clearwater Republican*'s acquisition of the older *Orofino Tribune*, didn't come on the scene until 1912. The paper is sometimes confused with the *Clearwater Progress*, publishing just a short piece up the river at Kamiah. Both papers have long and distinguished histories in their own right. The *Tribune* considers 1912 its founding year, and held a centennial celebration in 2012; its immediate predecessor was the *Clearwater Republican*. Not long after its founding in 1912, the *Republican* absorbed the *Orofino Tribune* to create the *Clearwater Tribune*. However, the *Orofino Tribune* dates back to 1905, and the *Orofino Courier* even further, having come into being just as the 19th century was drawing to a close.

As Alannah Allbrett reported in a centennial story in the *Tribune* in March 2012: "The first newspaper to get a toehold in Clearwater County, in May 1899, was the *Orofino Courier*. It was published by the Greer Brothers, using a small Army press which was common in those days because it was relatively easy to move and to set up. The *Orofino*

Tribune, a democratically slanted paper, came into being in September 1905. W.C. Foresman was the editor and the publisher."

She said of the *Courier*: "The paper was located in a little, wooden clapboard building below Canada Hill (behind the former Health and Welfare building) on the corner of Third and Johnson Avenue. The paper was printed with page one being on the right side, where the last page would be positioned today, so one would read it from the back to the front."

Two other papers appeared briefly in this period – the *Orofino News*, published by W.M. Chandler, which was founded in 1903, and *The Options*, published by Charles Offsetter, which was publishing by April 1905 and may pre-date that.

After the *Tribune* came to the fore, its Democratic leanings spawned a Republican rival. Emerging in March 1912, the new paper was named, appropriately enough, the *Republican*. However, the product of the merger ended up in the hands of I.R. Crow, who wasn't shy about his Democratic leanings. As Allbrett went on to note: "Publishers of the time were not expected to be 'neutral' on any given issue; they were in fact, allowed to express political and personal opinions. In 1916, then publisher of the *Clearwater Tribune*, I.R. Crow, was stumping in the gubernatorial campaign trying to get Moses Alexander (re-)elected." As it happened, he succeeded. Alexander, a Democrat first elected in 1914, won re-election in 1916.

Many of Idaho's weeklies passed into corporate hands at some point along the way, but not the *Tribune*. It is owned and operated by the Stanton family, without any outside assistance.

While the *Tribune* has no print competitor, it does have a subscription-based online competitor – Window on the Clearwater. The online news operation publishes six days a week. It is run by Nancy Butler, a Boise State graduate with 35 years of journalism experience.

Western Canyon Chronicle   Parma

Owner: Beth Campbell
Address: 25927 Stephen Lane, Parma, ID 83660
Phone: 208-514-7534
URL: No operating website, but Facebook page at www.facebook.com/WCChronicle
Established: 2002
Published: Wednesday
Market: Western Canyon County, including Parma, Wilder, Greenleaf, and Notus
Circulation: Unlisted
Editor, Publisher & Owner: Beth Campbell, write2wcc@gmail.com

Parma, which boasted 506 families in the 2010 census, is the largest of several farm communities on the northwestern corner of Canyon County. Short distances to Ontario, just over the Oregon border to the west, and Caldwell, Nampa, and Boise, equally near to the east, have limited the community's commercial development, and its roster of newspapers.

The *Parma Review* was a mainstay for most of the last century. Founded in 1909, it finally ran its course in 1993. Throughout its history, it was the main Canyon County newspaper west of Caldwell. Sometimes it was the only one.

Nine years went by before the *Western Canyon Chronicle* came on the scene in an attempt to fill the void. It is owned and operated by Beth Campbell. Campbell registered the domain name westerncanyonnewspaper.com for the *Chronicle*, but let it lapse in March 2013. The paper maintains a limited presence on Facebook.

In addition to Parma, it covers the communities of Greenleaf, Notus, and Wilder.

Independent Enterprise   Payette

Owner: Wick Communications
Address: 124 S. Main St., Payette, ID 83661
Phone: 208-642-3357
URL: www.argusobserver.com/independent (subscription required for full access)
Established: 1890
Published: Wednesday
Market: Payette County
Circulation: 2,100
Publisher: John Dillon, johnd@argusobserver.com (joint with Ontario, Oregon)
Editor & General Manager: Scott McIntosh, scottm@argusobserver.com (joint with Ontario, Oregon)
Deadline: Monday

All three cities in Payette County – Payette, Fruitland and New Plymouth – have supported newspapers at one time or another. But Payette's *Independent Enterprise*, the product of a 1937 merger, has had the field largely to itself the last half century. And Payette has generated what little competition it's gotten over the years, not neighboring Fruitland or New Plymouth.

Once an independent weekly, the paper is now a subsidiary of the *Ontario Argus-Observer*, a daily owned by Wick Communications, based in Arizona. The printing, business and editorial operations have all been merged. Wick publishes 28 newspapers and 18 specialty publications in 12 states. It is based in Sierra Vista, located in southeastern Arizona.

A paper called the *Three Rivers Chronicle* emerged in Payette in 1996, but lasted less than a year.

Idaho State Journal   Pocatello

Owner: Pioneer Newspapers
Address: 305 S. Arthur Ave., Pocatello, ID 83204
Phone: 208-232-4161
URL: www.idahostatejournal.com (subscription required for e-edition, full access)
Established: 1890
Published: Monday through Sunday AM
Circulation: 17,100
Market: Bannock and adjacent counties to Wyoming and Utah borders
Publisher: Andy Pennington, apennington@journalnet.com
Editor: Ian Fennell, ifennell@journalnet.com

Like Nampa and Idaho Falls, Pocatello got started as a transportation hub, spurred early in its history by landing substantial industrial development and Idaho's second large state institution of higher education – Idaho State University. For a brief time in the early 1960s, it was Idaho's most populous city, surpassing Boise.

Like most mid-sized cities, Pocatello had a variety of newspapers in the years leading up to World War II. In those days, Utah's *Salt Lake Tribune* also circulated widely in Southern Idaho, and it maintained a bureau in Pocatello. The well-known journalist and public official Perry Swisher served as its Pocatello correspondent for some years. But locally, the main two were the *Tribune* and *Post*, both publishing in the afternoon. The *Tribune* emerged as dominant.

The *Pocatello Tribune* entered the field first, getting its start in 1890. A trio of old newspaper hands from Salt Lake – typesetter C.H. Fersternmaker, ad salesman William Wallin and reporter George Ifft – bought the paper two years later and began publishing it out of upstairs offices in Pocatello's recently erected opera house. After buying out Fersternmaker, the remaining partners tried to take the paper daily in 1897. They failed in a first attempt, but succeeded five years later, and the *Tribune* and its successors have published daily ever since.

The original *Idaho State Journal* entered the field as a morning counterpart to the two afternoon papers in the 1930s. The owners of the *Tribune* soon bought it to serve as their morning edition. But they shut it down in 1942, as the war began to drain readership and resources.

When the Tribune-Journal Company bought the *Post* in 1949, its executives decided that this merger called for a fresh name, so they revived the old *Idaho State Journal* instead of going with *Tribune-Post* or *Post-Tribune*. The paper continued to publish on the afternoon cycle well into the 1990s, after most dailies had converted to morning.

The Ifft family, which remains active in Idaho newspapering to this day, ran the *Journal* from 1949 to 1984. In addition to serving as publisher for many years, G. Nicholas Ifft III, very much a journalist, wrote a column signed ING until late in life. Eventually, the Iffts sold several Northwest newspapers, including the *Idaho State Journal*, to Pioneer in a package deal.

The *Journal* is one of several Idaho dailies no longer operating its own press. Since 2000, Pioneer has been printing its Pocatello and Logan, Utah, dailies, along with several area weeklies, at a regional press plant in Preston.

Citizen   Preston

Owner: Pioneer Media Group (formerly Pioneer Newspapers)
Address: 77 S. State St., Preston, ID 83263
Phone: 208-852-0155
URL: www.prestoncitizen.com (subscription required for e-edition, full access)
Established: 1890
Published: Wednesday
Market: Franklin County
Circulation: 2,950
Publisher: Greg Madson, gregm@prestoncitizen.com
Editor: Rod Boam, editor@prestoncitizen.com
Deadline: Monday

Franklin, barely north of the Utah line, dates to 1860, making it the oldest permanent town in Idaho. It was founded by settlers migrating north from Salt Lake City, apparently thinking they were still in Utah. Today, Franklin is best known for supplying alcohol and lottery tickets to people who really do live in Utah. It never developed into one of the county's larger communities.

Oxford, some miles to the northwest, was the first town in Franklin County with a newspaper, Founded in 1879 as the *Idaho Enterprise*, it only lasted three years. The only other town here with a newspaper history is Preston, the county's seat of government and commercial center. Being agriculturally oriented, its mainstays are farm supply and food processing.

Preston's first newspaper was the *Standard*, which debuted in 1901 and flamed out in 1902. The *Franklin County Citizen*, launched in 1912, had more staying power. Today's *Preston Citizen*, which publishes every Wednesday, is a direct descendant. The paper was locally owned for many decades by the Citizen Publishing Company, which also owned the Montpelier *News-Examiner*. It has a long history of running relatively complex and analytical stories about its home county.

When Seattle-based Pioneer Newspapers moved in to establish a printing plant to serve its dailies in Pocatello to the north and Logan to the south, it was also able to acquire the *Citizen* and *News-Examiner*. Now known as the Pioneer Media Group, it prints papers at the same plant.

Like Logan, Franklin County lies in the Cache Valley. Thanks to geography, Logan thus serves as more of a commercial and cultural center for the valley's residents than any of Idaho's cities. Either way, the Pioneer group has the area covered since the *Logan Herald Journal* also is a Pioneer paper.

Times   Priest River

Owner: Hagadone Newspapers
Address: 5809 Highway 2, Suite C, Priest River, ID 83856
Phone: 208-448-2431
URL: www.priestrivertimes.com (unrestricted)
Established: 1914
Published: Thursday
Market: Western Bonner County.
Circulation: 1,500
Publisher: David Keyes, dkeyes@bonnercountydailybee.com (joint with Bonner County)
Managing Editor: Terri Ivey, tivie@priestrivertimes.com
Deadline: 10 a.m. Monday

Despite the name, the timber town of Priest River is actually located on the banks of the Pend Oreille River, near where the Priest River flows into it. The city has managed to maintain a significant economic base for more than a century now, but not without plenty of ups and downs. As its website notes, "Periodic downturns in timber's fortunes have been the norm over the years, but recent efforts to expand and diversify the economy have helped to address the problem."

Newspapers began appearing around the dawn of the 20th century, but only one managed to hold its ground over the decades – the *Priest River Times*, founded in 1914. It was locally owned through much of its history, but like other papers in the Idaho Panhandle, was eventually acquired by the Hagadone Corporation out of Coeur d'Alene.

The *Times* also publishes a free-distribution TMC product called the *Times Weekly*. In addition to being inserted into the regular weekly edition of the paid-distribution *Times*, circulation 1,500, it is mailed to 9,500 non-subscribers.

As the paper's website notes: "Thanks to advertisers, the *Times Weekly* is delivered into everyone's mailbox each week for FREE! It is also the second section of the *Priest River Times*. Advertisers get exposure in 11,000 homes."

Standard Journal   Rexburg

Owner: Pioneer Newspapers
Address: 23 S. First E, Rexburg, ID 83440
Phone: 208-356-5441
URL: www.rexburgstandardjournal.com (subscription required for e-edition, full access)
Established: 1888
Published: Tuesday, Thursday and Saturday
Market: Madison and Fremont counties
Circulation: 5,371
Publisher: Scott Anderson, sanderson@uvsj.com
Managing Editor: Mike Henneke, editor@uvsj.com

Rexburg, which spurted from 17,000 residents to more than 25,000 during the first decade of the new millenium, was founded by Mormon pioneer Thomas Edwin Ricks. Rexburg is home of one of Idaho's three LDS temples and the Idaho branch of Salt Lake City's Brigham Young University, which has grown dramatically. Madison County's largest city and seat of government, it was incorporated in 1883.

Like so many others towns, Rexburg was a competitive newspaper town in the first half of the century. Though there were others, including the colorfully named *Rexburg Silver Hammer*, the leaders in the field were the *Rexburg Standard* and the *Rexburg Current Journal*. The first was run (with financing from local business people) by Republican activist Lloyd Adams, the second by the Democratically affiliated Porter family. By 1942, Adams had given up newspaper publishing to establish a law practice. He ended up selling to the Porters, who merged the two papers into the *Standard Journal*. They held onto the paper for decades. Along the way, they were able to pick up the weekly *Herald-Chronicle* in nearby St. Anthony, to the north.

The Porters sold the *Standard Journal* to Pioneer Newspapers, now the Pioneer Media Group, in December 2000. Pioneer was not interested in the *Herald-Chronicle*, so it was shut down.

The *Standard Journal* for a time expanded from weekly publication to five days a week, but has cut back to three, producing editions on Tuesday, Thursday, and Saturday.

Jefferson Star   **Rigby**

Owner: Post Company
Address: 134 W. Main St., Rigby, ID 83442
Phone: 208-745-8701
URL: www.jeffersonstarnews.com (subscription required for full access)
Established: 1906
Published: Wednesday
Market: Jefferson and Clark counties
Circulation: 1,950
Editor: Earlene Poole, info@jeffersonstarnews.com
Deadline: 5 p.m. Friday

Rigby, located about mid-way between Rexburg and Idaho Falls in southeastern Idaho, only boasts about 4,000 residents. In Jefferson County, whose other communities are Hamer, Mud Lake, Lewisville, Menan, Ririe, Roberts, Terreton, and Monteview, that's enough to make it the largest city and seat of government. Rigby has been growing in recent years, which is good for the newspaper's economic environment. However, it is increasingly becoming a bedroom community for much larger Idaho Falls, which isn't so good.

Its main line of papers, a succession with *Star* in the name, got its start in 1906. They remained in local ownership until the 1990s, operating as Pioneer Publishing. More recently, both the *Star* and the *Pioneer* in Shelley soon were acquired by the Post Company, whose flagship is the *Post Register* in Idaho Falls.

Elsewhere in Jefferson County, weekly newspapers have also been published in Menan and Roberts, but not in almost a century.

Recorder Herald   **Salmon**

Owner: Rick Hodges
Address: 519 Van Dreff St., Salmon, ID 83467
Phone: 208-756-2221
URL: No online presence, but reporter Leslie May Shumate posts stories at http://lmshumate.com/article.php with a news alert subscription through LMS Enterprises
Established: 1886
Published: Thursday
Market: Lemhi County
Circulation: 3,100
Publisher & Owner: Rick Hodges, unlisted
Editor: Sheila Johnson, unlisted
Reporter: Leslie Shumate, lms@lmshumate.com
Deadline: Monday

For almost a century, Salmon's population has hovered around 3,000. That makes it the most remote community its size in Idaho, which has plenty of remote places, and one of the most stable overall. It is two hours or more to the nearest midsized cities – Idaho Falls to the south and Missoula, across the Montana state line, to the north. Laid out in the late 1860s by George Shoup, Idaho's last territorial governor and first state governor, it long has served as a supply and processing center for logging, ranching and mining.

Apart from scattered copies of a mining flier, Salmon's first newspaper was *The Idaho Recorder*, which debuted in 1886. Now the *Recorder Herald*, it continues to publish – without, its current editor says, having ever missed an issue.

The intervening decades saw a flurry of local papers come and go, some with colorful names like the *Hoot Owl*, the *Idaho Hydraulic Gold Miner* and the *Lemhi Daily Spud*. But the *Recorder* persevered. Its only serious competition came from the *Salmon Herald*, founded in 1914, and that ended in 1927 when the rival papers merged.

In his memoir *Crossing the Line*, editor Sam Day, later of the *Intermountain Observer*, wrote of his experience editing the *Recorder Herald* in the early 1960s: "In Lemhi County, everyone read the *Recorder Herald*. I was virtually the only reporter in town – the only one in hundreds of miles. I had the newspaper entirely to myself, with a blank check from the absentee owners to edit the news as I saw fit. I waged frequent battles with bureaucrats of every stripe, accustomed to thinking of the public's business as their private affair." But he didn't stay long.

The *Recorder Herald* has been owned for some years by Salmon resident Rick Hodges, and Sheila Johnson has served as editor since the 1990s. It has only had eight publishers in its history.

"We are strictly a local newspaper," Johnson said. "We've pretty much held steady. ... It's like the *Recorder Herald* has a life of its own."

The paper continues to circulate south to Mackay and west to Challis. It manages to reach small, remote outposts around Lemhi County.

It does not have online presence, though. "We are a newspaper and we will probably remain a newspaper," Johnson said.

Bonner County Daily Bee   Sandpoint

Owner: Hagadone Newspapers
Address: 310 Church St., Sandpoint, ID 83864
Phone: 208-263-9534
URL: www.bonnercountydailybee.com (unrestricted, subscription required for e-edition)
Established: 1965
Published: Tuesday through Sunday AM

Market: Bonner County
Circulation: 6,000
Publisher: David Keyes, dkeyes@bonnercountydailybee.com
Editor: Caroline Lobsinger, clobsinger@bonnercountydailybee.com

The definitive history of Bonner County newspapering was penned for the Bonner County Historical Society by Gary Pietsch. And he should know: His family played a major role in making that history through its founding and long-time ownership of the *Sandpoint Daily Bulletin*.

Sandpoint was among the later communities founded in northern Idaho, around the turn of the 20th century when timber and railroad interests connected on the north side of Lake Pend Oreille. It has become a retirement, vacation and even something of an arts center (given its scenic location) in more recent years.

The first paper to serve the city was the *The Kootenai County Republican*, which debuted in Rathdrum on May 19, 1899, Pietsch reports. At the time, Kootenai encompassed territory out of which three other counties would later be carved: Bonner, Boundary, and Benewah.

On July 12, 1901, owner John F. Yost moved the *Republican* to Sandpoint. Rathdrum had two other papers at the time, but Sandpoint was virgin territory, so the move made sense economically. Yost sold to new arrivals Al Filson and George Barker in 1903, but, Pietsch writes, they soon had a falling out. After selling his interest to Filson, Barker bought the *Priest River Enterprise*, moved it to Sandpoint and began publishing it as the *Pend d'Oreille Review* in 1905. By then, Filson had already drawn a competitor called the *Northern Idaho News*. And it continued publishing in Sandpoint until 1944.

The Pietsch family came on the scene in 1924, when Laurin E. Pietsch and J.L. Stack launched the *Daily Bulletin*, a mimeographed sheet published Monday through Saturday. They distributed it free of charge for the first four months, then began charging a quarter a month. Laurin Pietsch bought out his partner in 1926 and two of his rivals in 1929 – the newly founded *Daily Panidan* and longer running *Pend d'Oreille Review*. He shuttered the *Panidan* immediately, but continued to publish the *Review* as a weekly until 1936, according to Gary Pietsch's account. In 1940, the *Daily Bulletin* reduced its frequency and dropped "Daily" from its title. Four years later, it merged with the *Northern Idaho News* to create the *Sandpoint News-Bulletin*.

The Pietsches had the field to themselves until 1966, when Pete and Adele Thompson launched the *Bee Hive*. Eleven years later, the Pietsches sold to the Thompsons, ending a family involvement spanning more than half a century.

The Thompsons published both papers for a time, then merged them to create the *Sandpoint Daily Bee*. They sold the paper to Duane

Hagadone in 1984 and he renamed it the *Bonner County Daily Bee* four years later.

The biggest story in the paper's history was the Sundance Fire, which started with a lightning strike on Sundance Mountain on Aug. 23, 1967. *Bee* columnist Bob Gunter reports: "By Sept. 1, the fire was burning the surrounding timberland at the rate of one square mile every six minutes – the fire was six miles wide and 25 miles long. More than 2,000 firefighters fought to control the blaze."

Pioneer   Shelley

Owner: Post Company
Address: 154 E. Center St., Shelley, ID 83274
Phone: 208-357-7661
URL: www.theshelleypioneer.com (subscription required)
Established: 1905
Published: Wednesday
Market: Northern Bingham County
Circulation: 1,400
Editor: Shirley Thompson, news@theshelley.pioneer
Deadline: Noon Monday

The potato, specifically the russet-burbank, reigns supreme in Shelley. The high school mascot is a giant spud wielding a scepter. The locals call him Boomer. The big doings every year is Spud Day. Among other things potato, it offers participants the opportunity to jump into a giant pit of mashed potatoes and compete in a tug of war. The town boasted only 4,400 souls in the 2010 census. And it lies less than a 10-minute drive from the much larger and more cosmopolitan Idaho Falls.

However, it's a hardy place that has maintained its own identity. This has helped support continued publication of the *Pioneer*, which has had Shelley all to itself since 1909, five years after the town's founding.

For some years it was owned by Ken Carr, who also ran the *Jefferson Star* at Rigby. The *Pioneer* is now owned by the Post Company of Idaho Falls, which owns the daily there along with weeklies in Rigby and Challis.

Caribou County Sun   Soda Springs

Owned: Stanford M. "Mark" Steele
Address: 169 S. First St. W, Soda Springs, ID 83276
Phone: 208-547-3260

URL: No online presence
Established: 1931
Published: Thursday
Market: Caribou County
Circulation: 2,755
Editor, Publisher & Owner: Mark Steele, ccsun10@aol.com
Deadline: Monday

Soda Springs, a ranching and mining community, is one of the older cities in Idaho. And it holds some rather odd distinctions as a result. It has been associated with three counties – Oneida, Bannock and Caribou. It has served as the designated county seat of two of them – first Oneida, then Caribou, which wasn't carved out of Bannock until 1919.

The first newspaper to sink roots in Soda Springs was the *Chieftain*, which arrived in 1906 and departed in 1931. The *Chieftain* was followed in 1933 by the *Soda Springs Sun*, which later became the *Caribou County Sun*, as its ambitions broadened.

Mark Steele has owned and operated the paper for several decades, and he's seen lots of change, in both the community and the newspaper industry, over the years.

Steele observes that a lot more locals are working elsewhere these days, making Soda Springs more of a bedroom community. And that's not good for newspapering, as community cohesion helps build a solid economic and social base. One result, he said, has been a decline in home-delivery subscriptions, with an only partially offsetting increase in spot rack and counter sales. "It's slow," he said. "We've taken hits, obviously."

But Steele, who has the *Sun* printed to the south in Brigham City, Utah, isn't looking to the Internet as his salvation. He has resisted; the *Sun* is one of a handful of Idaho papers with no web presence.

Gazette Record   St. Maries

Owner: Hammes family
Address: 610 Main Ave., St. Maries, ID 83861
Phone: 208-245-4538
URL: www.gazetterecord.com (subscription required)
Established: 1913
Published: Wednesday
Market: Eastern Benewah County
Circulation: 3,300
Editor, Publisher & Owner: Dan Hammes, dan@smgazette.com or editor@smgazette.com
Deadline: Monday

Logs still float down the St. Joe River, just as they did more than a century ago when the river's twisting location between vast timber stands and the eminently floatable Lake Coeur d'Alene suggested a good location for a timber depot. That depot evolved into St. Maries (where from a bridge you often can still still those logs in the river), whose secluded home in heavily timbered hills far from major transportation lines, coupled with its continued reliance on the logging industry, have kept it in a state approaching suspended animation.

Local journalism debuted with the launch of the *St. Maries Courier* in 1901. Alas, it only lasted four years. The *Record* followed on April 29, 1913. Four years later, the *Gazette* arrived to mount a competitive challenge. The rivals slugged it out for only seven months before merging on June 4, 1918. The *Benewah County News* made a run at the *Gazette Record* from 1935 to 1937 before giving it up.

The Hammes family has owned and operated the *Gazette Record* and several other associated businesses in town for more than half a century. Robert and JoJane Hammes bought the paper in 1958. They sold it to their son, Dan, and his wife, Cindy, in 1992.

Dan, whose family holdings today include a local Internet service, and a book and office store, said he's been sustaining some advertising slippage, but circulation seems to be holding up pretty well. He attributes the latter partly to a firm resolve to limit online news to paid subscribers. "We put everything behind the paywall," he said. "We've always done it that way, and we make money on that."

The paper is delivered by mail, the usual mode in recent years for locally oriented weeklies.

Times-News   Twin Falls

Owner: Lee Enterprises
Address: P.O. Box 548, Twin Falls, ID 83303
Phone: 208-733-0931
URL: www.magicvalley.com (subscription for full access)
Established: 1904
Published: Monday through Sunday AM
Market: Magic Valley counties of Twin Falls, Elmore, Camas, Blaine, Gooding, Jerome, Lincoln, Minidoka, and Cassia
Circulation: 17,915 weekday, 20,404 Sunday (ABC)
Publisher: John Pfeifer, jpfeifer@magicvalley.com
Editor: Autumn Agar, aagar@magicvalley.com

The *Twin Falls News*, a Republican paper, got its start almost simultaneously with the city in October 1904. The *Twin Falls Times*, a Democratic counterpoint, launched just a block down the street about six months later. They competed ferociously for decades, through upturns, downturns and even bankruptcies. When one of them announced its conversion from weekly to daily, the other covered the move within the hour.

They joined forces in 1932, publishing separately initially, one on the morning cycle and the other on the evening, before fully integrating as the *Times-News*. Today, it publishes mornings seven days a week.

One of its signal accomplishments, coming in a moment of almost magical promotional insight, was coining the nickname Magic Valley for its circulation area. But beyond that, the *Times News* long has been a dominant news and editorial presence around the Magic Valley, and a detailed provider of what one former editor liked to call "chicken dinner news."

Howard Publications, effectively a division of Scripps, picked up the paper in 1968 and set about expanding its reach throughout the region. Lee Enterprises, a national operator based in Iowa, accelerated that process after it scooped up the Howard papers in 2002.

During the 1990s, Lee set about acquiring nearly all of the Magic Valley's smaller papers, including the *Wood River Journal* at Hailey, *South Idaho Press* at Burley, *Gooding County Leader* at Gooding and *Northside News* at Jerome. It eventually shut them all down. Lee also picked up the *Daily Free Press*, across the Idaho/Nevada line in Elko. It continues to publish that paper as a satellite operation of the *Times-News*.

Signal-American   Weiser

Owner: Pronghorn Publishing and Harvest Moon Inc.
Address: 18 East Idaho St., Weiser, ID 83672
Phone: 208-549-1717
URL: www.signalamerican.org (unrestricted)
Established: 1882
Published: Wednesday
Market: Washington County
Circulation: 2,115
General Manager: Sarah Imada, mgr@signalamerican.org
Editor: William Anderson, scoop@signalamerican.org
Deadline: Noon Monday

Around the opening of the 20th century, the farm supply and river crossing community of Weiser, seat of Washington County, seemed poised for growth. It appeared to have a bright future as a transportation hub, linking major routes west into Oregon, north into northern Idaho and southeast to Utah, via the Idaho capital of Boise. But a string of decisions ended up pushing the main rail lines, the Interstate 84 freeway, and the key road and rail junctions to the west.

Weiser, situated at the confluence of the Weiser River with the mighty Snake, is perhaps best known these days as the home of the National Oldtime Fiddlers' Contest. It evolved in 1953 out of a fiddling contest originating in 1914.

The *Signal* was the first newspaper to enter the field, launching in 1882. The *American* followed in 1907, when prosperity still seemed like it might be just around the corner. They merged business operations in the 1960s, but continued to publish separate editions, the *American* on Monday and the *Signal* on Thursday. They merged in earnest in 1985, creating the *Signal American*. It publishes on Wednesday.

Oregon Newspapers

By city, in alphabetical order

Democrat-Herald   Albany

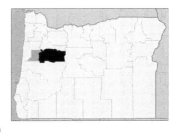

Owner: Lee Enterprises
Address: 600 Lyon St. SW, Albany, OR 97321
Phone: 541-926-2211
URL: www.democratherald.com (subscription required for full access)
Established: 1865
Published: Monday-Friday PM, Saturday and Sunday AM
Market: Linn County
Circulation: 14,092 weekday, 14,779 Sunday (ABC)
Publisher: Rick Parrish, rick.parrish@tdn.com (joint with Corvallis)
Editor & General Manager: Mike McInally, mike.mcinally@lee.net (joint with Corvallis)

Albany got its start as a farming and manufacturing city with its earliest settlers, the Montieth and Hackleman families, which had various differences, few stronger than on politics: The Montieths and their allies were Democrats, and the Hacklemans and their friends were Republicans, and the two maintained a hedge splitting the sides of town where each was dominant.

That forms some of the background for the *Albany Democrat-Herald*, which traces its heritage back to the *Albany Democrat*, founded in 1859, and *Albany Herald*, founded 20 years later. The *Democrat* was a vocal advocate for the Confederate cause during the Civil War, when it was still publishing as a weekly. It went daily in the 1870s, post-war. The paper was owned and operated by former New York lawyer Fed Nutting from 1882 to 1912, a run of 30 years. An even longer run began in 1918, when the paper was acquired by local farmer and businessman W.L. Jackson. The *Democrat* and its successor, the *Democrat-Herald*, remained in his family until the death of his son, Glenn, in 1980.

The *Democrat* bought out its rival daily in 1925 for the princely sum of $25,000 to create the *Democrat-Herald*.

Serving a predominantly blue-collar community accustomed to taking its leisure in the evening, the *Democrat-Herald* published on the PM cycle until 2010. As a by-product in recent years, that facilitated press-sharing with its Lee-owned sister paper in Corvallis, the long-AM *Gazette-Times*.

The papers now take turns on the Albany press, which includes units salvaged from the old Corvallis press when it was dismantled. The *Democrat-Herald* prints first, on a midnight cycle, and the *Gazette-Times* follows.

The two papers share advertising, production, circulation and accounting departments, and several elements of their news departments, including sports, business and photo. They also publish a joint Sunday morning edition under a *Mid-Valley Sunday* flag.

The collaboration between the two papers is a relatively recent phenomenon, resulting from a series of ownership changes.

After Glenn Jackson inherited majority interest in the *Democrat-Herald* from his father in 1949, he bought out his minority partner and began buying Oregon weeklies. He came to own nine of them in all, and retained them until his death in 1980.

The Jackson papers were bought by Capital Cities/ABC, a large media chain swallowed up in 1996 by an even larger one – Disney. Disney retained ABC, ESPN and other elements, but sold the Cap Cities newspapers to the Iowa-based Lee Enterprises chain in 1998.

Lee had already acquired the Corvallis *Gazette-Times* by then, and quickly began to explore synergies between the two neighboring dailies. In recent years, they have even come to share an editor and publisher – Mike McInally, who came to Corvallis as publisher after a long editing career in the Lee bastion of Montana.

The name most associated with the *Democrat-Herald* in recent decades was Hasso Hering, a German-born newspaperman who joined the staff in 1977 and took the editorial helm the following year. He continued as editor and/or publisher until his retirement in mid-2012.

Daily Tidings   Ashland

Owner: Dow Jones Local Media Group, a division of Newcastle Investment Corp. (formerly Ottaway Newspapers Inc.)
Address: 111 N. Fir Street, Medford, OR 97501
Phone: 541-776-4411
URL: www.dailytidings.com (subscription required for full access)
Market: Coverage: Ashland area.
Established: 1876
Published: Monday through Saturday PM

Market: Ashland area
Circulation: 1,916 (ABC)
Publisher: J. Grady Singletary, gsingletary@mailtribune.com (joint with Medford)
Editor: Robert L. Hunter, bhunter@mailtribune.com (joint with Medford)

Ashland is an aberration of an Oregon city. Located outside the Willamette Valley, its community base includes Southern Oregon University and the Oregon Shakespeare Festival, which give it a cultural environment far removed from most other southern or eastern Oregon cities. It certainly is distinctive from nearby Medford, which may help explain why it has retained a local daily newspaper that is one of the smallest in the region.

Like its big brother to the north, the Medford *Mail Tribune*, the *Ashland Daily Tidings* is owned by the Dow Jones arm of Rupert Murdoch's News Corp. One of the smallest dailies it the state, the six-day *Tidings* has no office of its own. Its five reporters work out of *Mail Tribune* quarters in Medford, where the paper is paginated and published.

The Medford and Ashland papers are the only ones in the state employing a metered charging system for online news. The first three stories in a given month are free without registration, and the next seven with registration. More frequent visits require a subscription.

The *Tidings* Internet presence piggybacks on the *Mail Tribune* web operation.

Ashland was part of the Glenn Jackson group, based in Albany. Through a series of sales involving Capital Cities Communications, ABC and the Walt Disney Co., it landed with the national Lee Enterprises chain. Lee sold the paper to Ottaway Newspapers Inc., a formerly independent newspaper group then operating as a subsidiary of Dow Jones & Co, in 2002.

In the spring of 2013, Murdoch began shopping the Dow Jones group through the New York investment house Waller Capital. In September, he found a buyer – Newcastle Investment Corp., a subsidiary of the Fortress Investment Group.

Fortress owns GateHouse Media, whose stable includes 78 dailies in 21 states, along with 235 weeklies and 91 shoppers. The company said its plan was to reorganize the heavily debt-ridden GateHouse via Chapter 11 bankruptcy, then merge it with Dow Jones Local Media to create a new parent company called New Media.

The Daily Astorian   Astoria

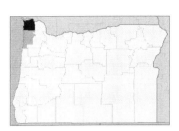

Owner: EO Media Group
Address: 949 Exchange St., Astoria, OR 97103
Phone: 503-325-3211
URL: www.dailyastorian.com (subscription required for full access)
Established: 1873
Published: Monday through Friday PM
Market: Clatsop County
Circulation: 7,001 (SO)
Editor & Publisher: Steve Forrester, sforrester@dailyastorian.com
Managing Editor: Patrick Webb, pwebb@dailyastorian.com

In 1810, the Pacific Fur Company, a trading company owned by John Jacob Astor, founded Fort Astoria as a permanent trading post. Unlike so many such efforts, this one took root, and Astoria has been a permanent community ever since – the oldest in the Northwest.

Newspapers came considerably later. Founded by DeWitt Clinton Ireland, Astoria's first paper began life on July 1, 1873, as the *Tri-Weekly Astorian*. It went daily three years later, becoming by turns *The Daily Astorian*, *The Daily Morning Astorian* and the *Morning Astorian*.

In 1930, the *Astorian* merged with the *Evening Astorian-Budget*. Adopting a *Budget* publication cycle dating back to 1893, it became the *Evening Astorian-Budget*. Though remaining on the PM cycle, it reverted to *The Daily Astorian* in 1960.

The corporate entity, the Astorian-Budget Publishing Company, was merged into the East Oregonian Publishing Company in 1973. In 2010, the company replaced its 40-year-old press in Astoria with a five-year-old press acquired from the Chicago Sun-Times. In addition to *The Daily Astorian*, it uses that press to print the *Chinook Observer*, the *Seaside Signal* and coastal weeklies from Steve Hungerford's Country Media group. By 2013, the company, founded to publish the *East Oregonian* newspaper in Pendleton, had broadened its holdings in Oregon and Washingon to the point where it decided to adopt a new name more reflective of that — the EO Media Group.

The company is owned by the Forrester family. It got its start in newspaper ownership with the late J.W. "Bud" Forrester's marriage to Eleanor Aldrich, whom he met at Oregon State University.

Record-Courier   Baker City

Owner: Brinton Estate, dba C.M. Brinton & Sons LLC
Address: 1718 Main St., Baker City, OR 97814
Phone: 541-523-5353
URL: www.therconline.com (subscription required for full access)
Established: 1901
Published: Thursday
Market: Baker County
Circulation: 2,301 (SO)
Publisher: Greg Brinton, news@therconline.com
Editor: Debby Schoeningh, news@therconline.com
Deadline: 3 p.m. Monday

The *Record-Courier* was created by merger in 1931. The *Courier* originated in Baker City, but the *Record* originated in Haines, a neighboring Baker County community. It remains the only newspaper ever published in Haines.

Charles McKay Brinton, who had previously published newspapers and run print shops in North Dakota, Montana, and Washington, bought the *Haines Record* and *North Powder News* (located in those cities) in 1928. The *News* fell victim to the Great Depression, but the *Record* survived. His family traces its roots all the way back to William Penn. It's first house, a 1704 colonial, still stands in West Chester, Pennsylvania. C.M.'s many adventures included publication of newspapers on the Sioux and Blackfoot Indian reservations. C.M.'s son, Byron Charles Brinton, who was born in a family print shop in Fessenden, N.D., served as editor from 1934 to 1999 and publisher from 1959 until 2004. He sold to his son Byron Dorsey Brinton. Byron D., known as Ron D., died in 2005 at the age of 59. The paper passed to another third-generation family member – Ron's brother, Greg Charles Brinton.

Though the *Record-Courier* faced stiff competition from the *Baker City Herald* (see that entry), which only recently cut back from daily to tri-weekly, Byron C. refused to accept advertising for either tobacco or liquor during his 65-year run at the helm. He said he believed his was the first paper in the country to take such a stand.

Ron D. got his start in the family business sweeping the floors for 45 cents an hour. He said that supplied him with enough money to get a regular candy fix next door at Our Market.

The family bought its first offset press, a Goss Unitube, in 1970. It replaced the Unitube with a three-unit Goss Community in 1980. However, like the competing *Herald*, it now contracts its printing out to its larger northeastern Oregon neighbor, the *La Grande Observer*.

In a concession to electronic times, it is now offering an e-edition to paid subscribers, in a PDF format.

Herald   **Baker City**

Owner: Western Communications
Address: 1915 First St., Baker City, OR 97814
Phone: 541-523-3673
URL: www.bakercityherald.com (unrestricted)
Established: 1870
Published: Monday, Wednesday and Friday PM
Market: Baker County
Circulation: 2,615 (SO)
Publisher: Kari Borgen, kborgen@bakercityherald.com (joint with LaGrande)
Editor: Jayson Jacoby, jjacoby@bakercityherald.com
Deadline: 9:30 a.m. day of publication

Baker City was the original name of the paper's home community, which is situated about 45 miles south of La Grande in Oregon's northeastern corner. Residents voted to drop "city" in 1910 and to restore it 80 years later.

The *Herald* lost its long-held status as the smallest daily in Oregon – and, for that matter, one of the smallest anywhere – when it converted to a tri-weekly publication cycle on June 1, 2009. It is printed on the press of its larger sister paper to the north, the *La Grande Observer*. The *Herald* and *Observer* have long been owned by the Chandler family's Western Communications. The company is based in Bend, home of its flagship paper, *The Bulletin*.

The *Herald* was founded as the *Bedrock Democrat* in 1870. It went through iterations in the ensuing decades before becoming the *Baker Democrat-Herald*. When Baker became Baker City in 1990 (to better distinguish it from Baker County), the paper became *Baker City Herald*.

One of the biggest headline stories of recent years chronicled the January 4, 2003, arrest of Edward Morris, who was convicted of murdering his wife and children in the Tillamook State Forest. Another came in 2007, when Portland-area resident Doris Anderson survived 13 days on her own in the Eagle Cap Wilderness vicinity after the family vehicle got stuck.

In 2013, the paper launched an e-edition, available to home-delivery subscribers in a PDF format at no extra cost. The *Herald*'s website remains free, but only a limited selection of stories is posted.

Western World   **Bandon**

Owner: Lee Enterprises
Address: 1185 Baltimore Ave. SE, Bandon, OR 97411.
Phone: 541-347-2423

URL: www.bandonwesternworld.com (unrestricted)
Established: 1912
Published: Wednesday
Market: Bandon area (Coos County)
Circulation: 1,537 (SO)
Owner: Lee Enterprises
Publisher: Jeff Precourt, jeff.precourt@theworldlink.com (with Coos Bay, Reedsport)

In 1851, French fur traders discovered gold at Whiskey Run Beach, on the Southern Oregon coast near Bandon. That drew settlers who soon became engaged in a range of other commercial activities, including farming, logging, fishing, and shipping. The city, situated at the mouth of the Coquille River, was named after settlers from Bandon, Ireland. It was incorporated on February 18, 1891.

The first newspaper to serve the area was the *Curry County Recorder*, founded in the hamlet of Denmark in 1883 by P.O. Chilstrom and J.M Upton. They renamed it the *Southwest Oregon Recorder* in 1884 and, following relocation of their enterprise to Bandon, the *Bandon Recorder* in 1887. It served residents not only of the coastal enclave of Bandon, but also of the surrounding farming and fishing communities.

The seeds of its demise were sown in 1912, with the founding of the rival *Bandon Western World*. It went into bankruptcy proceedings in 1915 and ceased publication in 1916.

In 2003, the paper was bought by Southwestern Oregon Newspapers, a subsidiary of Lee Enterprises. Lee also owns other properties in the region, including the daily *Coos Bay World*, and manages them as a group.

Valley Times   Beaverton

Owner: Pamplin Media Group
Address: 6605 S.E. Lake Road, Portland, OR 97222
Phone: 503-684-0360
URL: www.beavertonvalleytimes.com (unrestricted)
Established: 1921
Published: Thursday
Market: Beaverton area (Washington County)
Circulation: 3,857 (SO)
Publisher: Christine Moore, cmoore@commnewspapers.com (joint with Tigard)
Managing Editor: Christina Lent, clent@commnewspapers.com (joint with Tigard)
Deadline: Noon Friday

The *Valley Times* got its start in 1921, when Beaverton still lay largely outside the Portland metropolitan orbit. Since, it has become one of the largest and most prominent of Portland's suburban communities.

However, with the help of its newspaper, it has still managed to maintain an identity of its own. The paper remained in local ownership until 1981, when longtime owner and publisher Hugh Edward McGilvra sold it to the Baker family, owner of the *Eugene Register-Guard*.

At the time, the Bakers were in the process of assembling a stable of weeklies in the Portland suburbs. They eventually came to hold six in all. In January 1988, the Baker family went into partnership with the Smith family, owner of the Eagle Newspapers chain of mostly suburban weeklies, to create Community Newspapers. It encompassed both families' holdings, including the *Valley Times*, with Eagle serving as the managing entity.

In 1996, the partners sold their collection of suburban Portland newspapers to Steve and Randalyn Clark, who continued to operate them under the Community Newspapers banner. Four years later, they sold to the Pamplin Media Group, which has amassed extensive holdings in the metro area.

Bulletin   **Bend**

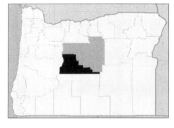

Owner: Western Communications
Address: 1777 S.W. Chandler Ave., Bend, OR 97708
Phone: 541-382-1811
URL: www.bendbulletin.com (subscription required for full access)
Established: 1903
Published: Monday through Sunday AM
Market: Deschutes, Crook, and Jefferson counties
Circulation: 29,294 weekday, 28,992 Saturday, 29,351 Sunday (ABC)
Publisher: Gordon Black, gblack@bendbulletin.com
Editor: John Costa, costa@bendbulletin.com

The Bulletin was founded in 1903 by Portland entrepreneur Max Lueddemann, who saw opportunity in the sagebrush communities beginning to develop on Oregon's dry east side. He founded papers first at Shaniko and Antelope, then set his sights on Bend – all the while continuing to live in Portland himself. The paper, produced on a hand press housed in a log schoolhouse, debuted on March 27.

Lueddemann missed his bet in Shaniko and Antelope, but not in Bend. Starting with nothing more than a sawmill, irrigation system, and handful of houses, it gradually came to dominate Central Oregon, and, to a large extent, the entire two-thirds of the state lying east of the Cascade Range. And all of this was faithfully chronicled by the *Bulletin*, which flexed its muscles in tandem.

Early on, the *Bulletin* had a competitor, the *Deschutes Echo*. But it swallowed up that rival in 1904.

Bend got a big boost in 1915, when Shevlin-Hixon announced plans for a sawmill with a projected workforce of 500 and projected output of 80 million board feet a year. The *Bulletin*, an enthusiastic supporter, used the development as leverage in a successful campaign to have Deschutes County carved out of Crook County in 1916, with Bend serving as its county seat. It also took the opportunity to take the paper daily, publishing on the PM cycle. As Bend continued to grow as a residential, commercial and industrial center, not to mention tourist mecca, the *Bulletin* added a Sunday morning edition to its otherwise PM lineup. Eventually, it converted to full-fledged seven-day publication on the AM cycle.

Most of its history has been encompassed in just two ownerships – those of Robert W. Sawyer and Robert C. Chandler.

Sawyer, a prominent Bend businessman, bought the paper in 1919 and published it until 1953. Then, ready to retire, he put it up for sale. Bend's prospects shone so bright, the offering drew strong interest from major newspaper chains, which were willing to pay top dollar. But Sawyer was taken with a shoestring bid tendered by Chandler, a young U.S. Army veteran who grew up on a farm in California's fertile Tulare County.

What he lacked in resources, Chandler made up for in credentials. After completing studies at Stanford University, he got his start at small papers in Northern California, then graduated to the *San Francisco Chronicle, Denver Post,* and United Press International. To make the deal work, Sawyer settled on a down payment of just $6,000.

Chandler ran the paper for the next 43 years, until succumbing to prostate cancer in 1996, but never claimed the title of publisher. He served as editor of the paper throughout his career, both in title and in fact, and was very proud of it. Publishers reported to him in his newsroom office, and they earned his wrath if they ever forgot it.

He was intensely loyal to UPI, and was one of the last owners anywhere to abandon the failing service in favor of The Associated Press. He saw opportunity in the *Bulletin*'s ability to dominate all of Central Oregon, not just Bend or even Deschutes County, so he dropped "Bend" from the name in 1963.

Along the way, Chandler began picking up other papers as opportunities arose, mostly in Oregon, and operating them under the Western Communications banner. He came to own the *La Grande Observer, Baker City Herald, Hermiston Herald, Redmond Spokesman,* and *Burns Times-Herald* on Oregon's dry side, the *Curry Coastal Pilot* on the southern Oregon coast, the *Triplicate* on the northern California coast and the *Union-Democrat* in Sonora, California.

After his death, the papers passed to his eight children. His youngest daughter, Betsy McCool, continues to represent the family's interests in her capacity as chairman of the board.

The company has sold the *Hermiston Herald* and and *Burns Times-Herald*, but the rest of its holdings remain intact.

Curry Coastal Pilot   Brookings

Owner: Western Communications
Address: 507 Chetco Ave., Brookings, OR 97415
Phone: 541-469-3123
URL: www.currypilot.com (unrestricted)
Established: 1946
Published: Wednesday and Saturday
Market: Southern Curry County
Circulation: 6,168 (SO)
Publisher: Charles R. Kocher, publisher@currypilot.com
Editor: Scott Graves, sgraves@currypilot.com
Deadline: Noon the day prior to publication

Brookings was founded as a company town in 1908 by the Brookings Lumber and Box Company, which used nearby stands of Coast Range timber as its wood supply. It has tried repeatedly but unsuccessfully to annex its unincorporated sister community of Harbor, so much of the local population lies outside city limits. In recent decades, lumbering and fishing have declined, and the community has become more of a bedroom community for retirees and employees of the Pelican Bay State Prison just across the state line in Crescent City, California.

The county's other two substantial cities, Port Orford and Gold Beach, lie well to the north. Gold Beach, the most central, serves as county seat.

Like the *Triplicate*, its sister paper in Crescent City, the *Pilot* is printed at a plant mid-way between the two in Smith River. Both the papers and the plant are owned by Western Communications, a family group based in Bend.

The *Pilot* posts selected elements of its reports on the web, where readership is unrestricted. However, it is about to begin publishing a subscription-only e-edition in a PDF format.

Like many papers, daily and weekly both, it has moved to a narrower format. It converted to a 23-inch width in October 2012.

The Times   Brownsville

Owner: V&H Media LLC
Address: 343 Main St., Brownsville, OR 97327
Phone: 541-466-5311
URL: www.thebrownsvilletimes.com (news not posted online, but PDFs available through SmallTownPapers)
Established: 1888
Published: Wednesday
Market: Brownsville area (Linn County)
Circulation: 783 (SO)
Owners & Publishers: Vance and Holly Parrish, thetimes089@centurytel.net
Deadline: Noon Monday

Brownsville was founded as Calapooya, an alternate spelling for the Calipooia River, on whose banks it lies. It originally served as Linn County seat, but lost that distinction to Albany early on.

Local newspapering began when George Dyson founded the *Advertiser* in 1878. The *Advertiser* succumbed in short order, but hard on its heels came the *Times, Banner,* and *Informant.* Homer Davenport of Silverton, who went on to become a nationally renowned cartoonist, suggested the *Times* venture to his friend Albert Cavender, then working at the *Woodburn Independent.* Cavender took him up on it, and his enterprise was the one that survived. F.M. Brown bought the paper in 1906 and published it for many years. The paper's best known editor in those years probably was D.H. Talmadge, who went on to become a highly regarded columnist at *The Oregonian.*

Don Ware, now in his second four-year term as mayor of Brownsville, served as editor, publisher, and owner of the *Times* for many years. He said he saw no conflict between his newspaper and municipal roles, as both involved looking out for the best interests of Brownsville. Finally deciding to retire at the age of 76, he sold the *Times* to Vance and Holly Parrish in January 2012, but agreed to stay on as editor for a time through the transition. In addition to Brownsville, the paper serves the nearby Linn County communities of Shedd, Halsey, and Crawfordsville.

Times-Herald   **Burns**

Owner: Survival Media LLC
Address: 355 N. Broadway, Burns, OR 97720
Phone: 541-573-2022
URL: www.burnstimesherald.info (unrestricted)
Established: 1887
Published: Wednesday
Market: Harney County
Circulation: 3,445 (SO)
Editor: Randy Parks, rparks@burnstimesherald.info

The *Burns Times-Herald* has long boasted on its mast, "Covers Harney County Like the Sagebrush." And in the vast and open arid cattle country it serves, on Oregon's dry eastern flank, that's saying something.

The paper was owned for many years by Western Communications, a family-owned newspaper group based in Bend. But in June 2003, the company sold to Scott Olson, who had spent the previous six years publishing the *The Vidette* in Montesano, Washington, the last three as owner. Though Olson would go on to found the *Springfield Times* in 2008 and buy the *Creswell Chronicle* in 2011, in Oregon's Willamette Valley, he only retained the *Times-Herald* for a little over two years.

Following a brief intervening ownership, Sue Pedersen led a five-member group of employees that agreed to buy the paper for $400,000 in 2006, creating Survival Media as the vehicle. They took out second mortgages, pooled their savings and landed a state grant to come up with the $100,000 down payment.

Pedersen cashed out her stake and left the paper in March 2013, but her partners are continuing to cover Harney County "like the sagebrush."

The Herald   **Canby**

Owner: Pamplin Media Group
Address: 241 N. Grant St., Canby, OR 97013
Phone: 503-266-6831
URL: www.canbyherald.com (subscription required for full access)
Established: 1906
Published: Wednesday and Saturday
Market: Canby area (Northern Marion County)
Circulation: 5,388 (SO)
Publisher: William D. Cassel, wcassel@eaglenewspapers.com
Editor: John Baker, jbaker@canbyherald.com
Deadline: Noon Friday

Canby got its start in 1857 as Baker Prairie. It was later renamed for Edward Richard Sprigg Canby, a Civil War general who died in the Modoc War at the hands of infamous native warrior Captain Jack. Platted in 1870 and incorporated in 1893, it counted about 16,000 residents when the 2010 census was taken. Though it lies within a county of almost 300,000 and a metropolitan statistical area of almost 2.5 million, it has managed to maintain a rural and independent nature.

Canby's local newspaper, *The Herald*, publishes Wednesday and Saturday. It shares its Saturday content with the *Woodburn Independent*, which lies across the line in northern Marion County. It also shares its publisher, William Cassel, but with the *Mollala Pioneer* and *Wilsonville Spokesman*.

The *Herald* was purchased by Eagle in 1972, one of 11 papers the company acquired during the 1970s, which marked its period of greatest expansion. The company converted the group of four papers from broadsheet to tabloid in the spring of 2012. Then, in January 2013, it sold them to Pamplin Media Group in a package that also included the *Madras Pioneer* and *Newberg Graphic*.

The *Herald* and its three companion papers continue to be printed at Eagle's web press plant in Salem.

Illinois Valley News   Cave Junction

Owner: W.H. Alltheway LLC
Address: 321 S. Redwood Highway, Cave Junction, OR 97523
Phone: 541-592-2541
URL: www.illinois-valley-news.com (unrestricted access to e-edition posted in PDF format)
Established: 1937
Published: Wednesday
Market: Cave Junction area (Southwestern Josephine County)
Circulation: 2,459 (SO)
Publisher: Dan Mancuso, dan@illinois-valley-news.com
Editor: Kevan Moore, kevan@illinois-valley-news.com

The *Illinois Valley News* was founded in 1937 in what was then the unincorporated community of Cave City, self-proclaimed gateway to the Oregon Caves National Monument, south of Grants Pass. Located at Highway 199's junction with Highway 46, leading to the monument, Cave City incorporated and became Cave Junction. The first issue of the new paper consisted of just four pages. It featured ads from points as distant as Medford and Grants Pass, to the north and east.

Bob Rodriquez, formerly news editor at the *Curry Coastal Pilot* in Brookings, bought the paper with his wife, Jan, in February 1986. They ran it for almost 25 years, the longest stint of anyone in the paper's history, before selling it to Dan Mancuso in 2010. According to a story by Scott Jorgensen, Rodriquez got his start in newspapering as a copy boy at the *San Diego Evening Tribune* in 1963. "I got to see every part of the process of producing a daily paper," he told Jorgensen. He spent eight years at the *Pilot* before acquiring the *Valley News* from another longtime owner – Bob Grant. He said it took some creative financing on both ends to make the deal work.

The Chief   Clatskanie

Owner: Clatskanie Chief Publishing Co., a partnership of Philip and Deborah Steele Hazen and their daughter, Amanda Gail Moravec
Address: 148 N. Nehalem St., Clatskanie, OR 97016
Phone: 503-728-3350
URL: www.clatskaniechiefnews.com (unrestricted)
Established: 1891
Published: Thursday
Market: Northern Columbia, eastern Clatsop counties: Rainier, Westport, Knappa, and Svensen
Circulation: 2,407 (SO)
Editor & Publisher: Deborah Steele Hazen, chief@clatskanie.com
Deadline: Noon Wednesday

The Chief is an independent family-owned newspaper that has served the people of Northern Columbia County and Eastern Clatsop County for more than a century. Founded by F.T. Shute, in 1891, it has been owned and operated by the Steele family since February 1922. The family is now into its fourth generation of active management and ownership.

The patriarch was William Arthur "Art" Steele, who covered the Black Sox scandal for a Chicago daily early in his career, then headed west, landing in Lewiston. Holder of degrees from Linfield and Yale, he was just 25 when he acquired the Chief. He went in with a partner who only lasted two months.

The paper carries a Thursday date, as it reaches subscribers in Thursday's mail. However, it is printed Wednesday morning and reaches newsstands Wednesday afternoon. About 1,550 papers are mailed to subscribers. Street sales account for the rest of its distribution. The Chief also publishes a free-distribution TMC with a press run of 7,650. Both the newspaper and its TMC offshoot are printed at The Daily Astorian.

It maintains an unrestricted website featuring all of its front page stories and a limited selection of other items. It also has 250 residents paying $10 a year to subscribe to a breaking news e-mail service, an outgrowth of a devastating storm that struck in December 2007.

The Times-Journal   Condon

Owner: Macro Graphics of Condon LLC
Address: 319 S. Main St., Condon, OR 97823
Phone: 541-384-2421.
URL: www.smalltownpapers.com/newspapers/newspaper.php?id=386 (no website of its own, but PDF available here through SmallTownPapers)
Established: 1886
Published: Thursday

Market: Gilliam, Wheeler, and Sherman counties
Circulation: 1,467 (SO)
Co-Publishers: McLaren and Janet Stinchfield, times-journal@jncable.com
Editor: McLaren Stinchfield, times-journal@jncable.com

Newspapering in central Oregon's lightly populated ranching communities began with the founding of Wheeler County's *Fossil Journal* in 1886 by Scotsman James S. Stewart. The *Condon Globe* followed in 1891 and the *Condon Times* in 1900, both in neighboring Gilliam County. The *Globe* and *Times* consolidated in 1919 to create the *Globe-Times*, and it acquired the *Fossil Journal* in 1975 to create the *Times-Journal*. Though based in Condon, the paper also serves Fossil, Mitchell, Spray, Arlington, and Lonerock.

McLaren (Mac) Stinchfield and his wife, Jan, are the fourth generation to own the *Times-Journal*. The family involvement began with a great-great uncle – Scotsman William Christie, founder of the *Times*. The paper's heritage through the *Globe*, founded by Sloan P. Shutt, makes it the oldest continuously operated business enterprise in Condon. The Stinchfields went in with B. Rockne Wilson to purchase the paper in the fall of 1976, shortly after the merger. Two years later, they bought Wilson out.

The newspaper has been published from a sandstone building on Condon's South Main Street since 1930. The building was constructed in 1903 of stone quarried at Lost Valley. It was built to house a bank, but the Bank Saloon, billed as "a gentleman's retreat," ended up being the initial tenant.

The World   Coos Bay

Owner: Lee Enterprises
Address: 350 Commercial Ave., Coos Bay, OR 97420
Phone: 541-269-1222
URL: www.theworldlink.com (unrestricted)
Established: 1878
Published: Monday through Thursday PM and Saturday AM
Market: Coos County
Circulation: 8,646 weekday, 8,694 Saturday (ABC)
Publisher: Jeff Precourt, jeff.precourt@theworldlink.com (joint with Bandon, Reedsport)

Coastal settlements around Coos Bay go back to 1853. The first was actually the community of Marshfield. But for many years, contact was easier over the ocean from San Francisco that over the mountains from other Oregon communities. So Coos Bay and its long stretch of adjoining towns made up a very separate and distinct community. Some of that history is reflected in the local newspaper name: *The World* newspaper was first published in 1878 as *The Coast Mail*.

During the next few decades, a long series of mergers and name changes took place. Then Sheldon Sackett bought the paper, ushering in several decades of stability under family ownership. The paper was known as the *Marshfield Times* when Sackett bought it in 1930. He moved it from Marshfield to Coos Bay and renamed it the *World*.

Sackett also owned other media outlets, including KISN, a Portland radio station. Upon his death in 1968, sons John and David took over. On July 2, 1973, John and David announced sale of the paper to the Scripps League, a national chain controlled by the Scripps family.

Through the Southwestern Oregon Publishing Company, the *World* acquired the *Bandon Western World* in 2003 and Reedsport *Umpqua Post* in 2004, and in 2005 Lee Enterprises purchased Southwestern Oregon Publishing. *The World* publishes the two weeklies at its plant in Coos Bay. It also provides them with editorial and operational direction.

Published as a five-day daily, the paper launched its website in 1999.

Valley Sentinel   Coquille

Owner: Beacon Communications
Address: 61 E. First St., Coquille, OR 97423
Phone: 541-396-3191
URL: http://www.thesentinelepaper.com (unrestricted access to e-edition in PDF format)
Established: 1882
Published: Wednesday
Market: Coos County
Circulation: 3,010 (SO)
Editor, Publisher & Owner: Jean Ivey, jeanivey@mycomspan.com
Deadline: Noon Monday

Trapping and exploration brought European transplants to the Southern Oregon coast as early as 1828. The first settlement was established at Empire City, now part of Coos Bay, in 1853. Later that year, the territorial legislature fashioned Coos County out of Umpqua and Jackson counties. The legislature financed wagon roads from Coos Bay to Jacksonville in 1854 and Roseburg in 1857, facilitating development in the county's timbered interior, where Coquille lies.

In 1896, the legislature allowed residents of the county to choose a county seat. Though Coos Bay was and still is several times larger, and the coast was already dotted with other fishing and port towns, they chose the interior logging town of Coquille.

Local newspapering began in 1882, before the community earned county seat status, with the founding of the *Coquille City Herald*. The weekly newspaper continued publishing as the *City Herald* or *Herald* until 1917, when it morphed into the *Coquille Valley Sentinel*. The *Valley Sentinel* was owned by H.A. Young from 1927 until 1952. It was later owned by Fred Haas for a time, then Bob and Betty Van Leer, longtime owners of the *Curry County Reporter* in Gold Beach. Competitors came and went, including the *Coquille City Bulletin*, published from 1901 to 1904, and the *Coquille Tribune*, published from 1933 to 1947.

G. Fredrick Taylor bought the paper in 1989, following a 30-year career with the *Wall Street Journal*. He published it until May 1, 2000, when he sold it to Del and Janet Richardson of Troy, Idaho.

Jean Ivey serves as editor, publisher, and owner of the *Valley Sentinel* today. Before becoming a newspaper owner, she spent 30 years ranching in Nevada. In another newspaper venture, she founded the *North Douglas County News* in Sutherlin in 2002. Six years later, she sold it to Becky Holm, who renamed it the *Douglas County News*.

Ivey has been highly vocal in local politics, sometimes stirring controversy. She helped fund Bob Main's 2012 Coos County commissioner campaign. A $1,500 contribution to Main was attributed to the *Sentinel* in state filings, but she said it actually came out of her own pocket. She described Main, one of 15 candidates, as a fellow Coquille resident who runs in the same circles she does. She said he shares her opposition to hiring a county administrator. Ivey got so upset with Coquille City Councilor Linda Short that she canceled Short's subscription, returned her money and allegedly refused to accept an ad from her when she announced for mayor against a *Valley Sentinel* correspondent. Ivey told a Coos Bay *World* reporter that Short would "never have a *Sentinel* again."

Gazette-Times   Corvallis

Owner: Lee Enterprises
Address: 600 S.W. Jefferson Ave., Corvallis, OR 97333
Phone: 541-753-2641
URL: www.gazettetimes.com (subscription required for full access)
Established: 1862
Published: Monday-Saturday AM and joint Sunday AM with Albany Democrat-herald as Mid-Valley Sunday
Market: Benton County
Circulation: 11,072 weekday, 10,951 Sunday (ABC)

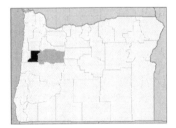

Publisher: Rick Parrish, rick.parrish@tdn.com (joint with Albany)
Editor & General Manager: Mike McInally, mike.mcinally@lee.net (joint with Albany)

Corvallis (the word translates to "heart of the valley") is one of Oregon's oldest communities. It dates back to the 1840s, when it was called Marysville. For a brief period, in fact, it served as Oregon's territorial capital. Corvallis went on to become a major processing and supply center for the farming and logging industries, and home of the land grant college that would eventually become Oregon State University. OSU combined strengths in agriculture, forestry, and teaching with the state's leading engineering program, and that led to development of one of Oregon's major high tech centers.

The early history of the Corvallis newspaper, the *Gazette-Times*, is deeply interwoven with partisan politics. And that was certainly not uncommon at the time.

The *Corvallis Gazette* was founded in 1862 as a Union and Republican-leaning counterpart to *The Democratic Crisis*, a Confederate and Democratic-leaning publication that got its start in 1859. Ironically, the *Gazette* inherited as its first editor T.B. Odeneal, former editor of *The Democratic Crisis*, who was converted to the Union side with the election of Republican Abraham Lincoln in 1860. Oregon tended to support the North rather than the South in the Civil War, but *The Democrat*, serving nearby Albany, was a dedicated backer of the Confederate cause. Interestingly, the *Gazette* evolved into a Democratic-leaning paper itself in the post-war years.

The other partner in the merger that would eventually create the *Gazette-Times*, the *Corvallis Times*, is a descendant of the *The Corvallis Chronicle*. It was launched in 1886 as a Republican counterweight to the now Democratic leaning *Gazette*. The *Gazette* was purchased in 1884 by a trio of men closely allied with the Oregon Pacific Railroad, which dominated local politics at the time. When Editor C.A. Cole refused their orders to support a pro-railroad Democrat in an 1886 Senate election, they fired him.

Sensing an opening, local Republicans launched the *Chronicle* and hired Cole as its first editor. The paper failed in short order, but local businessman Robert Johnson bought its presses at a sheriff's sale and founded *The Corvallis Times*.

In the early 1900s, Charles L. Springer purchased the *Gazette* and N.R. Moore purchased the *Times*. And both had designs on taking their papers daily. Springer went daily with the *Gazette* on May 1, 1909, but soon realized he lacked the resources to continue on his own. So he merged his operation with Moore's to create the daily *Corvallis Gazette-Times*, which published its first edition on July 2, 1909.

Kansas-transplant Claude Ingalls bought out Springer in 1915 and Myron K. Myers bought out Moore in 1923. Ingalls' son, Robert, later shared ownership with Myers' son, Bruce. They sold the paper to Lee Enterprises on Oct. 1, 1969. Lee later came into ownership of the neighboring *Albany Democrat-Herald* and *Lebanon Express* as well, and began to operate them jointly.

Sentinel   Cottage Grove

Owner: News Media Corporation
Address: 116 N. Sixth St., Cottage Grove, OR 97424
Phone: 541-942-3325
URL: www.cgsentinel.com (subscription required for full access)
Established: 1889
Published: Wednesday
Market: Southern Lane County
Circulation: 3,210 (SO)
Publisher: Jessica Baker, publisher@cgsentinel.com
Editor: Jon Stinnett, cgnews@cgsentinel.com
Deadline: 5 p.m. Friday

Shortly after the Lane County community of Cottage Grove was established in 1887, its population swelled to more than 3,000 with discovery of gold in nearby creeks, touching off the Bohemia mining boom. That provided the basis for a weekly newspaper, and the *Sentinel* was established in 1889.

Other papers came and went in the early years. Horace Mann launched the *Messenger* in 1897. Two years later, he sold it to C.J. Howard, who renamed it the *Bohemia Nugget*. The *Nugget* was aimed at miners at first, to the point that it prominently featured industry news and advertising. It later came into the hands of Bohemia Mining promoter Frank Hard. Under the leadership of Walter Conner and Joe DuBruille, another early paper, the *Leader*, later bought out the Nugget. In 1918, the *Sentinel* bought out the *Nugget* in turn.

Lee Enterprises acquired the *Sentinel* in 1997. Nine years later, Lee sold it to the current owner, News Media Corporation. Not to be confused with Rupert Murdoch's News Corp., this News Media Corp. owns 75 community shoppers and weeklies printed at 10 plants spread across nine states.

The Chronicle   Creswell

Owner: S.J. Olson Publishing
Address: 34 W. Oregon Ave., Creswell, OR 97426
Phone: 541-895-2197.
URL: www.thecreswellchronicle.com (unrestricted but limited)
Established: 1965
Published: Thursday
Market: Creswell area (Lane County)
Circulation: 754 (SO)
Publisher: Scott J. Olson, publisher@springfieldtimes.net (joint with Springfield)
Deadline: Noon Monday

The *Chronicle* debuted on September 30, 1909, the year Creswell incorporated. It has since undergone two lapses in publication, at least two changes in name and no less than 16 changes in ownership.

The paper's first run lasted eight years, ending in 1917. Publication did not resume until 1946, a lapse of almost 30 years, then ceased again in 1950. Its third incarnation began in 1965, and it continues to this day. During at least a portion of its history, it was published as the *New Era*.

Both *The Chronicle* and the *Springfield Times*, a neighboring Lane County weekly launched in 2008, after its long-time predecessor failed, are owned by Scott J. Olson through S.J. Olson Publishing. The company is based in the Eastern Oregon ranching community of Burns, where Olson and his wife, Jeanne, previously owned and operated the *Times-Herald* for more than two years.

Olson bought the *Chronicle* from Helen Hollyer on October 21, 2011. She had purchased it from Todd M. Hakes on April 1, 2004.

"*The Creswell Chronicle* is a nice addition for our group of weekly newspapers," Olson said at the time of his purchase. "We will continue of offer in-depth news coverage for the Creswell community and will be able to offer a broader audience for advertisers."

Before making the move to Burns, he had spent six years editing and publishing *The Vidette* in Montesano, Washington, the last three as owner. A group of former employees has since pooled its resources to buy the Burns paper.

Polk County Itemizer-Observer   Dallas

Owner: Eagle Newspapers
Address: 147 S.E. Court St., Dallas, OR 97338
Phone: 503-623-2373
URL: www.polkio.com (unrestricted)
Established: 1875
Published: Wednesday
Market: Polk County
Circulation: 4,751 (SO)

Publisher: Nancy J. Adams, nadams@polkio.com
Managing Editor: Kurt Holland, kholland@polkio.com
Deadline: 5 p.m. Friday

Newspapering in the Polk County seat of Dallas began in 1875 with the founding of the *Polk County Itemizer*. The *Polk County Observer* followed in 1888, and they continued their competition for more than 40 years before finally calling a truce and merging forces in 1927.

The name most associated with the papers in recent years is that of Joe Blaha, who got his start in the circulation department at the *San Francisco Examiner*. He first took the helm in 1966.

Blaha left briefly to oversee the *Daily Journal* in Ukiah, California, introducing it to a new building featuring a new web offset press. But he returned in 1971, dividing his time initially between running the paper and helping its owner, then known as Blue Mountain Eagle but now known as Eagle Newspapers, establish a major new print plant in Salem. In 1978, when Eagle bought the *Lake Oswego Review*, he became publisher there. He helped orchestrate the spinoff of the *West Linn Tidings* during his tenure.

During the 1970s, Eagle went on a major acquisition binge. Among the properties it acquired were the weekly newspaper serving the neighboring cities of Monmouth and Independence, and it went on later to merge them into its Dallas operation.

The paper's current publisher, Nancy Adams, was hired by Blaha in 1973 to write society news. Editor Kurt Holland was hired away from *The Bulletin* in Bend.

The Enterprise   Drain

Owner: Sue Anderson
Address: 309 First St., Drain, OR 97435
Phone: 541-836-2241.
URL: www.354.com/drain/enterprise.htm (limited to page of city website)
Established: 1950
Published: Thursday
Market: Northern Douglas County
Circulation: 764 (SO)
Editor, Publisher & Owner: Sue Anderson, drainenterprise@earthlink.net
Deadline: Noon Tuesday

Newspapering in Drain, off Interstate 5 between Eugene and Roseburg, began in 1885 with the *Drain Echo*. It merged with *The Leader* in 1895 to create the *Echo-Leader*. The *Enterprise* was founded in 1922, though its current incarnation only dates back to its revival by the

Anderson family in 1950. A logging community, Drain was also served during the early 1900s by the *Nonpareil* and *Watchman*.

The paper is currently owned and operated by Suzanne "Sue" Anderson, who also has been mayor in Drain since 2002, a dual role not unprecedented in rural Oregon.

She inherited the paper from her parents, Lowell and Betty Anderson. Lowell and Betty met and married while working together at the *Oregon Statesman* in her native Salem. After their marriage in 1950, his father helped them buy the *Drain Enterprise*, and it would become a lifelong labor of love for them. Lowell served as editor and publisher until his death in 1992. With his passing, Betty took over as publisher and Sue as editor. Betty Anderson died in 2007, after devoting 57 of her 80 years to the family's newspaper venture.

Wallowa County Chieftain   Enterprise

Owner: EO Media Group
Address: 209 N.W. First St., Enterprise, OR 97828
Phone: 541-426-4567
URL: www.wallowa.com (subscription required for full access)
Established: 1884
Published: Thursday
Market: Wallowa County
Circulation: 2,962 (SO)
Publisher: Marissa Williams, mwilliams@bmeagle.com (joint with John Day)
Editor: Robert Ruth, editor@wallowa.com
Deadline: 2 p.m. Friday

Few communities in Oregon are more off the beaten track – not located on any major highway – than those in its first northeast corner, in Wallowa County. Those they link to the La Grande area to the outside world, and the newspaper from there circulates in Wallowa, it remains its own distinct community.

The *Wallowa County Chieftain* dates to May 15, 1884, when H.S. Heckethorn published the first issue in Joseph. The idea was conceived at a community meeting called by Joseph merchant F.D. McCully, who was instrumental in securing passage three years later of a bill breaking Wallowa County off from Union County.

At least two dozen other Wallowa County publications have come and gone during the *Chieftain*'s more than 125-year run. It stands today as the county's only newspaper, having never missed an issue. The *Chieftain* spent its first nine years in Joseph before moving to Enterprise in 1893. It is by far the oldest continuing business in the county.

The *Chieftain* rotated through 11 managers between 1884 and 1911. Then Kansas newsman, George Cheney, took the helm and continued to hold it for the next three decades, seeing the paper through both World War I and the Great Depression. Illinois lawyer Gwen Coffin purchased the paper in 1941 and served as its editor and publisher for the next 30 years, selling it to his son-in-law, Don Swart. Don's son, Rick, who got his start shoveling snow off the *Chieftain*'s front sidewalk at the age of 7, took over in 1998.

He sold to the Forrester family's Pendleton-based East Oregonian Publishing Company (now the EO Media Group) two years later, but stayed on as editor for several more years.

News   Estacada

Owner: Pamplin Media Group
Address: 307 S.W. Highway 224, Estacada, OR 97023.
Phone: 503-630-3241
URL: www.estacadanews.com (unrestricted)
Established: 1904
Published: Wednesday
Market: East Central Clackamas County
Circulation: 1,520 (SO)
President: J. Mark Garber, mgarber@theoutlookonline.com (joint with Gresham)
Executive Editor & General Manager: Steve Brown, sbrown@theoutlookonline.com (joint with Gresham)
Deadline: Noon Friday

By the 1890s, six fiercely competitive electric rail companies had lines crisscrossing Portland and its immediate suburbs. Eventually, they all came under the umbrella of the Oregon Water Power and Railway Company, which set about meeting their biggest common need – cheap electrical power – by erecting a series of hydroelectric dams on the Clackamas River.

A forerunner of Portland General Electric, OWPR began with construction of the Cazadero Dam in 1904, using Estacada as its home base. The fledgling community got a rail line, post office, and newspaper in quick succession in 1904. The following year, it incorporated. The flurry of development opened up a huge expanse of timber and provided a means to get it to market. For good measure, the community also began to develop resort facilities for Portlanders eager for scenic getaways in the woods, starting with the Hotel Estacada.

The *Estacada News* has been there to chronicle it all from the very start.

The paper was published as the *Estacada News* from 1904 to 1908, the *Estacada Progress* from 1908 to 1916 and *Eastern Clackamas News* from 1916 to 1928. In 1916, *The Morning Oregonian* called the paper, then being published every Thursday by R.M. Standish, "a fine little sheet" enjoying "a good advertising patronage."

Back under the *Estacada News* mantle since 2004, it has become part of a network of Pamplin Media Group papers covering virtually every nook of the Portland Metropolitan Area.

The Register-Guard Eugene

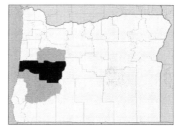

Owner: Baker family
Address: 3500 Chad Drive, Eugene, OR 97408
Phone: 541-485-1234
URL: www.registerguard.com (subscription required for e-edition, full access)
Established: 1862
Published: Monday through Sunday AM
Market: Lane County
Circulation: 50,729 weekday, 51,976 Saturday, 54,027 Sunday (ABC)
Editor & Publisher: Alton F. (Tony) Baker III, tony.baker@registerguard.com
Chief Operating Officer: David Pero, david.pero@registerguard.com
Managing Editor: Dave Baker, dave.baker@registerguard.com

Historically a timber and university community, Eugene was founded in the 1850s and incorporated in 1862. Newspapering there started immediately – in fact, as the first buildings were going up.

J. B. Alexander founded the *Eugene Guard* in 1862, but sold it the following year to J.W. Skaggs. Within a matter of months, Skaggs sold it to the Thompson & Victor partnership, the Thompson half of which had founded the *Eugene Herald* in 1859 and operated in for 18 months. After changing hands several more times in relatively short order, it was purchased by John and Ira Campbell in the late 1870s. They took it daily in 1890. The *Morning Register* was founded in 1905, making it a Johnny-come-lately by comparison. It published on an AM schedule while the *Guard* published on a PM schedule.

E.J. Finneran bankrupted the *Guard* in 1916. The University of Oregon School of Journalism published the paper while it was in receivership, with the legendary Eric Allen serving as editor.

After another series of sales, Alton F. Baker Sr., whose father had published the *Cleveland Plain Dealer*, bought the paper in 1927. And the Baker family has owned it ever since. Alton Baker bought out the *Morning Register* in 1930 to create the *Eugene Register-Guard*, now published in the morning itself. The *Register-Guard* became Oregon's second-largest daily when *The Oregonian* absorbed *The Oregon Journal* in 1982, claiming Portland all for itself.

Alton F. (Bunky) Baker Jr. inherited the newspaper in 1961. He passed it on to his brother, Edwin, who passed it on in turn to Alton F. (Tony) Baker III. It is one of the few regional dailies in the United States still in family ownership.

The newspaper began limiting free access to its locally produced news content in June 2013, joining, as it noted in its announcement, hundreds of other newspapers around the country that charge for digital content." Previously, it had been charging $2 a week for its e-edition, but not for access to news posted on its website. The *Guard*'s home page, wire content, obituaries and entertainment listings remain accessible to all, as do a limited number of its local stories. But once a visitor has reached his quota for local stories, he must take out a subscription for continued access. Electronic access comes free with a print subscription. It may also be purchased separately.

"The reason is simple ... ," Editor and Publisher Tony Baker said in announcing the change. "Circulation revenue must supplement advertising revenue for our digital content, just as it does for print."

Siuslaw News   Florence

Owner: News Media Corp.
Address: 148 Maple St., Florence, OR 97439
Phone: 541-997-3441
URL: www.thesiuslawnews.com (subscription required for full access)
Established: 1890
Published: Wednesday and Saturday
Market: Coastal Lane County
Circulation: 4,903 (SO)
Publisher: John Bartlett, publisher@thesiuslawnews.com
Editor: Theresa Baer, editor@thesiuslawnews.com
Deadline: Noon Monday for Wednesday, noon Thursday for Saturday

The twice-weekly *Siuslaw News* began life in 1890 as the *Siuslaw Oar*, reflecting its maritime location on the Lane County coast, I the pretty coastal town of Florence. It became *The West* on October 9, 1891, and published under that name until January 7, 1921. The *News* covers Western Lane County from Yachats on the north to Gardiner on the south.

Dave Holman bought the paper in 1958 and served as editor and publisher for 21 years. Upon his retirement on June 19, 1979, he was succeeded by his son, Paul. Paul Holman started with the paper in 1975. He stayed on for another 22 years after replacing his dad as publisher, a

26-year run in all. Holman sold the paper to the News Media Corporation, whose stable includes 75 publications in nine states, in 2000. He stayed on one year to assist with the transition.

Robert Serra served as the paper's editor for the last 24 years of the Holman reign and the first seven of the subsequent News Media reign. He is now president of Pacific Publishing, which publishes Central Oregon Coast phone directories out of Florence.

News-Times   Forest Grove

Owner: Pamplin Media Group
Address: 2038 Pacific Ave., Forest Grove, OR 97116
Phone: 503-357-3181
URL: www.fgnewstimes.com (unrestricted)
Established: 1886
Published: Wednesday
Market: Southern Washington County
Circulation: 3,096 (SO)
Editor: Nancy Townsley, ntownsley@fgnewstimes.com
Publisher: John Schrag, jschrag@fgnewstimes.com
Deadline: Noon Friday

Forest Grove has a much longer history and much better established identity than many of the Portland suburbs. As a result, the *News-Times* dates back more than 125 years – much longer than is typical for its sister publications.

Forest Grove was settled in the 1840s, platted in 1850 and incorporated in 1872. The first community in Washington County to become a full-fledge city, it was named for a grove of oak trees that still stands on what is now the campus of Pacific University. Papers serving Forest Grove in the early years included the *Monthly, Independent, Hatchet, Express, Index, Press,* and *Venture.*

At least two of them pre-date the *News-Times* and its direct ancestors. The *Monthly* was published as early as 1869 and the *Independent* as early as 1873. The *News* and *Times* combined forced to produce the *News-Times* on March 9, 1911 – more than a century ago. Originally, it was the *Washington County News-Times.*

In the 1970s, the Baker family, owner of the *Eugene Register-Guard,* began to amass a stable of weeklies in suburban Portland. Forest Grove's *News-Times* was one of them, along with the papers serving neighboring Tigard, Tualatin, and Beaverton. The Smith family's Eagle Newspapers, run by former governor Elmo Smith and former congressman Denny Smith also had begun to acquire suburban Portland weeklies by then. In January 1988, the two families pooled eight of their papers, including the *News-Times,* under the Community Newspapers mantle, and entrusted their management to Eagle Newspapers. The partners sold the group to Steve Clark in 1996. Four years later, he sold them to Eagle's principal rival in the market, Robert B. Pamplin Jr.'s Pamplin Media Group.

Like other Pamplin papers, the *News-Times* is printed at a plant in Gresham, home of the company's twice-weekly *Outlook*. It is sold on newsstands and home-delivered by mail.

Curry County Reporter   Gold Beach

Owner: Matt and Kim Hall
Address: 29821 Ellensburg Ave., Gold Beach, OR 97444
Phone: 541-247-6643
URL: www.currycountyreporter.com (unrestricted but very limited)
Established: 1914
Published: Wednesday
Market: Southern Curry County
Circulation: 2,351 (SO)
Editor & Publisher: Matt Hall, currycountyreporter@gmail.com (joint with Port Orford and Myrtle Point)

Gold Beach is a community of 2,500 toward the far southern end of the Oregon coast. It was founded as Ellensburg in the 1850s and later known as Ellensburgh, then Ellensburg again. It was renamed Gold Beach in 1890 after gold was discovered at the mouth of the Rogue River by placer miners. It has served as the seat of Curry County since 1859, but was not incorporated until 1945. Mail boats based in Gold Beach have been delivering mail upstream to Agness since 1895. The run is one of only two remaining in the U.S. today.

Gold Beach got its first newspaper, *The Gazette*, in 1893. It only lasted three years, publishing its final edition August 28, 1896. *The Curry County Reporter* was established in Gold Beach in 1914. It is most closely associated with two related families, the Van Leers and the Walkers.

The newspaper's longest ownership was under Robert "Bob" and Betty Van Leer, who purchased it from Wickes Shaw. The Van Leers met at the University of Missouri School of Journalism. After marrying in 1952, they headed west, settling initially in Eureka, Calif. They moved to Gold Beach to buy the *Reporter* in 1956, and ran it as partners for 41 years.

Initially, the printing was done in-house with a small sheet-fed printer, but the Van Leers soon switched to web offset printing under contract.

The Van Leers' daughter, Molly, started working full time at the paper in 1977. When they opted to retire in 1997, they turned it over to her to run in conjunction with her husband, Jim. The Walkers acquired the *Port Orford News*, at the northern end of Curry County, the same year. They continued to run that paper until 2003, when they sold it to Matt and WillowSong Hall.

Joel Summer and Rebecca Macko bought the *Reporter* in January 2006, after the Walkers began transitioning into retirement with a move to Salem. In August 2012, the Summer-Macko tandem sold it to Matt and Kim Hall, Matt having divorced and remarried. That returned the two Curry County weeklies to common ownership. In announcing the sale, Summer said, "It was very important to us to find a buyer here in Curry County, and Matt and Kim fit that bill to a tee.

"Working 70 to 80-hour weeks for nearly seven years, without a day off, finally got to us. We're a small shop, and we sold ads, composed ads, did the editing, writing, photography, page layout, circulation and distribution, and classified."

Matt is playing the lead role in Gold Beach, Kim in Port Orford. Matt has previous experience with the Coos Bay *World* and papers in Alaska. In June 2013, they added a third paper, the *Myrtle Point Herald* in neighboring Coos County.

Daily Courier   Grants Pass

Owner: Courier Publishing Co.
Address: 409 SE Seventh St., Grants Pass, OR 97526
Phone: 541-474-3700
URL: www.thedailycourier.com (subscription required for full access)
Established: 1885
Published: Monday through Saturday PM
Market: Josephine County
Circulation: 12,683 (ABC)
Publisher: Dennis Mack, dmack@thedailycourier.com
Editor: Kevin Widdison, kwiddison@thedailycourier.com

Hudson's Bay Company trappers, following the Siskiyou Trail, began frequenting heavily timbered Southern Oregon in the 1820s. Settlers, following the Applegate Trail, began taking up donation land claims in the 1840s. Gold was discovered in the Illinois Valley in 1851 and at Sailor Diggings in 1852, triggering an influx of fortune seekers. The county was created in 1856 with Sailor Diggings as its seat of government. The county seat was moved to Grants Pass in 1886. By then two major developments had occurred: The Oregon & California Railroad came through and picked Grants Pass for a depot, and the economic mainstay shifted from mining to logging.

Local newspapering was introduced by the weekly *Argus* on March 13, 1885, a little over a year after completion of the railroad on Christmas Eve of 1883. The weekly *Rogue River Courier* followed three weeks later. The *Argus* soon faded, but the *Courier* flourished and went daily.

The story of the *Grants Pass Daily Courier*, as it is known today, is basically the story of the Voorhies family. The family has owned the newspaper since 1897, when Amos Voorhies, an out-of-work printer from Michigan, acquired it with a partner, whose interest he bought out two years later. Amos served as publisher or co-publisher of the newspaper almost up to the time of his death in 1960 at age 91. His son, Earl, served as co-publisher first with Amos and later with his own son, John. Earl died in 1971.

Today, John owns the paper, but Dennis Mack serves as publisher. He's the first person outside the family to hold the post since 1897.

The Voorhies family has always prided itself on being active in the community and staying on the cutting edge of technology. Amos was a leader in developing the Oregon Caves as a tourist destination, and he always made sure the newspaper got all the latest equipment, as soon as it became commercially available.

The paper publishes six days a week, Monday through Saturday, on the PM cycle.

It was one of the last dailies in the state to establish a major news presence on the web, not making the move until about 2005. It adopted a paid subscription model from the outset, charging by the day, week, month, or year to meet varying user needs.

Editor Dennis Roler said in August 2013, "We cut back from six editions a week to five in March. We now print Tuesday through Friday and Sunday. We used to print Monday through Saturday. Realistically, I see a good chance we will have to reduce staff in the next five years. We may also have to cut another day off the publication schedule. It's going to depend on where revenues meet expenditures, with a little left over for profit. That's what my cloudy crystal ball says now. I wish I could say things look brighter, but I can't."

The Outlook   Gresham

Owner: Pamplin Media Group
Address: 1190 N.E. Division St., Gresham, OR 97030.
Phone: 503-665-2181
URL: www.theoutlookonline.com (unrestricted)
Established: 1911
Published: Tuesday and Friday

Market: Eastern Multnomah County
Circulation: 7,434 (SO)
President: J. Mark Garber, mgarber@theoutlookonline.com (joint with Estacada)
Executive Editor & General Manager: Steve Brown, sbrown@theoutlookonline.com (joint with Estacada)
Deadlines: Noon Wednesday for Tuesday, noon Tuesday for Friday

Gresham, whose 2010 population of 105,000 made it Oregon's fourth largest city, after Portland, Eugene and Salem, started life as Campground (it was a popular overnight camping spot for pioneers making their way to Portland or south into Oregon's fertile Willamette Valley). When the community petitioned for a post office in 1884, it sweetened the deal by offering to name the town after then-Postmaster General Walter Q. Gresham. The name stuck.

The city incorporated in 1905. Six years later, H.L. St. Clair founded *The Gresham Outlook* under the auspices of the Outlook Publishing Company. It operated under that name until 1991, when it dropped the Gresham element, becoming simply *The Outlook*. Lee Irwin and Walt Taylor bought the paper in 1960, and Irwin served as its publisher for the next 22 years. He was succeeded briefly by Robert Caldwell, who went on to become editorial page editor at *The Oregonian*, then by Steven J. Clark on April 4, 1983.

The Glenn Jackson group, whose flagship was the *Albany Democrat-Herald*, bought four papers from Irwin and Taylor on February 10, 1977 – the Gresham *Outlook*, *Sandy Post*, *Newport News-Times* and *Lincoln County Leader*. Irwin remained publisher at the *Outlook* till retirement.

The Jackson papers were sold to one of the largest American media chains, Capital Cities/ABC, which was swallowed by an even larger one in 1996: Disney. Disney sold the Cap Cities newspapers to the Iowa-based Lee Enterprises chain in 1998. Lee retains ownership of some of the old Jackson papers, including the *Albany Democrat-Herald*. However, Robert B. Pamplin Jr.'s Pamplin Media Group picked up the Gresham and Sandy papers in 2000.

The Outlook is the only twice-weekly in the Pamplin stable. Most of its other publications, including its flagship, the *Portland Tribune*, come out weekly; the rest publish monthly or twice-monthly.

The Outlook is the dominant newspaper in East Multnomah County. It is equipped with a large printing press, which Pamplin uses to publish most of its community papers.

Hells Canyon Journal   Halfway

Owner: Hells Canyon Publishing
Address: 145 N. Main Street, Halfway, OR 97834

Phone: 541-742-7900
URL: www.smalltownpapers.com/newspapers/newspaper.php?id=163 (no website of its own, but PDFs available through SmallTownPapers)
Established: 1984
Published: Wednesday
Market: Eastern Baker County
Circulation: 1,099 (SO)
Editor & Publisher: Steve Backstrom, hcj@pinetel.com
Deadlines: Friday for advertising, Monday for news, with exceptions as warranted

Baker County was carved out of Wasco County in 1862 and named for an Oregon senator who died fighting for the Union at Ball's Bluff. Sparsely populated, it lies in Oregon's dry northeastern corner, bordering Idaho on the east. The community of Halfway takes its name from its location between the unincorporated hamlets of Pine and Cornucopia. Halfway itself is incorporated but counted only 288 residents in the 2010 census. A farm and ranch community, one of 43 dotting the sagebrush of Baker County, it made national waves in 1999 when it agreed to go by Half.com for a year as part of a publicity stunt by an e-commerce company. It lies about 55 miles east of Baker City, the county seat and dominant local population center.

The *Hells Canyon Journal* began publication in Halfway in 1983 as a free weekly circular. It was preceded by a similar but short-lived free-distribution weekly known as the *Pine Eagle Bulletin*. The paper was put on a paid subscription footing in 1988. It is printed in La Grande, a 200-mile round trip, on the press Western Communications uses to print the *La Grande Observer* and *Baker City Herald*.

While the *Journal* is based in Halfway, it also serves Pine Valley, Eagle Valley, Oxbow-Brownlee, and the the ranches interspersed between them. That gives it a total population base of almost 2,000.

A series of four ownership changes in its first six years of existence culminated in creation of Hells Canyon Publishing Inc. in 1989. And that brought some welcome stability.

"The *Hells Canyon Journal* exists only as a print publication – something of an anachronism in today's media environment," noted Editor and Publisher Steve Backstrom. That's more by necessity than design, he says, "Based in one of the smallest of the small towns served by Oregon's weekly papers, the paper has limited resources. ... And it serves communities with a large population of retirees. In this environment, given its limited cash flow, ownership has decided to avoid diverting resources away from the print edition to try and extend its viability as long as possible."

Backstrom said the paper actively seeks side work to help subsidize its continued publication: "Based in such a small community, the HCJ takes on other printing and publishing projects as available to enhance its cash flow and subsidize the existence of a weekly newspaper in what would otherwise be a drastically underserved small media market."

Gazette-Times   Heppner

Owner: Sykes Publishing LLC
Address: 188 W. Willow St., Heppner, OR 97836
Phone: 541-676-9228.
URL: www.rapidserve.net/Gazette (news not posted online, but PDFs available through SmallTownPapers)
Established: 1883
Published: Wednesday
Market: Morrow County
Circulation: 1,421 (SO)
Publisher: David Sykes, david@rapidserve.net
News Editor: Andrea Di Salvo, editor@rapidserve.net
Deadline: 5 p.m. Monday

The *Gazette-Times* has been most associated with the Crawford family, though the Crawfords did not found it and no longer own it.

Its oldest predecessor is the *Gazette*. The *Times* didn't come along until some years later.

Vawter Crawford began the family association when he joined the *Gazette* staff in 1890. At the time, the paper was being published by Otis and Alvah Patterson. In 1910, Crawford bought the *Gazette* from Fred Warnock. In 1912, he bought the *Times* from E.M. Shutt and merged the papers. Crawford moved the operation into the *Times* plant, because it was better equipped, according to an interview with his brother, O.G., published in 1963.

O.G. and another brother, Garfield, were also involved in publication of the *Gazette-Times* over the years. So was Vawter's son, Spencer, who took over for him. Spencer Crawford bought an Optimus 41 press in 1919 that wasn't replaced until 1963, according to O.G.

The paper was owned by another old-line Oregon newspaper family, the Heards, prior to their retirement in 1972. Charles and Dorothy Heard also owned, at various times, the *Herald* in Joseph, *Valley Herald* in Milton-Freewater, *Valley Record* in Cashmere, Wash., and *News* in Pilot Rock. It is currently owned by David Sykes through Sykes Publishing LLC.

The newspaper pre-dates the creation of Morrow County in 1884 from portions of Umatilla and Wasco counties. Heppner, which counted 1,300 residents in the 2010 census, has served as the county seat of government from the outset.

The county lies south of the Columbia River from eastern Washington. Morrow, a farm and ranch supply center originally known as Standsbury Flat after early settler George W. Standsbury, is situated virtually dead-center.

Heppner was virtually destroyed by a flash flood that struck on June 14, 1903. The flood sent a wall of water cascading down Willow Creek, killing an estimated 238 residents. It stands to this day as the deadliest natural disaster in Oregon history.

The Herald   Hermiston

Owner: EO Media Group
Address: 333 E. Main St., Hermiston OR 97838
Phone: 541-567-6457
URL: www.hermistonherald.com (subscription required for full access)
Established: 1906
Published: Wednesday and Saturday
Market: Western Umatilla County
Circulation: 1,301 (SO)
Publisher: Kathryn B. Brown, kbbrown@eastoregonian.com (joint with Pendleton)
Editor: Randy Thompson, rthompson@hermistonherald.com
Deadline: Noon Tuesday for Wednesday, noon Friday for Saturday

Pendleton, Umatilla County's earliest substantial settlement and long-time seat of government, has traditionally been its largest city as well. In fact, at one time, it was the fourth largest city in Oregon. However, in recent years, it has been overtaken by Hermiston, which lies along Interstate 84 to the west. Both are currently hovering around the 17,000 mark; the 2010 census pegged Hermiston as slightly larger.

The Eastern Oregon county abuts the Columbia River, which marks the boundary between Oregon to the south and Washington to the north. The county is heavily agricultural, with onions, melons, and wheat predominating and wine grapes joining the mix in recent years.

The *Hermiston Herald* was founded in 1906 by Horace Greeley Newport and William Skinner.

Jerry Reed got involved in 1969 and came into full ownership in 1974. Reed entered into a pooling of interests stock exchange with Elmo Smith's Eagle Newspapers in 1979, trading ownership of the *Herald* for a stake in Eagle, but continued to run the local operation as publisher. After a run of almost 20 years, Reed retired in 1992 and Eagle sold the *Herald* to the Chandler family's Bend-based Western Communications. It remained part of the Bend company, which also owned the *La Grande Observer* and *Baker City Herald*, for more than 15 years.

On April 30, 2008, Western Communications sold the paper to another family operation – the Forrester family's East Oregonian Publishing Company, now known as the EO Media Group, which among other paper also publishes the nearby *East Oregonian* at Pendleton.

While the *East Oregonian* has long been the Forresters' flagship paper, Hermiston has been growing faster than Pendleton in recent years, to the point where it has supplanted its neighbor as Umatilla County's largest city. That spurred the company's interest in adding the the *Herald* to its lineup.

The *Herald* publishes Wednesday and Saturday. It is printed on the *East Oregonian* press. Like its EO Media Group counterparts, it publishes aggressively on the web, but reserves full online access for subscribers.

Argus   Hillsboro

Owner: Advance Publications (Newhouse)
Address: 150 S.E. Third Ave., Hillsboro, OR 97123
Phone: 503-648-1131
URL: www.oregonlive.com/argus (unrestricted)
Established: 1873
Published: Tuesday and Friday
Circulation: 6,539 (SO)
Editor: Tom Maurer, tmaurer@hillsboroargus.com
Deadline: Noon Monday for Tuesday, noon Thursday for Friday

Hillsboro is the largest city in Washington County and the fifth largest in Oregon. The heavily urbanized county was created as Twality in 1843 and renamed Washington in 1849 – much earlier than most of the state's 36 counties. It claimed a population of 530,000 in 2010, with Hillsboro accounting for about 90,000, followed by Beaverton, Tigard, and Forest Grove. Hillsboro lies in the Tualatin Valley, on the west side of the Portland metro area. (The MAX train line ends there on the west, as it does in Gresham on the east.) Founded in 1842, it takes its name from early political leader David Hill. Once an orchard, vineyard, and woodlot processing and supply center, it has evolved into a bedroom community, commercial center and high-tech center in recent decades.

The *Argus* traces its ancestry back to Washington County's first newspaper – the *Forest Grove Independent*, founded in 1873. In December that year, the paper moved to Hillsboro and began publishing as the *Washington Independent*.

The *Argus* was founded on March 28, 1894 by R. H. Mitchell and C. W. Clow as a six-page weekly. Following a series of ownership changes, Emma C. McKinney purchased a half-ownership in 1904, introducing an ownership run that would extend an unprecedented 95 years. McKinney went on to become sole owner in 1909. She brought her son, W. Verne McKinney, on board in 1923. In January 1932, the McKinneys bought the *Independent* from S.C. Killen and merged it into the *Argus*. The paper published weekly until 1953, when it went twice-weekly.

Emma's grandson, Walt, joined the staff in 1941 and rose through the ranks to next assume the helm. He spent his entire 60-year career with the paper. The family sold the paper to Newhouse's New Jersey-based Advance Publications in October 1999, but he remained as publisher until his retirement on December 31, 2001.

Emma, W. Verne and Walt McKinney all accumulated numerous honors for their work with the, which was highly regarded throughout their tenure. All won induction into the Oregon Newspaper Hall of Fame as well.

The Argus shares ownership with the state's dominant metro, *The Oregonian* in Portland, giving it access to a robust web operation.

It also shares another rare distinction.

It now has an upstart competitor, the Pamplin Media Group's *Hillsboro Tribune*. The *Tribune* is currently being published twice-monthly on a free-distribution basis. However, both greater frequency and paid distribution could be in the offing as it gains its footing. *The Oregonian* has responded by launching a weekly in Forest Grove, where Pamplin publishes the *News-Times*. The Pamplin foray into Hillsboro effectively opens a second front in the competition between the two companies, where the front line in Portland is between *The Oregonian* and *Portland Tribune*.

News   **Hood River**

Owner: Eagle Newspapers
Address: 419 State St., Hood River, OR 97031
Phone: 541-386-1234
URL: www.hoodrivernews.com (unrestricted)
Established: 1905
Published: Wednesday and Saturday
Market: Hood River County
Circulation: 4,678 (SO)
Publisher: Joe Petshow, jpetshow@hoodrivernews.com
Editor: Kirby Neumann-Rea, kneumann-rea@hoodrivernews.com
Deadlines: Noon Monday for Wednesday, noon Thursday for Saturday

Hood River County was established in 1908 – relatively late in the process. It was named for Hood River, a tributary of the Columbia, which forms the county's northern border. The county is a bountiful producer of apples, pears, cherries, grapes, and other fruits. In fact, it leads the world in Anjou pear production.

Hood River is both the largest population center and seat of government. Lying about 30 miles due north of 11,000-foot Mount Hood, it was incorporated in 1895. It only counts about 7,000 permanent residents, but tourism is capable of doubling or tripling that at peak times during the year.

The local newspaper was founded in 1905. Three years later, it was purchased by Charles Sonnichsen and Hugh Ball, who continued to run it for decades. Sonnichsen served as publisher, Ball as editor. Both of them had extensive newspaper backgrounds, Ball most recently with the *Coos Bay Times*, and both were highly regarded.

Elmo Smith's Blue Mountain Eagle group – forerunner of today's Eagle Newspapers, run by Elmo's son, Denny – bought the paper in 1961. Elmo, serving as publisher of the *Albany Democrat-Herald* at the time, sent Denny to Hood River to run it. But Denny was an F-89 pilot and cold war tension led him to report for active duty in 1962. So Elmo dispatched his managing editor in Albany, Dick Nafsinger, to take over.

Nafsinger, only 28 at the time, spent the next 29 years building both the newspaper and the company into major forces in Oregon journalism – and, indeed, national journalism. Perhaps no one is more closely associated with the *Hood River News* than Nafsinger, who also came to play a leading role in the parent company during its formative years.

Blue Mountain Eagle   John Day

Owner: EO Media Group
Address: 195 N. Canyon Blvd., John Day, OR 97845
Phone: 541-575-0710
URL: www.myeaglenews.com (unrestricted, but subscription required for e-edition)
Established: 1868
Published: Wednesday
Market: Grant County
Circulation: 2,572 (SO)
Publisher: Marissa Williams, mwilliams@bmeagle.com
Editor: Scotta Callister, editor@bmeagle.com
Deadline: 5 p.m. Friday

Grant is one of eastern Oregon's sagebrush counties. Ranch country, there can be no doubt it counts more cows that it does people – fewer than 7,500 humans when the 2010 census was conducted. The county seat is Canyon City, which once claimed the largest population in Oregon, but now ranks second in its own county to John Day, about a mile to the north. Gold was discovered in 1862 on Whiskey Flat, drawing an estimated 1,000 miners in 10 days. When the deposits played out, as most soon did, the cattle industry returned to its place as chief economic driver.

John Day – named for the John Day River, which was named for a member of the 1811 Astor Expedition – began to eclipse Canyon City as early as the 1930s. Its 2010 population count was 1,744, making it easily the county's largest city.

John Day's *Blue Mountain Eagle* traces its heritage back to the *Grant County News*, originally based in Canyon City. It inherited its name from the *Long Creek Eagle*, founded in the northern Grant County community of Long Creek in 1889. The paper became the *Blue Mountain Eagle* when it relocated to Canyon City in 1898.

The *News* and *Eagle* merged in 1908, with owners Clinton P. Haigt and P.F. Chandler agreeing to serve as co-publishers. The arrangement continued until 1937. A devastating fire led the paper to make the move from Canyon City to John Day. John Day already had its own paper, the *Valley Ranger*, which the *Eagle* absorbed in 1944.

Elmo and Dorothy Smith bought the *Eagle* in 1948 from Chester and Vera Ashton, and it remained in Smith family ownership for the next 20 years. Smith, father of former congressman Denny Smith, who heads the Eagle Newspapers chain, got his start in newspapering with the *Ontario Argus* in 1928. It was the forerunner of today's *Argus Observer*. He launched a political career on the side by winning election to the Ontario mayorship in 1940, and served as governor of Oregon from 1956-57.

John and Donna Moreau bought the paper in 1968. Eleven years later, they sold it to the East Oregonian Publishing Company, now known as the EO Media Group. EO Media's holdings include the *East Oregonian* in Pendleton and *Herald* in Hermiston, Eastern Oregon's largest newspaper operations.

Keizertimes   Keizer

Owner: Wheatland Publishing Corp.
Address: 142 Chemawa Road N, Keizer, OR 97303
Phone: 503-390-1051
URL: www.keizertimes.com (unrestricted)
Established: 1979
Published: Friday
Market: Keizer area (Marion County)
Circulation: 2,320 (SO)
Publisher: Lyndon Zaitz, lzaitz@keizertimes.com
News Editor: Craig Murphy, editor@keizertimes.com
Deadline: 5 p.m. Monday

Keizer, abutting the northeast side of Salem, was founded by Thomas Dove Keizur, whose family arrived by wagon train via the Applegate Trail in the fall of 1843. It wasn't incorporated until November 2, 1982.

The *Keizertimes* was founded by John Ettinger in 1979, when Keizer was still just an unincorporated 25,000-resident suburb of Salem. Les Zaitz, a long-time investigative and state government reporter with *The Oregonian*, joined with his wife and *Oregonian* colleague, Scotta Callister, to purchase the paper in 1987. They continue to own it under the banner of the Wheatland Publishing Corporation.

Les' younger brother, Lyndon, runs the newspaper operation. He described the key to its success as "positive journalism that keeps Keizer residents informed of their community and keeps watch over city and fire district operations."

The printing is handled by Salem's Eagle Web Press, arm of the Eagle newspaper chain.

Herald and News   Klamath Falls

Owner: Pioneer Newspapers
Address: 2701 Foothills Blvd., Klamath Falls, OR 97601
Phone: 541-885-4410
URL: www.heraldandnews.com (subscription required for full access)
Established: 1906
Published: Tuesday through Sun AM
Market: Klamath County and portions of Lake County
Circulation: 13,119 (SO)
Publisher: Heidi Wright, hwright@heraldandnews.com
Editor: Steve Miller, smiller@heraldandnews.com

Klamath County, which shares its southern border with California's Siskiyou and Modoc counties, was, like those counties, named for an indigenous Native American tribe. When pioneers began moving into the heavily timbered country to settle in the 1840s, over the Applegate Trail, the Klamaths and Modocs took offense; the Modoc War of 1872-73 was one result. Klamath Falls was founded along a series of Link River waterfalls in 1867 and given the name Linkville, then renamed Klamath Falls in 1892. The city accounts for almost one third of the county's approximately 66,000 residents. It has served as seat of government since the county's founding in 1882.

The Klamath Reclamation Project was launched in 1906 as a way to siphon off more water for agriculture. Since the turn of the 20th century, flows have proven insufficient to meet competing claims by the tribal, agricultural, and wildlife conservation interests, leading to a fierce series of water rights battles sometimes spilling out of the courts and into the streets. Water has been the area's biggest story for a generation.

Against this backdrop, Fred Cronemiller and his wife launched the *Klamath Falls Evening Herald* in 1906 as a tabloid. Two years later, Ed Murray and W.O. Smith bought the paper and turned it into a six-day, four-page broadsheet selling for a nickel a copy. Murray bought out Smith in 1919. Two rival dailies folded in 1912, as did their successor in 1915. But in 1923, the *Klamath News* was launched and bitter rivalry ensued.

In early 1927, Murray sold out to Bruce Dennis, who later bought the *News* as well. In 1942, wartime newsprint rationing forced consolidation of the two papers.

The paper was later acquired by the Scripps League, which installed Joe Caraher as publisher in 1963. Former owner of the *East Side Journal* in Kirkland, Washington, Caraher remained at the helm until his retirement and continued to write a weekly column for the paper until his death in 2004 at the age of 92. He was inducted into the Oregon Newspaper Hall of Fame in 1990.

Pioneer Newspapers was spun off from Scripps in 1974 by James G. Scripps. It continues to own and operate the *Herald and News*.

The Observer   La Grande

Owner: Western Communications
Address: 1406 Fifth St., LaGrande, OR 97850
Phone: 541-963-3161
URL: www.lagrandeobserver.com
(subscription required for full access)
Established: 1896
Published: Monday, Wednesday and Friday
Market: Union and Wallowa counties
Circulation: 5,259 (SO)
Publisher: Kari Borgen,
kborgen@bakercityherald.com (joint with Baker City)
Editor: Andrew Cutler, acutler@lagrandeobserver.com

La Grande, which lies amid cattle and wheat country up in Oregon's far northeast corner, began life as Brownsville after early settler Benjamin Brown. Postal officials demanded its renaming in 1863 because a Brownsville already existed in the Willamette Valley county of Linn, on Oregon's wet western side. Legend has it that earlier French settler Charges Dause was so taken with the beauty of the Grande Ronde Valley, defined by Mounts Emily to the north and Harris to the south, and the Blue Mountains to the west, that he was prone to exclaiming,

"La Grande!" Hence the name. Union County seat and home of Eastern Oregon University, it was incorporated in 1865. It claimed a population of 13,000 in the 2010 census.

La Grande's first paper was the *Mountain Sentinel*, published from 1872 to 1886. *The Observer*, founded by George Currey, didn't come along until 1896. By then, three other papers had taken the field: *The Farmer*, the *Chronicle* and the *Gazette*, later known as the *Advocate*. *The Observer* fared so well, however, that it soon pushed its competitors aside.

It fluctuated between weekly and daily status over the ensuing years, depending on how its fortunes were faring. It eventually settled into a long-term pattern of daily publication, but cut back to a tri-weekly cycle early in 2012.

The paper has published under a variety of names, all built around the Observer theme. They include the *Morning Daily Observer*, *Eastern Oregon Observer*, *La Grande Evening Observer*, *La Grande Morning Observer* and *La Grande Weekly Observer*.

Following its absorption of the *La Grande Weekly Star*, the *Observer* also published for periods as the *LaGrande Weekly Observer-Star* and *The Observer-Star*. It did not become simply *The Observer* until June 1959.

The Observer was one of the first acquisitions Robert C. Chandler made when he began to build a newspaper company called Western Communications around the *Bend Bulletin*, which he acquired from Robert W. Sawyer in 1953.

But the man most closely associated with the paper in recent years was Robert "Bob" Moody, one of Chandler's key lieutenants. He served as publisher from 1974 to 1997, finally retiring in the wake of Chandler's death. Moody got his start in newspapering as a *Bulletin* carrier at the age of 11. He worked under then circulation manager Les Schwab, who would go on to establish a tire chain with outlets throughout the West. Schwab took Moody under his wing and promoted him to a management position in the circulation department while he was still in high school. He served three years as publisher of the *Redmond Spokesman*, a Western Communications weekly, before being tapped by Chandler for the publishership in La Grande.

He was eventually succeeded in La Grande by a man he had brought in as sports editor in 1977: Ted Kramer. Kramer has since retired.

Review   Lake Oswego

Owner: Pamplin Media Group
Address: 400 Second St., Lake Oswego, OR 97034

Phone: 503-635-8811
URL: www.lakeoswegoreview.com (unrestricted)
Established: 1920
Published: Thursday
Market: Lake Oswego
Circulation: 5,831 (SO)
Editor: Martin Forbes, mforbes@lakeoswegoreview.com
Deadline: Noon Friday

Who would guess that Lake Oswego, now one of Oregon's poshest residential enclaves, once served as the hub of a thriving Oregon steel industry? A town that got its start with the erection of a sawmill on Sucker Creek embraced the steel industry when it began to exploit a rich deposit of iron ore in 1861. At peak production in 1890, Lake Oswego, then known simply as Oswego, saw 300 millworkers smelt more than 12,000 tons of pig iron at three smelters. Key producers included the Oregon Iron Company, founded in 1865, which vowed to turn "Oswego" into the "Pittsburgh of the West."

The industry was already waning when the weekly *Oswego Iron Worker* had its brief run in the community in 1893-94. Other early papers included the *Times* (1916-18) and *Banner* (1918-19), followed in later years by the *Honk* (1942-45) and *Daily Report* (1968-69).

The *Review* began life as the *Western Clackamas Review*, then switched to the *Oswego Review*. It did not become the *Lake Oswego Review* until 1960, when Oswego annexed Lake Grove, acquiring the lake justifying the expanded name. The community burnished its reputation as a haven for the affluent in the 1930s and 1940s, when developers began to build handsome homes on 24,000 acres acquired from Oregon Iron & Steel.

In 1979, Eagle Newspapers acquired the *Lake Oswego Review*. Three years later, it spun off the *Tidings* in neighboring West Linn, adding to its growing suburban presence. In January 1988, Eagle went into partnership with the Baker family's *Eugene Register-Guard*, which also owned several suburban weeklies, to form Community Newspapers. In addition to the Lake Oswego and West Linn papers, it encompassed papers in Tigard, Tualatin, Beaverton, and Forest Grove.

The partners sold the group to Steve and Randalyn Clark in 1996. Four years later, the Clarks sold them to Eagle's' principal rival in the Portland suburbs, Robert B. Pamplin Jr.'s Pamplin Media Group.

Lake County Examiner   Lakeview

Owner: Pioneer Newspapers
Address: 739 N. Second St., Lakeview, OR 97630
Phone: 541-947-3378.

URL: www.lakecountyexam.com (unrestricted but limited)
Established: 1880
Published: Wednesday
Market: Lake County
Circulation: 2,409 (SO)
General Manager: Tillie Flynn, tflynn@lakecountyexam.com

Lakeview was founded in 1876 in Oregon's lightly populated southeastern corner as a supply center for early sheepherders, cattlemen, farmers, and loggers.

The *Examiner* was founded four years later by Charles Cogswell and Stephen Moss, who installed Frank Coffin as its first editor. Subscriptions ran $3 a year, discounted to $2.50 with payment in advance. The paper soon eclipsed and absorbed the *State Line Herald*, founded in 1878, and took on a decidedly Republican orientation. It not only survived the great Lakeview fire of May 22, 1900, but put out an extra on the event and lent its equipment to the rival *Lake County Rustler*, which had been burned out.

In 1905, C. Oscar Metzker acquired the *Examiner* and equipped it with its first linotype machine. The Cronemiller family, founder of the *Klamath Falls Evening Herald*, bought the paper from Metzker six years later. Upon the death of his father, Fred, in 1924, G.D. Cronemiller took the reins. He continued at the helm until 1935, when he sold to C.J. Gillette and Hugh McGilvra.

The paper is currently under the ownership of Pioneer Newspapers, owned by members of the Scripps family.

Express   Lebanon

Owner: Lee Enterprises
Address: 90 E. Grant St., Lebanon, OR 97355
Phone: 541-258-3151
URL: www.lebanon-express.com (unrestricted, subscription required for e-edition)
Established: 1887
Published: Wednesday
Market: Eastern Linn County
Circulation: 1,913 (SO)
Publisher: Mike McInally, mike.mcinally@lee.net (joint with Albany, Corvallis)
Managing Editor: Emily Mentzer, emily.mentzer@lee.net
Deadline: 3 p.m. Friday

The weekly *Express*, founded in 1887 by J.H. Sine, who also founded several other Oregon papers, was the first newspaper to serve the Linn County logging community of Lebanon. It was named for a railroad train, the Oregonian Railway's Lebanon Express, that did not fare nearly as well.

Two years later, a pair of Eugene newspapermen, George Alexander and Jack Adams, launched the *Lebanon Advance*. Alexander was the son of J.B. Alexander, founder of the *Eugene Guard*, a predecessor of today's *Eugene Register-Guard*. The papers merged to create the *Express-Advance* in 1897, and Alexander served as its editor until his retirement in 1936, a run of almost 40 years. A rival paper, the Republican-oriented *Lebanon Criterion*, joined the field in 1898. It operated briefly as the *Linn County Advocate* before returning to its original name, and gave the *Express* a good run for its money.

The *Express*, now owned by the national Lee Enterprises chain, based in Iowa, bought out the *Criterion* in 1924. Lee also owns a pair of nearby dailies, the *Albany Democrat-Herald* and *Corvallis Gazette-Times*, and has merged their business functions. It publishes all three papers on the *Democrat-Herald* press in Albany.

News Guard   Lincoln City

Owner: Country Media
Address: 930 S.E. Highway 101, Lincoln City, OR 97367
Phone: 541-994-2178
URL: www.thenewsguard.com (subscription required for full access)
Established: 1927
Published: Wednesday
Market: Northern Lincoln County
Circulation: 3,236 (SO)
Managing Editor: Jeremy Ruark, jruark@countrymedia.net

The *News Guard* actually pre-dates the community it serves by almost four decades. The newspaper got its start in 1927, but Lincoln City didn't come into being until March 3, 1965. The linear, coast-hugging community, defined by Highway 101, is the product of a merger of the predecessor communities of Delake, Occeanlake, Taft, Cutler City, and Nelscott. The name was chosen in a contest. It encompasses Devils Lake, which local Finns dubbed "Delake." It also encompasses Wecoma Beach, which had been annexed by Oceanlake earlier.

David and Margaret Juenke came to Lincoln City in 1967 to buy the *News Guard*. They owned and operated it until October 1, 1980, when they sold the *News Guard* and three other coast papers – the *Tillamook Headlight-Herald*, *Seaside Signal* and *Ilwaco Tribune* – to Scripps-Ifft Newspapers of Pocatello, Idaho.

The Juenkes had gone into partnership with Lee Irwin and Walt Taylor, owners of *Newport News Times* and *Gresham Outlook*, to acquire the *Tillamook Headlight-Herald* from the Moore family on January 4, 1973. Six months later, they purchased the *Seaside Signal* as well.

In 1976, the Juenkes bought out their partners, setting the stage for the 1980 sale to Scripps. Scripps closed the *Tribune*, serving Southwestern Washington's Long Beach Peninsula, and sent Circulation Manager Garph Lords of the *Idaho State Journal* in Pocatello over to run the three Oregon papers out of Tillamook. On July 15, 1983, Scripps-Ifft sold the three to Swift Newspapers, founded in 1975 by former Scripps League executive Philip Swift. Swift created a new subsidiary, Pacific Coast Newspapers, to run them.

Swift has come in recent years to specialize in media properties in western resort communities like Reno, Tahoe, Vail, and Aspen. It still owns Oregon's *Roseburg News-Review*, but has sold its coast holdings.

On February 1, 2003, the *News Guard* and *Headlight-Herald* were picked up by the husband and wife team of Joe Happ, who served as editor, and Kathleen Newton, who served as publisher. The *Signal* was sold to a different buyer.

Happ and Newton, which operated the papers under the mantle of Oregon Coast Newspapers LLC, sold to Steve and Carol Hungerford's Country Media in April 2007. Country Media, which already owned the *Cannon Beach Gazette*, went on to acquire additional coast properties, including the *Seaside Signal*. It is based in Tillamook.

The Pioneer   Madras

Owner: Pamplin Media Group
Address: 345 S.E. Fifth St., Madras, OR 97741
Phone: 541-475-2275
URL: www.madraspioneer.com (subscription required for full access)
Established: 1904
Published: Wednesday
Market: Jefferson County
Circulation: 3,773 (SO)
Publisher: Tony Ahern, tahern@madraspioneer.com
Editor: Susan Matheny, smatheny@madraspioneer.com
Deadline: 5 p.m. Friday

The *Pioneer* has the novel distinction not only of pre-dating its home city of Madras, which wasn't incorporated until 1910, but also its home county of Jefferson, which wasn't carved out of neighboring Crook County until 1914. In fact, its 1904 founding makes it not only Jefferson County's first newspaper, but also Crook County's, because it pre-dates Prineville's *Central Oregonian*.

Both papers were owned for many years by the Oregon-based Eagle Newspapers chain. However, Eagle sold them to the the Pamplin Media Group in separate 2013 transactions coming just a few months apart.

The *Pioneer* was launched by veteran Oregon newspaperman Timothy Brownhill with the aid of veteran Oregon printer Bill Rutter. They published it on a hand-press initially, offering annual subscriptions for $1.50. In 1905, Brownhill sold the paper to Max Lueddemann, founder of the *Bend Bulletin*. A whole series of ownership changes ensued over the next 20 years, with no one owner sticking around very long. William E. Johnson bought the paper in 1919. He sold it to George Pearce the following year, but began leasing it back in 1923.

As early as 1909, the *Pioneer* began promoting Madras as the "Gateway to Central Oregon." From early on, it provided sympathetic and supportive coverage of the nearby Warm Springs Indian Reservation. Fire swept the high desert community in September of 1924, and the building housing the *Pioneer* was one of the few emerging unscathed.

When Johnson died a few months later, his widow bought the paper and took over as publisher. Their daughter, Betty Welker, assumed the editorial helm in 1933.

Elmo Smith, a pioneering Oregon newsman and politician who went on to serve briefly as governor in the mid-1950s, bought the *Pioneer* in partnership with friend Bill Robinson in 1948. They created Blue Mountain Eagle, later shortened to Eagle, as the corporate vehicle. It was named after Smith's *Blue Mountain Eagle* newspaper in John Day, later sold to the the East Oregonian Publishing Company, now the EO Media Group.

Eagle continues to own and operate community newspapers in Oregon, Washington, and Idaho, but neither the *Pioneer* nor the *Central Oregonian* is among them. Eagle sold the *Pioneer* and five other Oregon weeklies to the Portland-based Pamplin Media in January 2013 and a few months later, the *Central Oregonian* as well.

McKenzie River Reflection   McKenzie Bridge

Owners: Ken and Louise Engelman
Address: 59059 Old McKenzie Highway, McKenzie Bridge, OR 97413
Phone: 541-822-3358.
URL: www.mckenzie.orenews.com (news not posted online, but PDFs available through SmallTownPapers)
Established: 1978
Published: Thursday
Market: Eastern Lane County
Circulation: 713 (SO)
Publisher: Ken Engelman, rivref@aol.com
Editor & General Manager: Louise Engelman, rivref@aol.com
Deadline: 5 p.m. Monday

The founding of Eastern Lane County's weekly *McKenzie River Reflection* in 1978 makes it one of the state's newer community newspapers. Co-owner and Publisher Ken Engelman said, "We're focused on bringing together the McKenzie River area's businesses and residents by covering community news and activities. Our 'beat' includes Cedar Flat, Camp Creek, Walterville, Deerhorn, Leaburg, Vida, Nimrod, Finn Rock, Blue River, Rainbow, and McKenzie Bridge ..."

The paper is printed by the Oregon Web Press in the Lane County seat of Eugene, which is some 55 miles to the west of the newspaper's headquarters on Highway 126.

It recently launched a paid e-edition in a PDF format, and the Engelmans said they've gotten a great response. "We're finally overcoming our resistance/anger over the intrusion of the Internet into the publishing realm," Engelman said.

An unincorporated hamlet at the extreme eastern edge of one of Oregon's largest and most populous counties, McKenzie Bridge seems an unlikely place to launch a newspaper. Lying on the rugged, swift-running McKenzie River, which cuts a jagged path through the heavily timbered Willamette National Forest, it is tucked in between two sets of springs, Rainbow and Belknap. It is home to a ranger station, which moved into Camp Belknap when the Civilian Conservation Corps moved out, but not much else.

McKenzie Bridge was once graced by the historic Log Cabin Inn, which was listed on the National Register of Historic Places, but it burned on March 29, 2006. Its economy is heavily dependent on outdoor recreation.

News-Register   McMinnville

Owner: Oregon Lithoprint Inc.
Address: 611 N.E. Third St., McMinnville, OR 97128
Phone: 503-472-5114
URL: www.newsregister.com (subscription required for full access)
Established: 1866
Published: Tuesday and Friday
Market: Yamhill County
Circulation: 8,808 (SO)
Publisher: Jeb Bladine, jbladine@newsregister.com
Chief Operating Officer: Guy Everingham, geveringham@newsregister.com
Managing Editor: Steve Bagwell, sbagwell@newsregister.com
Deadlines: 5 p.m. Friday for Tuesday, 5 p.m. Tuesday for Friday

In Telephone-Register days. (photo/courtesy, the News-Register)

McMinnville, with a 2010 population of 32,000, is the seat of predominantly rural Yamhill County.

The county has traditionally been dependent largely on logging and farming, but has become better known in recent years as the hub of Oregon's burgeoning wine industry. In addition to an array of wineries, wine bars, and associated restaurants, the city is home to Linfield College and the Evergreen Aviation Museum. It lies along Highway 18, the main route from Portland to the Spirit Mountain Casino and Central Oregon Coast, augmenting its tourism pull. Founder William T. Newby, an early immigrant on the Oregon Trail, named it for his hometown of McMinnville, Tennessee. Though just just 35 miles southwest of Portland, transportation limitations have kept it largely outside Portland's orbit.

The local paper, the *News-Register*, is a family-owned amalgam of several earlier papers. Its earliest progenitor was the *Courier*, founded in the nearby community of Lafayette in 1866, before Lafayette lost its county seat status to McMinnville. In 1872, the *Courier* moved to McMinnville and took a new name, becoming the *Yamhill County Reporter*. McMinnville was asserting its dominance in the county by then, though it would not become the county seat until 17 years later.

The *McMinnville News* was founded in 1901. Four years later, it merged with the *Reporter* to create the *News-Reporter*. During the intervening years, two other newspapers had been launched, the *Oregon Register* in Lafayette in 1881 and the *West Side Telephone* in McMinnville in 1886. They later merged to create the *Telephone-Register*, based in McMinnville.

In 1928, Iowa newsman Lars Bladine bought the *Telephone-Register* and sent his oldest son, Jack, out to run it. Four years later, he moved out himself with the rest of the family, including younger son Phil. The purchase launched a run of Bladine family ownership that continues to this day, with a transition from third to fourth generation leadership now under way.

The first handoff came with Lars' death in 1941, as Jack became publisher and Phil editor. Jack and Phil went on to buy the *News-Reporter* and merge it with their *Telephone-Register* on February 12, 1953, to create today's *News-Register*.

Phil became publisher with Jack's death in 1957, and held that title until 1991, when he handed the reins to son Jon E. "Jeb" Bladine. Jeb continues to head the company; his son, Ossie, serves as news editor. (One of the co-authors of this book, Steve Bagwell, is the paper's managing editor.)

The *News-Register* stole a march on the rest of the state's press by establishing a website in December 1995 and continues to publish aggressively on the web.

It has published as a weekly, twice-weekly, tri-weekly and daily at various points in its history. In recent years, it moved from a Tuesday-Thursday-Saturday cycle to a Wednesday-Saturday cycle, then to a Tuesday/Friday cycle when it switched from carrier to mail delivery late in 2012.

The paper is one of the few weeklies in Oregon – or the Northwest, for that matter – offering versions for the iPhone, iPad, Droid phone and other mobile devices through free downloadable apps. The apps were developed through a partnership with Agfa.

Mail Tribune　　　　　　　　　Medford

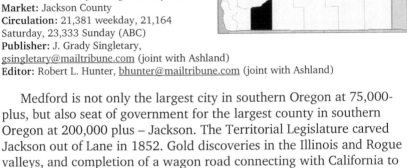

Owner: Dow Jones Local Media Group,a division of Newcastle Investment Corp.
Address: 111 N. Fir St., Medford, OR 97501
Phone: 541-776-4411
URL: www.mailtribune.com (subscription required for full access)
Established: 1906
Published: Monday through Sunday AM
Market: Jackson County
Circulation: 21,381 weekday, 21,164 Saturday, 23,333 Sunday (ABC)
Publisher: J. Grady Singletary, gsingletary@mailtribune.com (joint with Ashland)
Editor: Robert L. Hunter, bhunter@mailtribune.com (joint with Ashland)

Medford is not only the largest city in southern Oregon at 75,000-plus, but also seat of government for the largest county in southern Oregon at 200,000 plus – Jackson. The Territorial Legislature carved Jackson out of Lane in 1852. Gold discoveries in the Illinois and Rogue valleys, and completion of a wagon road connecting with California to the south and Douglas County to the north, led to an early influx of settlers. The main population center early on was Jacksonville, but the railroad bypassed Jacksonville in favor of Medford in the 1880s, and that shifted the balance.

The *Medford Mail* was founded in 1888 as a weekly, and went daily as the *Medford Morning Mail* in 1908.

The next year, the *Mail* was sold to veteran Oregon newsman George Putnam, owner of the rival *Medford Daily Tribune*. Putnam consolidated the papers into the *Medford Mail Tribune*.

Robert W. Ruhl bought an interest in the paper in 1911 and became majority owner when Putnam left for the *Capital Journal*, Salem's afternoon daily, in 1919. Both men were known for vigorous, courageous and sometimes contentious editorials. Both are considered major figures in Oregon journalism.

James Ottaway Jr., who gained national prominence in journalism through the family newspaper company, later came into the picture. Ottaway Newspapers Inc. acquired the *Mail Tribune* in 1973, three years after he took over as CEO from his father, an even more celebrated figure in journalism. The group became a subsidiary of Dow Jones & Co., owner of the venerable *Wall Street Journal*, in 1979. However, it continued to operate with a high degree of independence under the continued direction of the younger Ottaway.

Rupert Murdoch's News Corp. bought Dow Jones in 2007, over Ottaway's fierce opposition. It began operating the papers – then 25 in number, down from a peak of 40 – as the Dow Jones Local Media Group.

Ottaway picked up a smaller paper from Oregon's Jackson County, the *Ashland Daily Tidings*, in 2002. One of the smallest dailies in Oregon, the former Lee paper no longer has an office of its own. Its five reporters work out of the Mail Tribune building in Medford, where it is paginated and published.

The two papers are among the few in Oregon employing a metered charge system for online news, pioneered by the *Wall Street Journal*. The system is in wider use in Washington and Idaho. The first three stories in a given month are free without registration, and the next seven with registration. More frequent visits require a subscription.

In the spring of 2013, Murdoch began shopping the Dow Jones group through the New York investment house Waller Capital. In September, he found a buyer – Newcastle Investment Corp., a subsidiary of the Fortress Investment Group.

Fortress owns GateHouse Media, whose stable includes 78 dailies in 21 states, along with 235 weeklies and 91 shoppers. The company said its plan was to reorganize the heavily debt-ridden GateHouse via Chapter 11 bankruptcy, then merge it with Dow Jones Local Media to create a new parent company called New Media.

Valley Herald   Milton-Freewater

Owner: MS Media Circus
Address: 408 N. Main St., Milton-Freewater, OR 97862
Phone: 541-938-6688
URL: www.mfvalleyherald.com (subscription required)
Established: 2001
Published: Friday
Market: Northeastern Umatilla County
Circulation: 751 (SO)
Publisher: Melanie Hall, mel_valley@qwestoffice.net
Deadline: Noon Tuesday

Milton got its start as Freeport. When it was chosen as the site of a mill in the 1860s, it became Milltown, later shortened to Milton.

Freewater, Milton's neighbor to the immediate north, got its start in 1889 as New Walla Walla. It ended up being dubbed Freewater because its founders extended the offer of free water service as an inducement to settlers. When the long-time rivals opted to marry their fortunes in

1951, naming was a serious sticking point. They finally settled on the only name they could get a majority to accept – Milton-Freewater.

Local newspapering began with the founding of the *Milton Eagle* in 1887. The *Freewater Herald* followed in 1890 and morphed into the *Freewater Times* in 1900.

Herman and Dorothy Judd brought an end to a long and bitter competition by merging the two papers in 1951 to create the *Eagle-Times*, based in Milton. The merger mirrored that of the communities the two papers served and was carried out virtually simultaneously. However, the Freewater portion of the population felt the paper tilted toward its home base in Milton. And that created resentment.

Charles and Dorothy Heard, who had previously owned and operated the *Herald* in Joseph, launched the original version of the *Milton-Freewater Valley Herald* five years later.

In a story published in the *Walla Walla Union-Bulletin* in June 2012, Dorothy Heard told Rick Haverinen they had made the move over from Joseph to start a print shop. But she said local businessmen told her husband, "We want you to start a newspaper. That paper in Milton just ignores us."

Heard told Haverinen he sold the ads that kept the paper afloat, while she wrote and edited the stories, took the photos and wrote a weekly column. The paper prospered, and they were soon able to buy out the *Eagle-Times*. The Heards had owned and operated the Joseph *Herald* for nine years, from 1947 to 1956, prior to making the move to Milton-Freewater. After selling the *Valley Herald* in 1962, they went on to publish the *Cashmere Valley Record*, the *Pilot Rock News,* and *Heppner Gazette-Times* by turns before retiring in 1972.

After the Heards' departure, papers came and went under the *Valley Herald*, *Eagle-Times,* and *Valley Times* names. But the *Valley Herald* was revived in 2001 to compete with the *Valley Times*, and succeed in driving its rival out of business in 2003.

Dorothy Heard is now back in Milton-Freewater, authoring a weekly column for the *Valley Herald* in its latest incarnation under the ownership and oversight of Melanie Hall.

Pioneer   Molalla

Owner: Pamplin Media Group
Address: 217 E. Main St., Molalla, OR 97038
Phone: 503-829-2301
URL: www.molallapioneer.com (subscription required for full access)
Established: 1913
Published: Wednesday

Market: Southwestern Clackamas County
Circulation: 3,495 (SO)
Publisher: William D. Cassel, wcassel@eaglenewspapers.com (joint with Canby and Wilsonville)
News Editor: Peggy Savage, psavage@molallapioneer.com
Deadline: Noon Friday

Molalla is a city of 8,000 nestled in the foothills of the Cascade Range on the eastern side of the Willamette Valley. Though it is part of Clackamas County, population 375,000, and the Portland Metropolitan Area, population 2.2 million, it remains rural in character. Throughout its history is has served as a logging and farming supply center. The county seat is Oregon City, about a dozen miles north of Molalla. It was the site of the first federal court west of the Rockies, so when San Francisco was founded in 1849, the plat had to be filed there.

Molalla was named after the Molalla River, which was named in turn after a Native American tribe. It landed a post office in 1850, but came late to newspapering, as the *Pioneer* wasn't founded until 1913.

The paper has only changed hands twice in the last 50 years. Oregon-based Eagle Newspapers bought the *Pioneer* in the mid-1970s in a package deal with the *North Willamette News* and *North Willamette Press*. It kept the *Pioneer* intact, but merged the two smaller papers into other publications in its growing suburban stable. Like its sister publications in Canby and Wilsonville, the *Pioneer* is published on Eagle's web press in Salem. Also like them, it was converted in early 2012 from broadsheet to tabloid.

However, Eagle no longer owns the three Southern Clackamas County papers. It packaged them with three other Oregon weeklies in a January 2013 sale to the Portland-based Pamplin Media Group.

The Douglas County Mail   Myrtle Creek

Owner: Myrtle Tree Press
Address: 325 N.E. First Ave., Myrtle Creek, OR 97457
Phone: 541-863-5233.
URL: No web presence
Established: 1902
Published: Thursday
Market: Southern Douglas County
Circulation: 1,038 (SO)
Editor & Publisher: Robert L. Chaney Sr., dcmail@clearwire.net

Douglas County is one of the most timber-rich counties in Oregon, one of the most timber-rich states in the U.S. It was created in 1852 out of the portion of Umpqua County lying east of the Coast Range summit.

In 1856, more of Umpqua was shifted to Douglas, which was named after Stephen A. Douglas, a strong supporter of Oregon statehood.

Myrtle Creek lies well south of the much larger county seat of Roseburg, but they share dependence on cutting and processing of Douglas fir, which grows abundantly on the region's well-watered slopes, and positioning on Interstate 5, a West Coast arterial.

The local weekly *Umpqua Free Press* was founded in 1903. Serving a city of barely 3,500 that lies in the shadow of a city of more than 20,000, it's had a somewhat tenuous existence. But it has persevered.

Robert "Bob" Frederick Scherer gave up a 21-year career with the *Wall Street Journal* to buy the *Umpqua Free Press* in 1974. In doing so, he went from the largest circulation newspaper in the United States to one of the smallest. More than 35 years later, it still counts barely 1,000 subscribers.

Scherer, who died in July 2012, was born in South Dakota. He learned the journalism trade at the University of Missouri in Columbus. He came to Oregon after putting in two years of military service in Germany, and stayed long enough to put in stints with two dailies and earn a master's degree at the University of Oregon. He spent more than 20 years working in New York City for the *Journal*, but had a lifelong dream of owning his own paper and fulfilled it when he packed his bags for Myrtle Creek.

He expanded its reach, however, renamed it *The Douglas County Mail* and continued to publish for the next 27 years. He waited until he was ready to retire to finally sell it in 2001 to Robert Chaney, Sr.

Herald   Myrtle Point

Owners: Matt and Kim Hall
Address: 408 Spruce St., Myrtle Point, OR 97458
Phone: 541-572-2717
URL: No website
Established: 1889
Published: Thursday
Market: Southeastern Coos County
Circulation: 1,300 (SO)
Editor & Publisher: Matt Hall, mpherald@harborside.com
Deadline: Noon Monday

Early pioneers began to settle in Myrtle Point in the early 1860s. It was known as Ott, then Myersville, before becoming Myrtle Point. It drew the latter name from the myrtles lining the Coquille River as it winds its way west to the Pacific Ocean at Bandon. The three forks of the Coquille merge just above and below Myrtle Point, which lies well into Coos County's heavily forested interior. The community was platted in 1879 and incorporated in 1887. Its heritage is rooted in the twin pursuits of logging and farming, particularly dairy farming in the latter case. Though it still boasts only 2,500 residents, it experienced something of a boom when the railroad ran a line in from Coos Bay in 1893.

The *West Oregonian* introduced newspapering to Myrtle Point in 1889, just two years after the community's incorporation. A weekly, it morphed into the *Enterprise* in 1895 and the *Herald* in 1928. Other papers came and went over the years. The roster included the *Southern Coos County American*, published from 1917 to 1928, and the *Myrtle Creek Mail*, published from 1916 to 1982 – a run of more than 65 years.

Ken and Sherry Anderson bought the paper in 1998 and operated it until June 2013. They sold it to another husband and wife team, Matt and Kim Hall.

The *Herald* is the third Southern Oregon weekly to come under Hall ownership. They also own the *Curry County Reporter* and *Port Orford News* in neighboring Curry County. They started with the *News* and added the *Reporter* in September 2012, buying it from yet another husband and wife team – Joel Summer and Rebecca Macko.

Matt Hall spent four years at the *Klamath Falls Herald & News* before making the move to Port Orford. Earlier, he had worked for various newspapers along the Pacific Coast, in both the U.S. and Canada. In a story in the *Curry County Reporter*, he said the *Herald* was joining his "faith-based family newspapers." He said he considered the acquisition a "blessing from the Lord."

The Graphic   Newberg

Owner: Pamplin Media Group
Address: 500 E. Hancock St., Newberg, OR 97132
Phone: 503-538-2181
URL: www.newberggraphic.com (subscription required for full access)
Established: 1888
Published: Wednesday
Market: Northeastern Yamhill County
Circulation: 4,960 (SO)
Publisher: Allen Herriges, aherriges@newberggraphic.com
Managing Editor: Gary Allen, gallen@newberggraphic.com

The weekly *Newberg Graphic* and the city it serves were founded back to back, the newspaper in 1888 and the city in 1889. They were both pre-dated by George Fox University, founded by early Quakers in 1885 as the Friends Pacific Academy. The community has hosted a substantial

Quaker or Friends component ever since, which colors politics and social interaction. The community remained dry for decades, and the college remains so to this day.

In one of its early editions, the newspaper inventoried Newberg's assets this way: "15 business houses, representing nearly every line," plus "five good sawmills, one flouring mill, three grain warehouses, two fruit drying houses, a nursery, a brick and tile factory, another brick yard to start soon, a company organized to buy a fruit cannery, the prospect of a new roller process flouring mill and other manufacturing establishments." That's not to mention the college, which did not achieve university status until recently.

Over the years, competitors have come and gone. The roster includes the *Enterprise*, *Scribe*, *Valley News*, *Weekly*, *Times,* and *Chehalem News*.

The *Graphic* was acquired by Denny Smith's Eagle Newspapers in the mid-1980s. Eagle published it on a twice-weekly Wednesday-Saturday schedule until the end of 2012, then converted it to a Wednesday-only weekly. The *Graphic* is still printed at Eagle's web press plant in Salem. however, it is no longer owned by Eagle. The Portland-based Pamplin Media Group bought six Eagle weeklies, including the *Graphic*, in January 2013. Papers in Canby, Molalla, Madras, Wilsonville, and Woodburn were also included in the deal.

News-Times   Newport

Owner: News Media Corporation
Address: 831 N.E. Avery, Newport, OR 97365
Phone: 541-265-8571
URL: www.newportnewstimes.com (subscription required for full access)
Established: 1882
Published: Wednesday and Friday
Market: Southern Lincoln County
Circulation: 7,011 (SO)
Publisher: Jeremy Burke, publisher@newportnewstimes.com
Managing Editor: Steve Card, editor@newportnewstimes.com

At least 20 different newspapers have been published in or near Newport on Oregon's rugged and scenic central coast, starting with the *News-Times'* oldest ancestor, the *Yaquina Post*, in 1882. It was published five miles upriver from Newport by Colonel Collins Van Cleve, who later launched another local paper in the Willamette Valley to the east, the *Scio Press*.

In 1893, the year Lincoln County was carved out of Benton County, two more papers got their start: the *Yaquina Bay News* in Newport and *Lincoln County Leader* out of Toledo. Both would enjoy very long runs.

The *Post* was failing in Yaquina City, which was losing out economically, so it was moved to the bustling shipping and fishing center of Newport and rechristened the *Yaquina Bay News*. The move was orchestrated by a new owner, British newspaperman and cavalry officer Capt. John Matthews.

Descendants of Mathews continued to run the paper until 1941, after which a series of ownership changes ensued. The paper was purchased by Walt Taylor and Lee Irwin in 1964, and they set about making it the area's dominant paper. They bought out the *Lincoln County Times* in 1965, creating the *News-Times*, and swallowed the *Leader* the following year.

Glenn Jackson, owner of a chain headed by the *Albany Democrat-Herald*, added the paper to his stable in 1977. When he died, the papers were picked up by Capital Cities Communications. After mergers between Capital Cities and ABC, then Disney, the papers were sold to the national Lee Newspapers chain, based in Iowa. It combined them with the *Corvallis Gazette-Times*, which it had owned for many years, to establish itself as a major player in Oregon.

Dead Mountain Echo   Oakridge

Owner: Echo Publishing
Address: 48013 Highway 58, Oakridge, OR 97463
Phone: 541-782-4241
URL: No website
Established: 1973
Published: Thursday
Market: Southeastern Lane County
Circulation: 456 (SO)
Publishers: Larry and Debra Roberts, lroberts@efn.org
Editor: Larry Roberts, lroberts@efn.org
Deadline: 4 p.m. Monday

Lane County stretches all the way from the Oregon Coast to the Oregon Cascades. It shares that distinction with only one other county – Douglas, its next-door neighbor to the south. But it was vastly larger at the time of its creation in 1851, encompassing all of southern, and a portion of eastern Oregon.

In 1852, John Diamond and William Macy blazed a new Oregon Trail shortcut into the southern Willamette Valley. Known as the Free Emigrant Road, this Highway 58 forerunner cut through the Cascades at Willamette Pass and traversed the future townsite of Oakridge on its way west. And it served to double the population of the county virtually overnight. Originally known as Hazeldell, then Big Prairie, the community didn't gather enough people to qualify for a post office until

1888 or to qualify for incorporation until 1912, after the Southern Pacific ran a line through town. The railroad dubbed the settlement Oak Ridge, and that was shortened to Oakridge in the months leading up to incorporation.

The town depended on the logging and milling of Cascade Range timber until its two big mills folded in the mid-1980s. Its economy still relies on the timber industry to an extent, but has also diversified into outdoor recreation. Almost a century passed between the time the first explorers came through and the time the community got its first newspaper, the now long-gone *Oakridge Telegram*.

The *Telegram* was founded in 1947 by Gerry and Esther Beach Sittser. It was publishing an ambitious three times a week, and apparently making a go of it, until June 1973. Then Gerry Sittser died of leukemia at the early age of 62 and the hard times hit. His death put the operation under severe financial stress. Meanwhile, Oakridge's timber-based economy went into a tailspin.

If that weren't enough, a trio of young entrepreneurs founded a rival paper, the weekly *Dead Mountain Echo*, in April 1973. An eight-page tabloid featuring a livelier, more modern look, it soon began to cut into the *Telegram*'s circulation and advertising base.

Facing the prospect of bankruptcy, Esther Sittser suspended publication of the *Telegram* in November 1974, leaving the field to the upstart rival.

The three entrepreneurs, Mark Schwebke, 26, Dennis Keffer, 25, and Frank Drake, 21, had no previous experience in the newspaper business. They rotated publishing duties. Before long, they sold the operation to Larry Roberts, a 1965 graduate of Oakridge High School, who continues to own and operate it.

Argus Observer   Ontario

Owner: Wick Communications
Address: 1160 S.W. Fourth St., Ontario, OR 97914
Phone: 541-889-5387
URL: www.argusobserver.com (subscription required for e-edition, full access)
Established: 1896
Published: Tuesday through Friday PM, Sunday AM in partnership with *Payette Independent-Enterprise*
Market: Malheur County (plus Idaho's Payette and Weiser counties on Sunday)
Circulation: 6,837 (VAC)
Publisher: John Dillon, johnd@argusobserver.com (joint with Payette, Idaho)
Editor: Scott McIntosh, scottm@argusobserver.com (joint with Payette, Idaho)

Malheur County is a long, narrow strip of Oregon's arid southeast, bordering Idaho on the east and Nevada on the south. Ontario, the largest city, and Vale, the county seat, both are located in the county's northeastern corner, where most people live. It was first settled in the early 1860s by miners, cattle ranchers, and sheep ranchers. It earned independent county status in 1887, by which time an influx of Basque sheepherders from northern Spain had begun to arrive in significant numbers. Ontario, on the western, Oregon, side of the Snake River, was founded June 11, 1883.

The impetus was the pending arrival of the Oregon Short Line Railroad, which established a depot in the fledgling town. The railroad helped Ontario become a shipping center for livestock from the entire eastern two-thirds of Oregon and consequently develop one of the largest stockyards in the western United States. Development of a canal system capable of delivering irrigation water to farmers and stockmen also spurred the economy.

The local paper, the *Argus Observer*, is a direct descendant of a publication called *The Advocate*. It was established on January 6, 1897, in Vale. Partisan in nature, *The Advocate* supported Democrat William Jennings Bryan for president; it was owned and operated first by E.R. Murray, then by W. E. Lees.

Twice in its early history, *The Advocate* attempted to go daily, first in 1898 and again in 1904. Between those attempts, it moved from Vale to Ontario, becoming *The Ontario Advocate* initially and later the *Ontario Argus*.

In 1932, future Oregon governor Elmo Smith, became editor of the *Argus*. In 1936, he left to found *The Eastern Oregon Observer*, which started life as a free shopper published on a mimeograph machine, but became a full-fledged newspaper competing head to head with the *Argus*. He and his wife, Dorothy, borrowed $25 to finance the venture.

The *Argus* and *Observer*, both publishing twice-weekly at the time, merged in 1947 to create the daily *Ontario Argus Observer*.

At the time, Bernard Mainwaring and Don Lynch owned the *Argus*, while Robert E. Pollock and Jessica Longston owned the *Observer*. Smith had sold his interest in favor of acquiring other newspaper properties.

Wick Communications, which currently owns 28 small papers in 12 western states, bought the paper in 1968. It also owns the Payette *Independent-Enterprise*, located across the border in Idaho.

East Oregonian Building in Pendleton, circa 1930. (photo/Washington State Historical Society)

East Oregonian   Pendleton

Owner: EO Media Group
Address: 211 S.E. Byers Ave., Pendleton, OR
97801
Phone: 541-276-2211
URL: www.eastoregonian.com (subscription
required for full access)
Established: 1875
Published: Tuesday through Sunday AM
Market: Umatilla and Morrow counties
Circulation: 7,343 (SO)

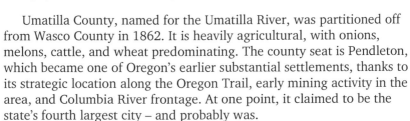

Publisher: Kathryn B. Brown, kbbrown@eastoregonian.com (joint with Hermiston)
Managing Editor: Daniel Wattenburger, dwattenburger@eastoregonian.com

Umatilla County, named for the Umatilla River, was partitioned off
from Wasco County in 1862. It is heavily agricultural, with onions,
melons, cattle, and wheat predominating. The county seat is Pendleton,
which became one of Oregon's earlier substantial settlements, thanks to
its strategic location along the Oregon Trail, early mining activity in the
area, and Columbia River frontage. At one point, it claimed to be the
state's fourth largest city – and probably was.

It remains one of the most important hubs of commerce in the eight
counties of arid eastern Oregon. However, it has been surpassed in its
home county in recent years by Hermiston, to its west. Both are
currently hovering around 17,000 residents, a lot by Oregon's dry-side
standards.

Pendleton's hometown paper, the *East Oregonian*, is the flagship daily in the Forrester family's EO Media Group. Formerly known as the East Oregonian Publishing Company, EO Media also publishes the neighboring *Hermiston Herald*, a small daily in Astoria, a five-state agricultural weekly based in Salem and a group of community weeklies scattered about Oregon and southwest Washington.

The *East Oregonian* was first published in Pendleton as a weekly newspaper in 1875 by M.P. Bull. C.S. "Sam" Jackson purchased it seven years later. He began publishing two editions a week in 1883 and six editions a week in 1888, publishing every day but Sunday. Jackson left in 1902 to take over the *Portland Evening Journal*. Edwin B. Aldrich became editor and part owner in 1908, and his descendants have owned it ever since.

Aldrich's eldest daughter, Amy Aldrich Bedford, started work at the EO in 1949 as the manager of the EO's commercial printing plant. She later became the promotions/public relations manager and continued in this position until her death in 2006. Another daughter, Eleanor, married budding journalist J.W. "Bud" Forrester Jr., and they came into ownership. Upon their deaths, the mantle passed to their sons, Mike and Steve.

In March 2012, the *East Oregonian* changed from weekday afternoon delivery to an all-morning. Like its sister five-day daily in Astoria, it publishes aggressively on the web, but requires a subscription for full access.

The Oregonian building (the most recent, at this writing) in downtown Portland. (photo/M.O. Stevens , Wikipedia commons, 2009)

The Oregonian   Portland

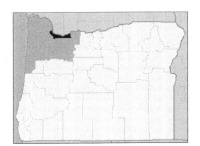

Owner: Advance Publications (Newhouse)
Address: 1320 S.W. Broadway, Portland, OR 97201
Phone: 503-221-8327
URL: www.oregonlive.com/oregonian (unrestricted, but e-edition limited to subscribers)
Established: 1850
Published: Monday through Sunday AM
Market: Oregon and Southwest Washington
Circulation: 228,909 weekday, 213,409 Saturday, 303,495 Sunday (ABC)
Publisher: N. Christian Anderson, canderson@oregonian.com
Vice President & Editor: Peter Bhatia, pbhatia@oregonian.com

The Oregonian Publisher N. Christian Anderson electrified the journalism community, and much of the larger community, when he announced the morning of June 20, 2013, that the paper would be cutting home delivery back to four days on October 1. He said *The Oregonian* would continue to publish seven days a week, selling out of stores and racks on the three weekdays being cut from its delivery schedule.

But following a pattern the Newhouse family has been imposing at papers it owns across the country, including major metro newspapers like the *Plain Dealer* in Cleveland, he said it would only offer home-delivery of the editions offering the most advertising support – those of Wednesday, Friday, Saturday, and Sunday. And he said the Saturday edition would be a truncated version built around sports and classified sections.

The limited-delivery idea was actually pioneered by Detroit Joint Operating Agreement partners Media General and Gannett, when they cut home delivery to three days at the *News* and *Free Press* in 2009. But the Newhouses have proven its most aggressive practitioners, working through their privately held, New-Jersey based holding company, Advance Publications.

The plan has several other elements, mirroring a pattern Advance developed through earlier rollouts in New York, Michigan, Ohio, Pennsylvania, Alabama, and Louisiana. Anderson said:

■ The paper would be substantially reducing its workforce effectively immediately. In fact, it began issuing layoff notices immediately after the announcement.

■ It would be trading its cavernous quarters on Southwest Broadway for more compact and cost-effective office space elsewhere.

■ It would be reorganizing into two divisions – The Oregonian Media Group, encompassing print and online news operations, and Advance Central Services of Oregon, encompassing accounting, personnel, and a range of other support functions.

■ It would launch a new e-edition to fill the Monday/Tuesday/Thursday void for its paid subscribers, dubbed MyDigitalO, but would maintain unrestricted access to its website and begin shifting more of its focus to its online operations overall.

While long-rumored and widely expected, the development still struck with stunning force. It promises to be a pivotal change for a paper of such size, dominance, reach, and long tradition.

The Oregonian was founded by Steven Coffin and William W. Chapman in 1850 as the *Weekly Oregonian*. They chose Thomas Jefferson Dryer of San Francisco as their first editor. There was little to suggest, at that point, its future as a major metropolitan newspaper. The land where downtown Portland was located had been claimed less than a decade before, and only a few buildings had been erected. Portland would not be incorporated until the following February, with an initial population of 800. Even by the standards of the times, it was barely big enough to support a newspaper.

Henry Pittock, who ran Dryer's hand-cranked press for him, came into possession of the fledgling paper in 1861 as compensation for back wages. He settled for room and board initially, but was later accorded a salary of $900 a year, and Dryer could not always cover it.

Very able and ambitious, Pittock purchased a steam-powered press and launched the *Morning Oregonian* as a daily on February 4, 1861. It was Portland's fourth daily, and competition was fierce, particularly with the better established *Times* and *Advertiser*. Pittock organized an elaborate system to obtain Civil War battle news ahead of his competitors. The *Times* and *Advertiser* were both relying on dispatches delivered by telegraph to the end of the line in Yreka, California, and ferried on north by steamship. Pittock had his telegrams rushed north by stagecoach and Pony Express rider, shaving several days off the travel time.

While Dryer had been driven by a desire to propagate Whig ideology, Pittock was driven simply by a desire to disseminate the news quicker and more efficiently than anyone else. And it proved the winning approach.

Harvey Scott, brother of women's suffrage advocate Abigail Scott Duniway, edited the paper from 1866 to 1872. But he was fired when Pittock sold to Henry Corbett and jumped to Ben Holladay's rival *Bulletin*. Corbett sold the paper back to Pittock in 1877. By then, the *Bulletin* had gone bankrupt.

The Oregonian, which had developed a staunchly Republican editorial orientation over the years (it did not endorse a Democrat for president until 1992), published its first Sunday edition in 1881. That helped it continue to develop its status in the market as Portland's pre-eminent newspaper.

The oldest continuously operated newspaper on the West Coast, and for many years the largest in the Northwest, *The Oregonian* originally was housed in a two-story building at the intersection of First and Morrison. It moved into a nine-story building at 6th and Alder in 1892 and to its present quarters on Broadway – perhaps soon to be vacated – in 1948.

S.I. "Si" Newhouse, founder of Advance Publications, bought the paper for $5.6 million In 1950.

For many years, *The Oregonian* shared the field with an evening sister paper, the six-day *Oregon Journal*. It was founded by C.S. "Sam" Jackson, publisher of Pendleton's *East Oregonian*, in 1902.

One of the signal events in the history of the two papers came in November 1959, when Stereotypers Local 49 struck them simultaneously over pressroom manning requirements. They published a joint strike paper for six months before resuming "normal" publication with a newly hired non-union workforce. Striking union workers published a daily strike paper of their own, *The Reporter*, from February 1960 to October 1964. The strike set the stage for Newhouse's acquisition of the *Journal* in 1961. But it left a bitter legacy with Oregon unions that lingers yet today.

Despite their shared ownership, the two papers remained fierce competitors until 1982, when Advance folded the *Journal* and merged its workforce into that of *The Oregonian*. The company cited declining ad support and readership for a fate that PM dailies were widely meeting – for the same reasons – all across the country.

The Oregonian once circulated in every corner of Oregon, and in large swaths of Washington to the north and Idaho to the east. To remain relevant to its far-flung network of readers, it employed a veritable army of correspondents. It has been steadily dismantling its correspondent system in recent years, and has been drawing in both its home-delivery and overall circulation areas. However, it has so far managed to maintain both its core reporting strength and dominance in the Northwest media landscape, underscored by a series of Pulitzers won under its current leadership.

Tribune   Portland

Owner: Pamplin Media Group
Address: 6605 S.E. Lake Road, Portland, OR 97222
Phone: 503-226-6397
URL: www.portlandtribune.com (unrestricted)
Established: 2001
Published: Thursday
Market: Greater Portland
Circulation: No paid circulation; free-distribution
President: Mark Garber, mgarber@commnewspapers.com
Executive Editor: Kevin Harden, kharden@commnewspapers.com
Deadline: Noon Friday

The *Portland Tribune* is a free-distribution weekly published Thursdays by the Pamplin Media Group. It is the flagship in an extensive network of mostly paid Pamplin weeklies serving cities throughout the Portland metropolitan area. The company, founded and led by Portland businessman Robert Pamplin Jr., also owns other media properties, including several Northwest radio stations.

The paper began life as a twice-weekly on February 9, 2001. It was the first paper to directly challenge *The Oregonian* on its home turf since that paper's owner, Newhouse's Advance Publications, acquired and then disbanded the rival *Oregon Journal* decades ago. The two companies have since gone head to head in suburban markets as well. When Pamplin announced it was launching a paper to compete with Advance's Hillsboro *Argus* in suburban Washington County, Advance countered by announcing plans for a new weekly on Pamplin turf in nearby Forest Grove.

The *Tribune* was launched on the eve of what would prove a long series of downturns and reverses for the newspaper industry, and it was by no means immune. It responded by cutting back to weekly publication in 2008, and by reducing the size of both its staff and press run, but has persevered.

The paper focuses primarily on metropolitan Portland and secondarily on the rest of the state. It makes no attempt to compete with *The Oregonian* on national/international news, or even Northwest news. But it also has featured extensive sports coverage from the outset, organized around Portland and Oregon teams. It is a reliable source of information on Oregon prep, college, and pro team, with context on the venues in which they compete – the NBA, the Pac-12, and so forth.

Pamplin maintains an extensive web presence for its network of papers through a central website, still featuring unrestricted access at this writing. It serves as local sponsor for the National Spelling Bee.

Willamette Week   Portland

Owner: City of Roses Newspaper Co.
Address: 2220 N.W. Quimby St., Portland, OR 97210
Phone: 503-243-2122
URL: www.wweek.com (unrestricted)
Established: 1974
Published: Wednesday
Circulation: No paid circulation; free-distribution
Publisher: Richard H. Meeker, rmeeker@wweek.com
Editor: Mark Zusman, mzusman@wweek.com

Willamette Week, an alternative weekly based in Portland, was launched as a paid-distribution publication in 1974. It was converted to free-distribution in 1984. Politics, business, and culture are the mainstays of its coverage. The paper was founded by a group headed by Ron Buel, who served as its original publisher. It was later acquired by the Baker family's *Eugene Register-Guard*.

Willamette Week staff members Richard Meeker, hired as a reporter in the startup days of 1974, and Mark Zusman, hired as a business writer in 1982, formed the City of Roses Newspaper Co. in 1983 to buy out the *Register-Guard*. Meeker installed himself as publisher and Zusman as editor, positions they still hold today, almost 30 years later.

At the time, *Willamette Week* had a paid circulation of about 12,000. Its circulation, and thus its influence, soared after it converted to free-distribution the following year.

It's proudest moment came in 2005, when reporter Nigel Jaquiss was awarded the Pulitzer Prize in investigative reporting. Jaquiss was honored for a May 2004 story exposing a deep, dark secret kept for decades by former Oregon Governor Neil Goldschmidt – that he had sexually abused the family's 14-year-old babysitter during his tenure as mayor of Portland. It was one of only a handful of Pulitzers won by a weekly, and especially rare for an alternative weekly. And it was the first awarded for a story originally published online, after Goldschmidt attempted to pre-empt *Willamette Week* by taking his story to *The Oregonian*.

The paper derives the vast majority of its revenue from display advertising. Personal ads and other forms of classified advertising once playing a significant contributing role, but have been largely usurped by Craigslist in recent years.

News   Port Orford

Owner: Matt and Kim Hall
Address: 519 10th St., Port Orford, OR 97465
Phone: 541-260-3638
URL: www.portorfordnews.net (under construction)
Established: 1958
Published: Friday
Market: Northern Curry County
Circulation: Approximately 600
Editor & Publisher: Matt Hall, portorfordnews@gmail.com (joint with Gold Beach and Myrtle Point)

Curry is a lightly populated county tucked into Oregon's southwestern corner. Bordered by the Pacific Ocean on the west and state of California on the south, it was named for George Law Curry, a governor of the territory. The county seat is Gold Beach, which lies well south of Port Orford. The county's other substantial city is Brookings, at its extreme southern end. All lie along the coast, which is no accident. The interior of the county long has been hampered by a limited transportation network. Mining had its moments early on, but Curry County's economic mainstays have traditionally been farming, fishing, and logging. It produces world-renowned Port Orford cedar and 90 percent of the nation's Easter lilies, along with cattle, sheep, blueberries, and nursery stock.

Port Orford, with about 1,100 residents, was founded in 1856. Early seafarer George Vancouver named nearby Cape Blanco for his good friend George, the Earl of Orford, and though Orford didn't stick with the cape, it did stick with the settlement that cropped up to the south.

For decades, the local paper, the *Port Orford News*, was owned by Lou and Ann Felsheim and operated by Pete and Nancy Peterson. The Felsheims, who made their home in Bandon, where they owned the

Bandon Western World, sold the *News* to Jim and Molly Walker on October 1, 1997. At the time, the Walkers also owned the *Curry County Reporter* in Gold Beach, passed down to them by Molly's parents, Bob and Betty Van Leer, who bought it in 1956. The Walkers sold the *News* to Matt and WillowSong Hall in June 2003. The Halls ended up divorcing and disposing of the paper, but after marrying Kim, Matt bought it back in partnership with her.

In September 2012, the Halls purchased the *Reporter*, which the Walkers had since sold to Joel Summer and Rebecca Macko. That gave them two of the county's three papers. In June 2013, they added yet another paper to the fold – the *Myrtle Point Herald*, purchased from longtime owners Ken and Sherry Anderson. It is located in neighboring Coos County.

Matt Hall spent four years working as an editor at the *Klamath Falls Herald & News* before taking over in Port Orford. Earlier, he had worked for various newspapers along the western coasts of the U.S. and Canada.

Central Oregonian   Prineville

Owner: Pamplin Media Group
Address: 558 N. Main St., Prineville, OR 97754
Phone: 541-447-6205
URL: www.centraloregonian.com (unrestricted)
Established: 1881
Published: Tuesday and Friday
Market: Crook County
Circulation: 2,829 (SO)
Editor & Publisher: Vance W. Tong, vtong@centraloregonian.com
Deadline: Noon Friday for Tuesday, noon Wednesday for Friday

Central Oregon's position on a high plateau east of the towering peaks of the Cascade Range hampered its development. The region's prosperity was concentrated in the Deschutes County seat of Bend rather than the Jefferson County seat of Madras or Crook County seat of Prineville. Bend was king of the realm when the economy depended on cutting and milling of Ponderosa pine, and never missed a beat when the mainstay gradually shifted to outdoor recreation.

Prineville, which accounts for almost half of the county's approximately 20,000 residents, was named for Barney Prine, its first merchant. When railroad tycoons James Hill and Edward Harriman established the first rail line into the region in 1911, they bypassed Prineville. Undaunted by the snub, city residents voted 355 to 1 to build a 19-mile shortline of their own, called the City of Prineville Railroad.

The *Central Oregonian* didn't come into being until 1922, about five years after completion of the shortline established rail access for local mills. But it traces its heritage all the way back to December 18, 1881.

Publisher Vance Tong said that's because the *Prineville News*, founded just one year after the *Ochoco Pioneer* came and went in a matter of months in 1880, is a direct ancestor. He explained it this way in a news account of his paper's history:

"It's still the same company. It's just a different name. Think of it as someone who just changed their name."

And changed it many times, truth to tell, as the *News* went through many permutations on its way to today's *Central Oregonian*. The *News* was absorbed by an upstart rival, the *Ochoco Review*, in 1884. After more than 30 years as the *Ochoco Review*, it became the *Prineville News* again in 1915. That wouldn't last either. It became the *Central Oregon Enterprise* in 1917 and the *Prineville Call* in 1920. It didn't transform itself into the *Central Oregonian* until 1922, when it absorbed two other local publications – the *Crook County Journal* and the *Western Stock Grower*.

It was publishing as a daily when Elmo Smith's Blue Mountain Eagle chain – forerunner of today's Eagle Newspapers, run by his son, Denny – picked it up in 1969. Under Eagle ownership, it acquired its own press in 1971 and cut back to twice-weekly publication in 1972.

Tong didn't arrive on the scene until 2002. And it fell to him to make another significant change, letting the paper's cadre of youth carriers go and converting to mail delivery. It wasn't popular, he said, but it had to be done. It was a major money-saver. "I love the nostalgia of kid carriers, and I wanted to keep them," he was quoted as saying. "It was a hard decision for us to make, but at the end of the day, we had to take certain actions to remain profitable."

In late June 2013, Eagle announced it was selling the *Central Oregonian*, after 44 years, to the Pamplin Media Group. Earlier in 2013, Eagle sold six other Oregon weeklies to Pamplin, including the *Madras Pioneer*, the *Central Oregonian*'s nearest neighboring paper. As part of the deal, Pamplin agreed to contract with Eagle for the printing of the new acquisitions at a commercial printing plant Eagle owns and operates in Salem.

The Spokesman   Redmond

Owner: Western Communications
Address: 226 N.W. Sixth St., Redmond, OR 97756
Phone: 541-548-2184

URL: www.redmondspokesmanonline.com (unrestricted, but limited to blog with events calendar)
Established: 1910
Published: Wednesday
Market: Northern Deschutes County
Circulation: 2,358 (SO)
Publisher: Steve Hawes, shawes@redmondspokesman.com
Editor: Leslie Pugmire Hole, lpugmire@redmondspokesman.com
Deadline: Noon Monday

Deschutes became the 36th of Oregon's 36 counties when it was cleaved from Crook on December 13, 1916. But has been more than making up for the late start. Over the last two decades, it has been the state's fastest growing, by far, reaching 160,000 by the 2010 census. The county was named after the Deschutes River. French-Canadians trapping for the Hudson's Bay Company dubbed it "Riviere des Chutes" – River of the Falls – for rapids that make it a major destination for whitewater rafters and kayakers these days.

Though not incorporated until 1910, Redmond has come in recent years to count more than 26,000 residents spread over 15 square miles. A high desert mecca for outdoor enthusiasts, it logged a population gain of almost 75% between 2000 and 2006 alone. The Johnny-come-lately city was named for Frank T. Redmond. It was platted by an irrigation company. It got a big boost when the Oregon Trunk Railway arrived in 1911, opening new markets.

The *Spokesman* was founded on July 14, 1910, eight days after Redmond's incorporation. That makes it the oldest continuously operated business in the community. It was the second of three papers launched in town around the same time, drawn by the twin prospects of incorporation and rail service. It followed The *Oregon Hub* and preceded *The Enterprise*, founded in 1913 by teenager Douglas Mullarky. The *Spokesman* bought out both of its competitors in 1914, and Redmond has been a one-newspaper town ever since.

The *Spokesman* was originally published by Henry and Clare Palmer. For a time, they also published *The Laidlaw Chronicle* in the nearby community of Tumalo, then known as Laidlaw.

However, the paper is most closely associated with Joe and Mary Brown, who published it for 40 years. The Western Communications group, based in nearby Bend, picked it up from them in 1971 and has owned it since.

The Umpqua Post   **Reedsport**

Owner: Lee Enterprises
Address: 2741 Frontage Road, Reedsport, OR 97467
Phone: 541-271-7474
URL: www.theumpquapost.com (unrestricted but very limited)
Established: 1996
Published: Wednesday
Market: Northwestern Douglas County
Circulation: 1,101 (SO)
Publisher: Jeff Precourt, jeff.precourt@theworldlink.com (with Bandon and Coos Bay)
Deadline: Noon Friday

The portion of coastal Umpqua County lying east of the Coast Range mountains was partitioned off to create Douglas County in 1852, just as settlement was beginning. The rest of Umpqua was absorbed into Douglas in a series of legislative actions in the 1850s and early 1860s. That left it ranging all the way from the coast to the Cascade Range, mirroring Lane County to the north. Reedsport was established on the estuary of the Umpqua River simultaneous with the creation of Douglas County. It was named for pioneer settler Alfred W. Reed.

The Southern Pacific extended a line south to Coos Bay in 1912, triggering Reedsport's transformation from a coastal hamlet doubling as a railroad construction camp to a true city. However, it was platted on marshland, so has been prone to repeated flooding, the most devastating coming in 1964.

The town traditionally relied on fishing, farming, and logging, but the closing of International Paper's Gardiner mill in 1999 virtually shut the door on the timber industry leg of that tripod. During the years since, it has striven to develop outdoor recreational opportunities like river and ocean sportfishing and cruising in the Oregon Dunes National Recreation Area.

From its offices in town, the *Umpqua Post*, also serves Winchester Bay, Gardiner, and Scottsburg – its three closest neighbors along Oregon's rugged southern coast. But it has one of the shortest histories in the industry. The *Post* was founded by Elizabeth Adamo and Nancie Hammond in 1996. By then, many Oregon papers had been in operation a century, and some could claim a century and a quarter.

After eight years at the helm, the Hammonds sold to the Pulitzer chain in 2004. But that relationship was brief, as Lee Enterprises scooped up Pulitzer the following year. Lee's largest concentration of papers is in Montana, but it also has a major and growing presence in Oregon.

Press   **Rogue River**

Owner: Valley Pride Publications LLC
Address: 8991 Rogue River Highway, Grants Pass, OR 97527
Phone: 541-582-1707.
URL: www.rogueriverpress.com (subscription required for full access)
Established: 1915
Published: Wednesday
Market: Northwestern Josephine County
Circulation: 1,582 (SO)
Publisher: Teresa Pearson, rrpress@rogueriverpress.com
Editor: Tammy Asnicar, editor@rogueriverpress.com

Rogue River was founded as Woodinville in 1876. It adopted Rogue River in 1912, taking the name of the river that runs through it. Ironically, "rogue" was a slur newly arriving settlers of European ancestry applied to the natives they were pushing aside. Though part of Jackson County itself, the community lies just a few miles east of the Josephine County seat of Grants Pass, a many-times-larger city that has long supported a daily. And its own county is dominated by Medford, an even larger city supporting an even larger daily. That tended to hamper development of local residency, commerce, and journalism.

The first local newspaper was the *Rogue River Argus*, which debuted on February 11, 1915. The *Argus* was followed by the *Times* in November 1951 and the *Press* in October 1972.

Unlike most of its neighbors, the *Press* remains locally owned. It circulates in Gold Hill as well as Rogue River. The current owner, Valley Pride Publications, is a venture overseen by Kendall and Nancy Birdsall of Rogue River, with their daughter, Teresa Pearson, also of Rogue River, who serves as publisher. Valley Pride bought the paper in 1994 from Dave and Heidi Ehrhardt, also of Rogue River.

"After nearly 12 years, we felt it was time to pursue other opportunities," Dave Ehrhardt said in announcing the sale. "The search for new owners led to an organization that we believe is a good fit to carry on the business and help it continue to grow into the future."

The News-Review   Roseburg

Owner: Swift Communications
Address: 345 N.E. Winchester St., Roseburg, OR 97470
Phone: 541-672-3321
URL: www.nrtoday.com (subscription required for full access)
Established: 1867
Published: Monday through Friday PM, Sunday AM
Market: Douglas County
Circulation: 16,549 (SO)
Publisher: Jeff Ackerman, jackerman@nrtoday.com
Editor: Vicki Menard, vmenard@nrtoday.com

Roseburg is the largest city and seat of government for heavily timbered Douglas County, which joins neighboring Lane to the north in stretching all the way from the Pacific Ocean on the west to the Cascade Range mountains on the east. Located in southern Oregon's surprisingly temperate Umpqua Valley, Roseburg started out taking the name of Deer Creek, a tributary of the South Umpqua. It adopted Roseburgh, later shortened to Roseburg, in honor of 1851 arrival Aaron Rose. In 1854, voters chose Roseburg to replace Winchester as the county seat. Instead of building a new courthouse in Roseburg, officials simply had the old one moved. Roseburg was incorporated in 1872. Home of Roseburg Forest Products, a major player in the southern Oregon timber industry, it has long depended economically on wood processing.

The local daily, the *News-Review*, traces its roots back to the Roseburg *Ensign*, which published its first edition on April 30, 1867. But they are exceedingly tangled roots.

The 1870s saw the advent of the *Roseburg Plain Dealer*, *Umpqua Ensign*, *Roseburg Pantagraph*, *Roseburg Western Star,* and *Douglas Independent*. Following in the 1880s were the *Roseburg Review*, representing the first manifestation of the *Review* nameplate, and the *Umpqua Herald*. The papers still surviving by the 1890s were joined by the *Roseburg Bugle Call* and *Roseburg Twice-A-Week Review* – two of the most unusual names in the annals of Oregon newspapering. The turn of the century ushered in the *Evening Roseburg Review* in 1902, the *Umpqua Valley News* in 1905, marking the first manifestation of the *News* nameplate, and the *Roseburg Spokesman* in 1906.

The parade of publishers, papers, and nameplates by no means ended there. Still to come were the *Roseburg Chieftain* and *Douglas County News*, both debuting in the 1930s and enjoying relatively short runs. And that doesn't account for the oldest local paper of all, the *Roseburg Express*. It published its first edition on November 17, 1859, but flamed out early on, leaving behind no direct descendants.

The *News* and *Review* joined forces to create the *News-Review* on April 8, 1920. And it proved strong enough to vanquish the rivals who came along to test the market in the '30s.

There can be no question about the biggest story to ever rock Roseburg. In the early morning hours of August 7, 1959, a fire at Gerretsen Building Supply spread to a nearby truck – a truck loaded with two tons of dynamite and more than four tons of equally explosive ammonium nitrate. The ensuing blast leveled eight blocks in the heart of the city's commercial district, killing 14 and injuring scores more. The cleanup took months and the rebuilding years. It forever changed the face of the city.

The paper currently is owned by Swift Communications. The company was founded in 1975 by Philip Swift, a former executive with the Scripps League newspaper group, as Swift Newspapers. Swift has come in recent years to specialize in media properties in western resort communities like Reno, Tahoe, Vail, and Aspen. *The News-Review* is its only holding in Oregon.

Statesman Journal   Salem

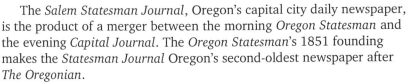

Owner: Gannett Co. Inc.
Address: 280 Church St. NE, Salem, OR 97301
Phone: 503-399-6611
URL: www.statesmanjournal.com (subscription required for e-edition, full access)
Established: 1851
Published: Monday through Sunday AM
Market: Marion and Polk counties
Circulation: 36,073 weekday, 32,751 Saturday, 41,450 Sunday (ABC)
Publisher: Steve Silberman, ssilberman@statesmanjournal.com
Executive Editor: Michael Davis, mdavis4@statesmanjournal.com

The *Salem Statesman Journal*, Oregon's capital city daily newspaper, is the product of a merger between the morning *Oregon Statesman* and the evening *Capital Journal*. The *Oregon Statesman*'s 1851 founding makes the *Statesman Journal* Oregon's second-oldest newspaper after *The Oregonian*.

At the time, *The Oregonian* had a Whig orientation. Democrat Asahel Bush founded the *Statesman* as a counterbalance. The paper was originally located in Oregon City, territorial capital then. When Oregon City lost that distinction to Salem in June 1853, the paper made the move as well. It became a reliable mouthpiece for the Democratic Party until Bush sold it in March 1863 to get into the banking business. The new owners toned down the partisanship and renamed it the *Salem Statesman*, but could not make a go of it and closed the doors in 1866.

Editor Samuel Clarke revived it as the *Salem Statesman and Unionist* in 1869, but soon dropped the "Unionist" element. It was acquired in 1884 by Jasper Wilkins, initially as a partner, then as sole owner. As editor, he brought in R.J. Hendricks, who went on to hold the position for 44 years. Along the way, it reclaimed its original name.

Will H. Parry established the *Capital Journal* on March 1, 1888, as a Republican counterweight. Ironically, in later years, *The Oregon Statesman* would become strongly Republican in its political orientation, while the *Capital Journal* would become strongly Democratic.

After a series of ownership changes, George Putnam bought the *Capital Journal* in 1923 and continued to edit and publish it for the next 30 years. He gave way to another long-time owner, Bernard

Mainwaring, in 1953. Charles Sprague, who went on to win the governorship as a Republican in 1938, bought the *Statesman* on the eve of the Great Depression in 1929. He, too, turned out to be a long-term steward.

The two papers each needed a new press, and neither family could afford the outlay on its own.

So in 1954, Mainwaring and Sprague agreed they would share both a building and a press, while still retaining fiercely independent editorial operations. They continued that arrangement until 1973, when they sold the papers to Gannett Co. Inc. as a package deal. Seven years later, Gannett, which was publishing nearly 100 newspapers at the time, merged the papers to create the *Statesman Journal*, publishing in the *Oregon Statesman*'s traditional morning time slot. By then, the *Statesman*, once the smaller of the two papers, had moved into a position of dominance. That mirrored a trend across the country of morning paper ascension at the expense of evening competition.

At one time, Gannett owned monopoly dailies in all three Northwest capitals – Salem, Olympia, and Boise. However, it sold its Olympia and Boise papers in 2005.

Through its parent company, the *Statesman Journal* purchased a pair of weeklies on its eastern flank – the *Silverton Appeal-Tribune* and the *Stayton Mail* – for $1.2 million in a bankruptcy court auction in November 1990.

In the fall of 2012, it decided to shut down its aging printing plant in downtown Salem and contract with *The Oregonian* in Portland for the printing of all three papers.

The *Statesman Journal* has adopted a metered system of online access. Print subscribers get free access to the paper's website, e-edition and mobile apps, but outside access is limited to a finite number of website views. Like most Northwest papers with only pay systems, the *Statesman Journal* charges the same for digital only as it does for a print/digital combination. That serves to discourage flight from the traditional print edition, which still pays the bulk of the bills.

Post   **Sandy**

Owner: Pamplin Media Group
Address: 17333 Strauss Ave., Sandy OR 97055
Phone: 503-668-5548
URL: www.sandypost.com (unrestricted)
Established: 1937
Published: Wednesday
Market: Northeastern Clackamas County

Circulation: 2,722 (SO)
Executive Editor & General Manager: Steve Brown, sbrown@theoutlookonline.com
(joint with Gresham)
Deadline: Noon Friday

Sandy lies along the northern edge of sprawling Clackamas County, at roughly its east-west midpoint. It looks west to the bulk of the county's 400,000 residents, concentrated in Portland's eastern and southern suburbs. It looks east to what is certainly Clackamas County's key feature and arguably the state's: 11,000-foot glacier- and timber-covered Mount Hood. Stretching along Highway 26, Sandy serves as the gateway to the ski resorts and other recreational amenities of the heavily used Mount Hood National Forest.

The local paper, the *Post*, was founded in 1937, making it a relative newcomer to the Oregon publishing scene. In addition to Sandy, perched on Mount Hood's majestic flanks, it serves smaller communities along a corridor extending from Boring to Government Camp.

The Post was among a group of four weeklies owned for many years by Lee Irwin and Walt Taylor, joining the *Gresham Outlook*, *Newport News-Times* and *Lincoln County Leader*. The Glenn Jackson group, headed by the Albany *Democrat-Herald*, picked them up on February 10, 1977. Upon Jackson's death, the papers were sold to Capital Cities/ABC, which was acquired by Disney in 1996. In 1998, Disney sold the former Jackson papers to another national chain, Lee Enterprises.

Lee retained some of the papers but sold the rest, including the Sandy Post, to Robert B. Pamplin Jr.'s Pamplin Media Group in 2000.

The South County Spotlight   Scappoose

Owner: Pamplin Media Group
Address: 33548 Edward Lane, Suite 110, Scappoose, OR 97056
Phone: 503-543-6380
URL: www.spotlightnews.net (unrestricted)
Established: 1961
Published: Wednesday
Market: Southern Columbia County
Circulation: 3,410 (SO)
Publisher: Darryl Swan, dswan@spotlightnews.net
Deadline: 11 a.m. Monday

Columbia County is a predominantly rural county stretching along the Oregon side of the Columbia River west of Portland's suburban fringe. Except for the interior logging community of Vernonia, its towns lie along Highway 30, which follows the westward course of the river. They include growing Scappoose in the southeastern corner, Clatskanie in the northwestern corner and the centrally located county seat of St.

Helens. Lumber and paper mills drive the economy, but the county supports an agricultural component and supplies Portland with commuting workers. The county seat was moved from Milton to St. Helens in 1857.

Scappoose, situated on the Scappoose River, is a Native American term for "gravelly plain." The first outside visitor was British sea captain Robert Gray, who sailed up the Columbia in 1792. Capt. Meriwether Lewis and Lt. William Clark of the Corps of Discovery followed in 1805-06. The city counted 6,592 residents in 2010.

By contrast, newspapering got a late start.

The *South County Spotlight* was founded in 1961 as a modest weekly tab called *The Scappoose Spotlight*, which ran no more than eight pages. Eventually, the *Spotlight* expanded its size and coverage, becoming a weekly broadsheet and extending its coverage area to nearby communities, including St. Helens.

Community Newspapers, an arm of the Pamplin Media Group, purchased the paper in 2007 from Art and Sally Heerwagen. Just four years later, it won general excellence honors in its division from the Oregon Newspaper Publishers Association. Like other Pamplin papers, the *Spotlight* is printed at the *Gresham Outlook* plant in eastern Multnomah County. It is distributed to subscribers in Wednesday's mail.

Former News Editor Stover Harger II said the print edition has a reputation in the county for "fierce, uncompromising, in-depth coverage of life in rural Oregon," but its web operation is less ambitious. "As with other papers of similar size, *The Spotlight* strives to maintain a web presence," he said. "But because of resources, it mostly utilizes its free website for high-profile breaking stories, quick updates and publishing the weekly edition."

Harger, who left in 2013 to join the staff of the *Vancouver Columbian*, said big stories in recent years detailed implosion of the Trojan nuclear plant cooling tower in 2006, the Rainier police chief's murder in 2011, and massive coal export plans this year. He also credited the *Spotlight* for documenting economic devastation stemming from paper mill layoffs in 2008 and efforts to make the notoriously dangerous Highway 30 safer.

Signal   Seaside

Owner: EO Media Group
Address: 1555 Roosevelt, Seaside, OR 97138
Phone: 503-738-5561
URL: www.seasidesignal.com (subscription required for full access)
Established: 1905

Published: Thursday
Market: Southwestern Clatsop County
Circulation: 1,032 (SO)
Editor & Publisher: Steve Forrester, sforrester@dailyastorian.com (joint with Astoria)

While spending the winter of 1805-06 at Fort Clatsop, at the mouth of the Columbia River, the Lewis and Clark Expedition's Corps of Discovery built a saltmaking cairn about 15 miles south, on the coast at Seaside. It chose a site just south of the Clatsop Plain, near a Clatsop Indian village known as Ne-co-tat. Clatsop County's oldest and largest city, named for fur magnate John Jacob Astor, was established just five years later as a fur trading post. But it would be many years before Seaside saw any settlement to rival that of Astoria.

The *Seaside Signal* was founded on March 25, 1905 by veteran newspaperman R.N. Watson. And by all accounts, he was a colorful character. The city got phones and electric lights during 1905 and 1906, two more trappings of civilization. It felt it had arrived.

In 1910, Watson sold to E.N. Hurd and W.B. Scott. Hurd went on to become one of Seaside's leading civic figures. Two communities were actually claiming the Seaside name at the time, and he succeeding in convincing them to merge. He conceived and pursued development of Seaside's iconic promenade, which critics dubbed "Hurd's Folly."

Hurd sold the *Signal* to Max Shafer in 1928, and he managed to shepherd it through the Great Depression.

The paper has undergone a whole series of ownership changes in recent decades. The stage was set for the first change when Lee Irwin and Walt Taylor, owners of the *Newport News-Times* and *Gresham Outlook*, and David Juenke, owner of the Lincoln City News Guard, went in together to buy the *Tillamook Headlight-Herald* in 1973.

The partners followed up in July 1976 by adding the *Signal* to their holdings. However, that ownership lasted just a matter of months, as Juenke and his wife, Margaret, bought out Irwin and Taylor later the same year. Four years later, on Oct. 1, 1980, the Juenkes sold all of their holdings to Scripps-Ifft Newspapers of Pocatello, Idaho, owner of papers in Montana and Idaho. Scripps picked up the weeklies serving Seaside, Tillamook, Lincoln City and Ilwaco, Washington, in a package deal. It shut down the *Ilwaco Tribune*, but continued to publish the three Oregon Coast weeklies from its base in Tillamook.

On July 15, 1983, it was Scripps' turn to sell. The papers went to Swift Newspapers, founded in 1975 by former Scripps League executive Philip Swift. Swift created a new subsidiary, Pacific Coast Newspapers, to operate them. Swift also came into ownership of an Oregon daily, the *Roseburg News-Review*, and eventually it decided to retain the *News-Review* and dispose of the weeklies.

That opened the door for Steven and Carol Hungerford, principals in Country Media. In a series of transactions in the early 2000s, they acquired the *Signal*, the *Headlight-Herald*, the *News Guard* and smaller papers serving Depoe Bay, Cannon Beach, and St. Helens.

Early in 2013, they sold their holdings in the North Oregon Coast communities of Seaside and Cannon Beach to the EO Media Group, formerly the East Oregonian Publishing Company. EO Media is longtime owner of *The Daily Astorian*, based in the northern coast's anchor city.

The Sun   Sheridan

Owner: Vining Publishing Company
Address: 136 E. Main St., Sheridan, OR 97378
Phone: 503-843-2312
URL: www.sheridansun.com (unrestricted)
Established: 1890
Published: Wednesday
Market: Western Yamhill County
Circulation: 1,070 (SO)
Editor, Publisher and Owner: Clinton Vining, news@sheridansun.com

Sheridan, a timber town tucked into the Coast Range foothills of Yamhill County, about 15 miles west of the county seat of McMinnville, was laid out in the mid-1860s by Absolem B. Faulconer. He had established a local homestead in 1847 and decided it was time he had company. The town was named for General Phil Sheridan, who earned notoriety as an Indian fighter before going on to earn Civil War acclaim. A controversial figure, particularly with Sheridan's neighboring Grand Ronde Indian Reservation, he is infamous for having once exclaimed, "The only good Indian is a dead Indian." Those pieces of history are not forgotten at the Grand Ronde reservation, only a few miles down Highway 18 from Sheridan.

The city has a listed population of 6,127, but almost 2,000 of them are residents of the Federal Correctional Institution, Sheridan, a federal prison built in 1989. And they don't get out much.

Since the extension of Highway 18 from McMinnville to Lincoln City in 1932, Sheridan and the neighboring West Valley timber town of Willamina have served as something of a gateway to the coast for a large swath of Willamette Valley residents.

The *Sun*, which serves Sheridan, Willamina and the tribal government center of Grand Ronde out of offices in Sheridan, got its start on February 6, 1890 as the *Sheridan Courier*. It began publishing under the *Sun* name on January 18, 1901, then as the *New Sun* from 1904 to 1908, when Oscar Hamstreet took over and changed the name back to the *Sun*. In 1913, fire destroyed his home as well as the newspaper office and plant. But he never missed an edition.

Hamstreet sold to Steen Johnson in 1929. The next ownership of note was that of Dean and Myrna Holmes, who published the paper from 1945 to 1963.

Elmo and Denny Smith's Eagle Newspapers chain, then known as Blue Mountain Eagle, bought the *Sun* in 1978, tapping George Robertson to run it. An unlikely choice – he was born in New York City, attended a seminary school, once planned to become a priest, spent his early adulthood in Boston and Los Angeles and had never heard of Sheridan before accepting the offer – he took over on October 5. Three years later, Eagle revealed plans to dispose of the paper. To the company's surprise, Robertson told a *Sun* reporter for a story published in 2010, he offered to buy the property. No bank would put up the financing, he told the *Sun*, so he borrowed the money from the family of his wife Gratia (and, he said, he paid back every penny).

Robertson remained in the capacity of owner, publisher, and editor until his retirement in 2008, when he sold to Clinton Vining. Vining has run the paper since through Clinton Vining Company LLC.

Vining is currently overseeing the paper from afar, entrusting on-site management to long-time correspondent Marguerite Alexander.

The Sun is one of three newspapers still publishing in Yamhill County, with the *McMinnville News-Register* and *Newberg Graphic*.

There was a fourth until June 2006, when the *Dayton Tribune* went under after 94 years of continuous publication, 68 of them in the same downtown building. George and Edwina Meitzen, both raised in newspaper families in Texas, published the *Tribune* for the last 42 years of its run. Unable to find anyone to take over, they finally shuttered the doors as they approached their 74th birthdays. They had been living in Lafayette and working for *The Oregonian* in Portland when they got a chance to acquire the *Tribune* in 1964. And they made a career of it.

"When George came home one day in 1964 with a smile on his face, I knew something was up," Edwina told the *News-Register* for a story on the paper's closing. "He told me he'd found exactly the right thing for us." And indeed he had.

The small city of Carlton (which is home, by the way, to Ridenbaugh Press, this book's publisher) just north of McMinnville has not had a local paper for more than 40 years. However, it did have several in the first half of the 20th century – the *Herald*, the *News,* and the *Sentinel*. Three miles further north, the still smaller town of Yamhill (hometown for *New York Times* columnist Nicholas Kristoff) once had the *County Journal* and the *Record*.

Appeal Tribune Silverton

Owner: Gannett Co. Inc.
Address: 399 S. Water St., Silverton, OR 97381
Phone: 503-873-8385
URL: www.silvertonappeal.com (unrestricted, but subscription required for e-edition)
Established: 1880
Published: Wednesday
Market: Eastern Marion County
Circulation: 1,067 (SO)
Publisher: Steve Silberman, ssilberman@statesmanjournal.com (joint with Salem)
News: Carol Currie, ccurrie@salem.gannett.com
Deadline: Week prior

Marion County got its start as a vast tract of territory called the Champooick District. The territorial legislature later shrank it and renamed it for Revolutionary War Gen. Francis Marion. In the heart of the fertile Willamette Valley, the county leads the state in agricultural production. About 100 different fruits and vegetables are grown, including peas, beans, carrots, corn, onions, and other row crops; a wide array of fruits and nuts on almost 11,000 acres of orchard land, notably cherries and hazelnuts; Christmas trees, nursery stock, wine grapes, and commercial timber; wheat, hay, grass seed, and other grasses and grain crops; and an array of livestock. But its leading product may be government, thanks to Salem's status as Oregon's capital city.

Silverton was founded by Polly Coon Price, who laid it out around a stately white oak. She named it after Silver Creek, now the salient feature in Silver Falls State Park. Silverton, lying well to the east at the base of the Cascade Range, accounts for only about 9,000 of Marion's 315,000 people.

The *Appeal Tribune* is the product of a merger, as its name suggests. Its roots run deepest on the *Appeal* side. That paper was founded by Henry G. Guild on May 17, 1880. In addition to the *Tribune*, whose founding date could not be determined with certainty, its early competitors included the *Marion County Record* (1894 to 1895), the *Silverton Torch of Reason* (1896 to 1903), *Silverton Semaphore* (1908 and 1909), and *Silverton Journal* (1913 to 1915). The lone commonality seems to have been fast flameouts.

The *Silvertonian*, founded in 1902, bought out the *Appeal* on Oct. 23, 1903 to create the *Silvertonian Appeal*. The paper published under that name through the middle of 1910, as the *Silvertoninan* from 1910 to 1914, then as the *Appeal* again for the next 16 years.

The *Tribune* went out of business at some point, but resumed publication on March 14, 1924. It published independently through August 1, 1930, then joined forces with the *Appeal* under the *Appeal Tribune* banner.

Joe Davis, who came into ownership in 1960, is the man most closely associated with the paper in recent decades. He went in with Frank Crow, owner of the nearby *Stayton Mail,* on a new web offset press in 1968. They combined forces because neither could afford the investment on his own. In 1975, Davis bought out the neighboring *Mount Angel News* and merged the two papers. He published the combined paper for a time as *The Silverton Appeal Tribune and The Mount Angel News,* reputedly the longest nameplate in Oregon newspaper history.

The *News* was founded in 1915 by the same man who founded the Silvertonian – Henry E. Browne. Mount Angel has not had its own paper since the 1975 merger. Crow sold the *Mail* to Howard and Mary Ann Woodall in 1982, along with his half-interest in the two papers' joint printing plant. Two years later, Davis sold the *Appeal Tribune* to them as well.

The Woodalls operated the papers under the banner of East Valley Newspapers until mid-1989, when they sold to Crow. He couldn't make a go of it, and declared bankruptcy about 18 months later.

The national Gannett chain, owner of the nearby *Statesman Journal,* submitted the winning bid to the court handling the proceedings, and the court approved a transfer of ownership on November 20, 1990. Gannett has operated them since in conjunction with the *Statesman Journal.* In 1998, it reverted to simply the *Appeal Tribune,* with no city designation, for the Silverton half of the package.

Times   Springfield

Owner: S.J. Olson Publishing
Address: 741 Main St., Springfield, OR 97477
Phone: 541-741-7368
URL: www.springfieldtimes.net (unrestricted)
Established: 2008
Published: Friday
Market: Western Lane County
Circulation: 1,443 (SO)
Publisher: Scott J. Olson, publisher@springfieldtimes.net (joint with Creswell)
Deadline: Noon Tuesday

By all rights, a city of 60,000 should be able to support a daily newspaper. However, Springfield has struggled to support a weekly, because it abuts the Lane County seat of Eugene, whose population of 156,000 makes it Oregon's second-largest city. Springfield, a blue-collar mill town, has played second fiddle to Eugene, a white-collar college town, ever since the Oregon & California Railroad bypassed it in favor of its arch-rival in 1871. Legend has it that Eugene businessmen paid railroad mogul Ben Holladay to cross the Willamette River at Harrisburg instead of Springfield, which could be true. The two cities lie at the confluence of the McKenzie and Willamette rivers, about 50 miles inland in the southern Willamette Valley. They are separated partly by the river and partly by Interstate 5.

William Stevens, who arrived in 1847, and Elias and Mary Briggs, who arrived the following year via Klamath Falls, were the first settlers to set up shop in Springfield. The two men joined in establishing a much-needed ferry service. The city was named for a spring. It has traditionally depended largely on wood-processing to support its economy, but has striven to diversify in recent years, with some success.

Springfield's current paper, the *Times*, was founded in 2008 by Scott and Jeanne Nelson. Former owners of Eastern Oregon's *Burns Times-Herald*, they own the *Springfield Times* and another Lane County weekly, the *Creswell Chronicle*, through Burns-based S.J. Olson Publishing Inc.

Scott spent six years as editor and publisher of *The Vidette*, a weekly serving Montesano, Washington, before venturing to Oregon to buy the *Times-Herald* in June 2003. He acquired the paper from Western Communications, a family-owned chain based in Bend, and published it for 2½ years before selling it to an employee group. His next venture was in Springfield, where he launched the *Times* on November 21, 2008.

Springfield was served by the *News*, once a thriving tri-weekly, for more than 100 years. The paper was given birth in 1903 and laid to rest in 2006.

But local newspapering dates even further back than that. Springfield's first newspaper was the *Nonpareil*, founded In 1896 by John Kelly. Kelly sold it to J.F. Woods in 1903, and Woods renamed it the *News*. Two generations of the Nelson family shepherded the *News* through much of the last half of the 20th century. John Nelson ran the paper for many years before turning it over to his son, Jack, in the mid-1970s. The *News* was subsequently picked up by Glenn Jackson, who built a collection of Oregon papers around the family centerpiece, the Albany *Democrat-Herald*. After his death, they were purchased by Capital Cities/ABC.

Disney swallowed Capital Cities in 1996 and two years later disgorged several of the former Jackson papers to Lee Enterprises. In 2006, Lee, struggling under a heavy debt load, concluded operations in Springfield no longer penciled out.

Olson went on to buy the neighboring *Creswell Chronicle* on October 20, 2011. He continues to publish both papers on a weekly basis.

The Chronicle   St. Helens

Owner: Country Media
Address: 1805 Columbia Blvd., St. Helens, OR 97051
Phone: 503-397-0116
URL: www.thechronicleonline.com (unrestricted)
Established: 1881
Published: Wednesday
Market: Columbia County
Circulation: 4,092 (SO)
Publisher: Don Patterson, advertising@thechronicleonline.com
Editor: Shari Phiel, sharip@thechronicleonline.com

The northern half of Washington County was partitioned off in 1854 to create Columbia County. It is named for the Columbia River, whose curving arc serves as its northern and eastern border. The county seat, originally in Milton, was moved to the bustling river port of St. Helens in 1857. The city, which accounts for about one quarter of the county's 50,000 residents, was founded as Plymouth in 1845 by Capt. H. M. Knighton. Five years later, it was changed to St. Helens in recognition of its view of Mount St. Helens across the river in Washington.

The local newspaper, the *Chronicle*, is descended from the *Oregon Mist*. This early ancestor, founded 1881, was later known less majestically as the *St. Helens Mist*. The city was also served briefly by the *Columbian* in the 1880s and the *Columbia County News* in the early 1900s.

The *Mist* ended up confronting two stronger competitors, the *Sentinel* in 1926 and *Chronicle* in 1936. The *Mist* bought out the *Sentinel* in 1933, creating the *Sentinel-Mist*. After decades as competitors, the *Chronicle* went on to acquire the *Sentinel-Mist* in 1968, producing the unlikely and unwieldy *Sentinel-Mist Chronicle*. The paper changed its name to the *St. Helens Chronicle and Sentinel-Mist* three years later. In 2009, it dropped the *Sentinel-Mist* component.

The paper is now owned by Steve and Carol Hungerford's Country Media, based in Tillamook. Founded in 2000, it has amassed a cadre of Oregon weeklies, mostly on the state's central and northern coast.

The Mail   Stayton

Owner: Gannett Co. Inc.
Address: 263 E. Ida St., Stayton, OR 97383
Phone: 503-769-6338
URL: www.staytonmail.com (unrestricted, but subscription required for e-edition)
Established: 1894
Published: Wednesday
Market: Eastern Marion County
Circulation: 790 (SO)

Owner: Gannett Co. Inc.
Publisher: Steve Silberman, ssilberman@statesmanjournal.com (joint with Salem)
Editor: Peggy Savage, salesmn@salem.gannett.com
Deadline: Week prior

Stayton lies about 12 miles southeast of Salem on Highway 22, which runs from Santiam Pass to the sea. A farm supply and light manufacturing center perched on the northern bank of the North Santiam River, it boasted a population of about 7,650 in the 2010 census. It joins several of its neighbors in having become something of a bedroom community for Salem, which doubles as Marion County seat and Oregon State Capitol. Stayton was founded in 1872 by Drury Smith Stayton, who had established a woolen mill and sawmill at the site. According to Wikipedia, he wanted to name the town for his daughter, Florence, but was rebuffed by postal authorities because Oregon already had a Florence on the coast west of Eugene.

The first newspaper, *The Sun*, was established by T.H. McGill in 1889. *The Mail* followed in 1894, and was joined by the *Times* and the *Siftings*. The *Standard* also tested the market briefly in 1916-17, during World War I. However, *The Mail* prevailed.

Lawrence E. Spraker, by all accounts a highly respected newsman, owned and operated the paper for the 25-year span between 1939 and 1964. He held both the editor and publisher titles. On October 1, 1964, he sold *The Mail* to newly created North Santiam Newspapers. It was a partnership of Robert W. Chandler, owner of *The Bulletin* in Bend, and two young men sharing Linfield College ties – Frank Crow of Seattle, 24, and John Buchner of Albany, 23.

Crow had been working in ad sales at the *Seattle Times*. Buchner, who would go on to a distinguished career with the *Albany Democrat-Herald*, had been Chandler's city editor in Bend. Crow later bought out his partners, gaining sole possession.

In 1968, Crow went in with Joe Davis, longtime editor and publisher of the neighboring *Silverton Appeal Tribune*, on a new web offset press capable of printing both papers. Neither man could afford the investment on his own. Both men sought to expand their operations, Davis by acquiring the *Mount Angel News* in 1975 and Crow by acquiring the *Junction City Times* in 1979. Before long, Davis folded the *News* into his *Appeal Tribune* and Crow divested himself of the *Times*.

In 1982, Crow sold *The Mail* to Howard and Mary Ann Woodall. Two years later, the Woodalls bought out Davis in Silverton as well, acquiring sole interest in the joint printing plant in the process, and founded East Valley Newspapers to oversee the operation.

Crow re-entered the picture by buying East Valley Newspapers in mid-1989. But the debt load was so great, he soon had to file for bankruptcy protection. The court put the company up for auction, and the national Gannett chain, publisher of *Salem Statesman Journal*, submitted the winning bid of $1.2 million. The judge awarded Gannett the two newspapers on November 20, 1990.

Gannett, which retains ownership, printed them at its plant in Salem for many years. When it closed that plant in the fall of 2012, and began contracting with *The Oregonian* for printing services, the Portland metro also began printing the two neighboring weeklies.

Douglas County News   Sutherlin

Owner: Becky Holm
Address: 352 S. Calapooia St., Suite A, Sutherlin, OR 97479
Phone: 541-459-0716
URL: www.douglascountynews.info (unrestricted but very limited)
Established: 2002
Published: Wednesday
Market: Northern Douglas County
Circulation: 2,142 (SO)
Editor, Publisher & Owner: Becky Holm, becky@douglascountynews.info
Deadline: 5 p.m. Friday

Sutherlin is a logging town of 7,800 incorporated in 1911, due north of Roseburg, Douglas County's seat of government and principal population center, on Interstate 5. The heavily timbered county encompasses nearly 1.8 million acres of commercial timberland. Not surprisingly, about one-quarter to one-third of the workforce is engaged in the wood products industry in some fashion. Overshadowed by its bigger, better-established neighbor city just to the south, longtime home of a daily, Sutherlin has a limited history with newspapering.

The local paper, a weekly, was established by Jean Ivey in 2002 as the *North County News*. She put her focus on the communities of Sutherlin, Oakland, Elkton, Yoncalla, and Drain, at the northern end of the county. When Becky Holm purchased the paper in February 2008, she gave it a countywide reach, expanding to serve Roseburg, Winston, and Reedsport as well. And she renamed it the *Douglas County News* to reflect that broader reach.

A sole proprietor, Holm has the paper printed in Eugene under contract. She said her mission is to provide "unbiased current news, uplifting and encouraging feature articles, and helpful information," designed to "enhance the community and world around us."

Holm summed up her online philosophy this way: "We don't put content online. If content is online, there wouldn't be a reason to purchase the paper." The newspaper's website does feature subscription information, contact information, community links and a PDF of the most recent front page.

The New Era   Sweet Home

Owner: Scott Swanson
Address: 1313 Main St., Sweet Home, OR 97386
Phone: 541-367-2135
URL: www.sweethomenews.com (unrestricted)
Established: 1929
Published: Wednesday
Market: Eastern Linn County
Circulation: 1,851 (SO)
Editor & Publisher: Scott Swanson, scott@sweethomenews.com
Deadline: Noon Friday

Sweet Home is a logging and mill town of 9,000 located along the south bank of the South Santiam River. It lies southwest of the larger Linn County cities of Albany and Lebanon on Highway 20, which traverses the entire state east to west. Settlers began arriving in the Sweet Home Valley in the early 1850s, creating Buckhead near the mouth of Ames Creek and Mossville just to the east. They merged to form Sweet Home in 1874 and the community incorporated in 1893.

The opening of the Santiam Wagon Road, a tollway connecting the Willamette Valley with Central Oregon via Santiam Pass, did a lot to spur early development. It was superseded by the McKenzie Highway, which crosses the Cascade Range via McKenzie Pass, in the 1930s. Eventually, the McKenzie Highway was superseded by Highway 20, which largely follows the old wagon road route.

The local paper, the *New Era*, was founded in 1929 by a doctor who decided Sweet Home needed a newspaper. It has been published continuously ever since, its publication day moving over the years from Friday to Thursday and eventually Wednesday. Unlike many of its brethren around the state, the paper remains family-owned. It prints at the Oregon Web Press in Albany, a commercial shop founded in 1985.

The paper is currently delivered entirely by mail, but it is considering options for a carrier-delivery component, perhaps in tandem with another paper.

Editor and Publisher Scott Swanson recalled, "Sweet Home was a booming place in the 1950s and 1960s. The governor and top legislators frequently visited back in the days when timber dollars were pouring in, so we had a lot of coverage of those kinds of events." He said the spotted owl controversy of the 1980s, covered by Alex Paul, stands out as the biggest story of recent decades.

The New Era publishes on the web at www.sweethomenews.com. Swanson said, "Our online presence has not been as aggressive as some Oregon non-dailies, partly because Sweet Home isn't on the cutting edge of technology and many of our readers still prefer the traditional formats. However, we are cognizant of the need to stay in step with the times."

A paywall is in the works and coverage will be expanded when the site is put on a paying basis. He said, "We'll be offering free photo downloads (low resolution), more breaking news (along with probable e-mail or text notification to subscribers of breaking stories), more timely posting of stories (we deliberately delay our Wednesday stories until the weekend to encourage purchase of the newspaper) and more, such as increased use of video."

Chronicle   The Dalles

Owner: Eagle Newspapers
Address: 315 Federal St., The Dalles, OR 97058
Phone: 541-296-2141
URL: www.thedalleschronicle.com (unrestricted)
Established: 1890
Published: Tuesday through Friday PM, Sunday AM
Market: Wasco County, Ore., and Klickitat County, Wash.
Circulation: 3,530 (SO)
Publisher: Marilyn Roth, mroth@thedalleschronicle.com
Editor: Kathy Ursprung, kursprung@thedalleschronicle.com

The Columbia River's Celilo Falls served as a fishing, gathering, and trading center for the Wasco, Paiute, and Warm Springs Indian tribes for 15,000 years before the first outsiders arrived in the early 1800s in search of fur for the European market. Celilo introduced a 12-mile run of like falls that had to be portaged. The early fur traders were French Canadian, and they named the run of rapids Les Grandes Dalles de la Columbia, which translates to The Great Falls of the Columbia. That soon got shortened to The Dalles, meaning The Falls.

The Dalles served initially as a way station on the Oregon Trail until the Barlow Trail was developed as a route through the Cascades in 1845. That began to spur settlement, as did passage of the Donation Land Claim Act by Congress five years later. Oregon's territorial legislature created Wasco County on January 11, 1854, at the time the largest county in the United States. The Dalles is the county's largest population center at almost 14,000, and serves as county seat.

The local paper is the *Chronicle*, a five-day daily. Dan Spatz probably told the story of the *Chronicle* best in an account that appeared in its own pages in 2001, saying:

"The Dalles is known for its history, and newspapers have been part of that heritage since Oregon statehood in 1859. The first newspaper in Eastern Oregon was published in The Dalles. In the following decades no fewer than 20 newspapers – competing dailies, a multitude of weeklies and even a monthly – would document the history of The Dalles, from its days as a military outpost on the frontier through the momentous events of the 20th century, into a new century and millennium.

"While *The Dalles Chronicle* today is the oldest newspaper in this region, it started out as a new kid on the block when its first edition hit the street on Dec. 10, 1890. By that time, there was already a 30-year tradition of newspapers here, and the *Chronicle* was only one of several Johnny-Come-Latelies to enter the fray."

That first newspaper arrived on the scene on April 1, 1859, only six weeks after Oregon achieved statehood. Called the *Journal* originally, and later the *Weekly*, it was commissioned by Capt. Thomas Jordan, commander of the local military post.

W.H. Newell bought the paper in 1860. Two years later, he launched a new paper in its stead, originally as the *Weekly Mountaineer* and later, starting in 1865, as the *Daily Mountaineer*.

The *Daily Journal* offered competition for a time, but flamed out fast. Competition was renewed on April 27, 1880, when R.J. Marsh and John Michell introduced the *Times*. The two papers merged in 1882 to create the daily *Times-Mountaineer*, with Michell taking the editorial helm and eventually buying out his partner.

Other daily and weekly papers came and went, including the *Tribune* (1875-77), the *Inland Empire* (1878-1880), the *Wasco Weekly Sun* (1881-94), *Oregon Democratic Journal* (1884-85), *Trade Journal* (1896), *Morning Dispatch* (1896) and *Baptist Sentinel* (1890s). There was also a monthly in the mix, the *Economist*, published in 1889-90.

The *Dalles Chronicle*, the lone survivor of all this activity, started inauspiciously in December 1890 as a semi-weekly. Over the course of the coming decade, however, the *Chronicle* made steady gains at the *Times-Mountaineer*'s expense, to the point where the T-M ceased daily publication in 1900 and all publication in 1904.

Spatz chronicled all of this in great detail in his story.

Competition resumed with the advent of the aptly named *Optimist*, a weekly, on June 19, 1906. It remained independent for 62 years before finally being swallowed by the *Chronicle* on Oct. 1, 1963, and the *Chronicle* continued to publish it for another five years after that. In the meantime, Martin Otos had established a weekly shopper called the *Reminder*. After the *Optimist* folded, it assumed the mantle of weekly competition.

After a series of ownership changes, Robert Howard came into possession in December 1949. He sold to the Scripps family, and the paper became part of the Scripps League. The Pulitzer chain bought out Scripps League in 1994, then two years later, it sold the *Chronicle* to Salem-based Eagle Newspapers, owner of the *Reminder*, and it has remained part of Eagle ever since.

The Times   Tigard/Tualatin

Owner: Pamplin Media Group
Address: 6605 S.E. Lake Road, Portland, OR 97222
Phone: 503-684-0360
URL: www.tigardtimes.com and www.tualatintimes.com (unrestricted)
Established: 1956
Published: Thursday
Market: Portland suburbs of Tigard and Tualatin
Circulation: 2,976 (SO)
Publisher: Christine Moore, cmoore@commnewspapers.com (joint with Beaverton)
Managing Editor: Christina Lent, clent@commnewspapers.com (joint with Beaverton)
Deadline: Noon Friday

Tigard was settled by a group that included the Wilson M. Tigard family, arriving in 1852. It was dubbed Tigardville in 1886, but that was shortened to Tigard in 1907. Long a Portland bedroom community on Portland's southwest flank, it did not formally incorporate until 1961. Tualatin takes its name from the Tualatin River, which flows between the two communities. Tigard lies along its northern bank and Tualatin its southern. They lie to the southwest of the larger suburban Washington County communities of Hillsboro, the county seat, and Beaverton.

Tualatin was originally known as Galbreath after founder Samuel Galbreath. After he built the first bridge over the Tualatin River in 1853, it became known as Bridgeport. It morphed into Tualatin, originally spelled Tualitin, on its way to incorporation in 1915. Though Tualatin lies mostly in Washington County, a portion slops over into Clackamas County to the east. In the 2010 census, Tigard had a population of about 48,000, Tualatin about 26,000.

The first paper in the area was the *Tualatin News*, which flamed out not long after its 1915 founding. The *Tigard Sentinel* had a longer run, publishing from August 1, 1924, to January 26, 1951. The *Tigard News* emerged, intent on filling the void, but failed. It was not until the *Times* came along in 1956 that the communities once again had a paper to call their own.

In the '70s, the Baker family, owner of the *Eugene Register-Guard*, began scouring the Portland metropolitan area for weeklies it could acquire. It came to own several of them, including the *Times*. Elmo and Denny Smith were pursuing the same sort of suburban strategy with their Eagle Newspapers chain. Along the way, they were able to acquire nearby papers, Clackamas County's *West Linn Tidings* and *Lake Oswego Review*. In January 1988, the Bakers and Smiths merged their holdings under the Community Newspapers umbrella, with Eagle serving as the managing partner. Their holdings included weeklies in Beaverton and Forest Grove in addition to Tigard, Tualatin, West Linn, and Lake Oswego.

The partners sold the group to Steve Clark in 1996. In 1999, he sold them to the Pamplin Media Group, which has now become the largest single player in the suburban Portland market with a far-flung network.

Headlight-Herald Tillamook

Owner: Country Media
Address: 1908 Second St., Tillamook, OR 97141
Phone: 503-842-7535
URL: www.tillamookheadlightherald.com (subscription required for full access)
Established: 1888
Market: Tillamook County
Published: Wednesday
Circulation: 6,176 (SO)
Editor & Publisher: Samantha Swindler, sswindler@countrymedia.net
Deadline: Noon Monday

Tillamook County, situated along Oregon's northern coast between Clatsop to the north and Lincoln to the south, became the state's 12th county in December 1853. Its boundaries were adjusted in 1855, 1870, 1887, and 1893 before being finalized in 1898. The county extends into the heavily wooded Coast Range, where a series of fires wreaked wholesale devastation on commercially valuable timber stands between 1933 and 1951. They came to be known collectively as the Great Tillamook Burn. Voters passed bonds enabling the state to acquire and replant the lands, creating the Tillamook State Forest. They are just beginning to become commercially viable again, more than half a century later.

Tillamook is the county's seat of government and dominant population center. Its economy revolves around fishing, farming, and logging, supplemented increasingly by tourism. One of the leading agricultural pursuits is dairy farming, which supports the city's nationally and even internationally known Tillamook Cheese Factory. Development along scenic Highway 101, which hugs the water as it makes its way along the West Coast, blocked part of the flood plain of the Wilson River. That has triggered repeated flooding in the low-lying city, a costly and continuing problem.

The local paper is the *Headlight-Herald*, an amalgam of a pair of predecessors. The *Headlight* emerged on the scene in 1888 and the *Herald* followed in 1896, but they didn't join forces until the spring of the Great Depression year of 1934. When they announced the merger in their respective pages, they promised readers: "Every effort will be made to attain and maintain for the combined newspaper the highest possible standard of excellence, to constantly endeavor to promote the interests of Tillamook city and county and to make it a publication in which the city and the county may well take pride."

Both papers were pre-dated by the *Kelchis Advance*, which published from December 18, 1880 to March 28, 1882. They just displayed more staying power. Other early Tillamook papers included the *Western Watchtower*, which apparently came and went in 1890, and the *Independent*, which tested the local publishing waters in 1902-03.

The first edition of the *Headlight-Herald* listed *Headlight* partner Thomas W. Walpole as editor and *Herald* owner George D. Borden as general manager. Within months, Borden bowed out, selling his interest to the partners on the *Headlight* side of the enterprise.

When Walpole died in 1940, he passed his ownership interest and the editor title to his son-in-law, D.A. DeCook. With DeCook's death four years later, they were bestowed on Elsie DeCook, DeCook's wife and Walpole's daughter. She went on to buy out her partners and continue operating the paper until her retirement in 1960.

The paper changed hands in 1961, 1965, 1969, and 1973, passing from the hands of one veteran newspaper family to another in each instance. Along the way, it absorbed the *Tillamook County News-Advertiser*. The partners in the 1973 purchase, consummated in January, included *Lincoln City News Guard* owner Dave Juenke.

The trio went on to buy the *Seaside Signal*. Juenke bought out his partners in 1976, giving him sole ownership in the three neighboring beach communities of Seaside, Tillamook, and Lincoln City.

Juenke cashed out on October 1, 1980, selling the three Oregon papers and southwestern Washington's coastal *Ilwaco Tribune* to Scripps-Ifft Newspapers of Pocatello, Idaho. Scripps closed the *Tribune* and consolidated the the three Oregon papers under the banner of Pacific Coast Newspapers, based in Tillamook.

On July 15, 1983, Scripps sold its Oregon coast holdings to Swift Newspapers. Swift, founded by former Scripps League executive Philip Swift in 1975, operated them under the Pacific Coast Newspapers umbrella. Swift also picked up the southern Oregon daily *Roseburg News-Review* during this period. Eventually, it decided to retain the daily and dispose of the weeklies.

After brief interim ownerships, the three coast weeklies were picked up by Steve and Carol Hungerford through Country Media. In a series of transactions in the early 2000s, they ended up with papers serving communities all down the Oregon Coast, including Seaside, Cannon Beach, Tillamook, Manzanita, Lincoln City, and Depoe Bay, plus the St. Helens Chronicle. Country Media also chose Tillamook as its home base.

Malheur Enterprise   Vale

Owner: Rick Nelson
Address: 289 'A' Street W, Vale, OR 97918
Phone: 541-473-3377
URL: No web presence
Established: 1909
Published: Wednesday
Market: Malheur County
Circulation: 1,253 (SO)
Editor, Publisher & Owner: Rick Nelson, malent@qwestoffice.net

When the West Coast was being settled in the 1840s and 1850s, Vale represented a major stop for weary pioneers plying the Oregon Trail. It also served as a supply center for farmers, miners, prospectors, and sheep and cattle ranchers. It is located at the northern end of Malheur County, which shares lengthy borders with Idaho and Nevada down in Oregon's aid and desolate southeastern corner. It lies about 12 miles west of the Idaho border, at the intersection of Highway 20 with Highway 26 and Bully Creek with the Malheur River.

Vale became the county seat in 1955, some 68 years after the county's founding. It supports a population of less than 2,000, just a fraction that of the larger border city of Ontario to the east.

The first paper to serve the community was the *Malheur Gazette*, which published from 1900 to 1908. The following year, Maj. L.H. French, a mining promoter, financed a new venture, the *Malheur Enterprise*. Launched on November 20, 1909, it remains in publication to this day. The paper's first publisher was B.M. Stone and its first editor John McGrath. Originally a Saturday publication, it sold for $2 a year. Newspaper historian George Turnbull said it featured "screaming headlines, red-hot editorials, and a general booster spirit."

After a series of ownership changes, the paper came into the possession of George Huntington Currey in 1917. Three years later, he traded it to Bruce Dennis for the *Baker Herald*. Dennis also owned the *La Grande Observer*, which he retained. He hired William Seeman to serve as editor of his new possession. Dennis sold the paper in the early '20s, and another series of ownership changes ensued, one every few years.

The longest run came under Winfield Brown, who owned the paper from 1924 to 1930.

The *Enterprise* is currently published and edited by Rick Nelson, who spent more than 20 years on the copy desk at the *Tacoma News-Tribune* before buying the paper from Julie Schaffeld in late 2006. (Before that, the paper was owned by the mother of current Idaho Press-Tribune Managing Editor Vickie Holbrook.) It maintains no web presence, not even on Facebook or a blog site.

The Columbia Press   Warrenton

Owner: Gary Nevan
Address: 160-B N.E. Fifth St., Warrenton, OR 97146
Phone: 503-861-3331
URL: www.thecolumbiapress.com (subscription required)
Established: 1922
Published: Friday
Market: Western Clatsop County
Circulation: 862 (SO)
Editor, Publisher & Owner: Gary Nevan, editor@thecolumbiapress.com
Deadline: 5 p.m. Tuesday

Established as a fur trading post in 1811, just a few years after the Lewis and Clark Expedition wintered in the area, Astoria is the oldest city in Oregon and one of the oldest in the West. But the original seat of government for Clatsop County was Lexington, forerunner of Warrenton. Astoria, the county's largest city, didn't assume the mantle until 1854.

Lexington was laid out in 1848 at the mouth of the Columbia River, across Youngs Bay from Astoria. It went through a period as Skipanon, the name of a river flowing through the heart of town, before taking the name Warrenton in honor of early settler Daniel Knight Warren. Having annexed neighboring Hammond, it now counts 5,000 residents, about half as many as Astoria. It was built on tidal flats, so it relies on dikes to prevent flooding. Historically, residents have made a living one of four ways: catching fish, canning fish, cutting logs or milling logs. However, the economy has turned toward tourism in a major way in more recent years.

The local paper is *The Columbia Press*, which was founded in Astoria. It once had the distinction of being the only Finnish language newspaper in Oregon, if not the nation. Located at the storm-wracked mouth of the Columbia River, early-day Astoria was populated in large measure by emigrants from the Scandinavian countries of Norway, Sweden, Denmark and, especially, Finland. Mostly fishermen by trade, they were drawn by a cold, wet, rugged, and fish-rich coast that reminded them of home.

Still based in Astoria, where it competed with *The Daily Astorian*, *The Press* became a county-wide English-language weekly in the 1940s as Finnish language skills began to wane. It made the move to Warrenton, where it adopted a Warrenton-Hammond focus, in 1978.

Gary Nevan bought the newspaper, previously owned and operated by Hal Allen, in 1988. He has owned and operated it ever since.

The storm of December 2007 produced the biggest news story of the last decade. It caused devastating flooding in much of northwestern Oregon.

The paper maintains a website limited to paid subscribers. It is printed by its nearest daily neighbor, the EO Media Group's *Daily Astorian*, under contract.

Tidings   West Linn

Owner: Pamplin Media Group
Address: 400 Second St., Lake Oswego, OR 97034
Phone: 503-635-8811
URL: www.westlinntidings.com (unrestricted)
Established: 1981
Published: Thursday
Market: West Linn area (Clackamas County)
Circulation: 2,731 (SO)
Publisher: J. Brian Monihan, bmonihan@lakeoswegoreview.com (joint with Lake Oswego)
Editor: Lori Hall, lhall@westlinntidings.com
Deadline: Noon Friday

Major Robert Moore, who emigrated to the Willamette Valley in the first wave in 1839, bought 1,000 acres on the west side of Willamette Falls from a local Indian chief. He platted a town he called Robin's Nest on it in 1843, across the river from Oregon City. The territorial legislature decided to call it Linn City after Lewis F. Linn, a Missouri senator supportive of western expansion. It remained so until 1913, when it joined its neighboring riverside communities of Bolton, Sunset, West Oregon City, and Willamette Heights in concluding that they only had one way to fend off eventual annexation by Oregon City – come together as a single entity and incorporate. The communities did just that, creating the city of West Linn.

Overshadowed by Oregon City, which was served by a daily newspaper, and later by neighboring Lake Oswego, served by a robust weekly, West Linn did not get a newspaper of its own – at least not one making more than a fleeting appearance – until 1981.

Eagle Newspapers, founded by one-time governor Elmo Smith, and run by his son, and one-time congressman Denny Smith, set the stage by picking up the *Lake Oswego Review* in 1979. The *Review*, which had been serving West Linn anyway, spun off the *West Linn Tidings* in 1981 under the direction of then-publisher Joe Blaha. That began a big brother-little brother relationship between those papers that continues to this day.

In January 1988, Eagle went into partnership with the Baker family's *Eugene Register-Guard*, which owned several suburban weeklies, to form Community Newspapers. In addition to the West Linn and Lake Oswego papers, it encompassed papers in Tigard, Tualatin, Beaverton, and Forest Grove, and Eagle assumed management responsibility for all of them.

The partners sold the group to Steve and Randalyn Clark in 1996. Four years later, the Clarks sold it to Eagle's principal rival in the Portland suburbs, the Pamplin Media Group.

Spokesman   Wilsonville

Owner: Pamplin Media Group
Address: 241 N. Grant St., Canby, OR 97013
Phone: 503-682-3935
URL: www.wilsonvillespokesman.com (subscription required for full access)
Established: 1985
Published: Wednesday
Market: Wilsonville area (Clackamas County)
Circulation: 3,338 (SO)
Publisher: William D. Cassel, wcassel@eaglenewspapers.com
Editor: Michelle Te, mte@wilsonvillespokesman.com
Deadline: 5 p.m. Friday

Alphonso Boone, grandson of Daniel Boone, established the Willamette River crossing of Boones Ferry in 1847. The community of Boones Landing grew up around it, and was eventually dubbed Wilsonville after its first postmaster, Charles Wilson. The settlement was originally part of Yamhill County, but was transferred to Clackamas in 1855. Lying along the north side of the river, where it is bisected by Interstate 5, it also slops slightly into Washington County to the west.

The paper got its start as the *Wilsonville Times* in 1985. It was launched by Eagle Newspapers' *Canby Herald* as a free-distribution shopper, the intent being reach Clackamas County turf the *Herald* was not able to reach with its paid edition.

The paper continued to serve as a free-distribution shopper, first as the *Times* and later as the *Spokesman*, until 2007. At that point, Eagle decided it had developed a enough of a market to stand on its own and converted it to a full-fledged paid-circulation weekly. The *Spokesman* shares its publisher, William Cassel, with its sister papers in Canby and Mollala. Like them, it is published on Eagle's web press in Salem.

However, the papers are no longer owned by Eagle. The Portland-based Pamplin Media Group bought them in a package deal with weeklies in Newberg, Madras, and Woodburn in January 2013.

Like its two sister papers, the *Spokesman* was converted from broadsheet to tabloid in 2012. Though it carries a Wednesday date, it is printed on Monday.

The *Spokesman* adopted a paywall prior to its acquisition by Pamplin, which has not implemented any system-wide paywall to date. A paid subscription provides the reader with full access to both the print and online versions. Breaking news stories and brief summaries of other stories are available online without a subscription, but the rest of the content is paywall-protected.

Independent   **Woodburn**

Owner: Pamplin Media Group
Address: 650 N. First St., Woodburn, OR 97071
Phone: 503-981-3441
URL: www.woodburnindependent.com (subscription required for full access)
Established: 1888
Published: Wednesday
Market: Northern Marion County
Circulation: 3,490 (SO)
Publisher: Nikki DeBuse, ndebuse@woodburnindependent.com
Editor: Lindsay Keefer, lkeefer@woodburnindependent.com
Deadline: Noon Friday

Woodburn probably is the only city anywhere named for a woodlot fire. Originally known as Halsey, it needed renaming because there already was a well-established community of Halsey to the south in Linn County. A railroad official witnessed the fire, triggered by a slash burn, and decided Woodburn would be a good option. The city owes its existence to the burst of rail building in the late 1800s. First William Reed and then Ben Holladay chose routes running through Woodburn, and the establishment of rail depots triggered residential and commercial development aimed at capitalizing on those services.

More than half its 24,000 residents claimed Hispanic heritage in the 2010 census. Many of the rest, members of, or descendants of, a large Old Believer community, are of Russian Orthodox heritage.

The local paper is the *Woodburn Independent*, which also serves Gervais, Hubbard, Donald, Aurora, St. Paul, and Mount Angel, neighbors in northern Marion County. It published its first edition on December 1,

1888, and continuously since. The paper was founded by Leonard McMahan, a Baker County native who served one term in the Oregon House of Representatives, then won election to the Marion County Circuit Court. He held the judgeship until his retirement in 1943.

The *Independent* has faced competition only twice in its long history – from the *Tribune* from 1911 to 1914 and the *Opportunity News* from 1965 to 1968.

Eagle Newspapers, founded by one-time governor Elmo Smith and run by his son and one-time congressman Denny Smith, bought the *Independent* in 1971. The paper is still printed on Eagle's web press plant in Salem, but is now owned by the Portland-based Pamplin Media Group. It was included in a package of six Oregon weeklies that Pamplin acquired from Eagle in January 2013. It published twice-weekly for some years, but has cut back to once a week, publishing Wednesdays.

Washington newspapers

By city, in alphabetical order

Daily World   Aberdeen

Owner: Stephens Media
Address: 315 S. Michigan St., Aberdeen, WA 98520
Phone: 360-532-4000
URL: www.thedailyworld.com (subscription required for e-edition, full access)
Established: 1889
Published: Monday through Sunday AM
Market: Western half of Olympic Peninsula, notably Grays Harbor County
Circulation: 14,100
Publisher: Bill Crawford, bcrawford@thedailyworld.com
Editor: Doug Barker, dbarker@thedailyworld.com

Washington has few good harbors on the Pacific, so Grays Harbor, one of those few, filled in early with settlements based on shipping, fishing and logging. In the late 1800s, Aberdeen began to achieve primacy among those settlements. As a result, newspapers began giving it a go there in the 1880s and 1890s.

Aberdeen's main paper has long been the *World*. Founded as the *Aberdeen Weekly Bulletin* in 1889, it went daily in 1900. It was sold to Tacomans Andrew Rupp, a political reporter and editorial writer, and John Gilbert, an editorial cartoonist, eight years later. They renamed it first the *World*, then the *Daily World*. The Rupp and Gilbert families continued to run the paper until 1967. They sold to Richard Lafromboise, whose death just a few months later led his heirs to sell in turn to the Donrey Media Group.

After a quarter of a century, Donrey sold to Stephens Media in 1993. Based in Las Vegas, its flagship is the *Las Vegas Review-Journal*. The company also owns papers in several other states, including Texas and Arkansas. Its holdings include a trio of Washington weeklies as well, The

North Beach News in Ocean Shores, the *South Beach Bulletin* in Westport and the *Vidette* in Montesano. Stephens made headlines in 2010 with its aggressive partnership with a Nevada law firm to search out copyright infringement cases online. It launched major lawsuits against perceived violators, including a number of bloggers around the country.

All three of the company's Washington papers, since August 2012, have been printed by the *Centralia Chronicle*'s Chronicle Printing Division. The *World* cited aging press equipment as the main reason. It said Lafromboise Communications had invested in a state-of the-art press in Centralia, promising more vivid color, sharper images and crisper production.

The paper historically published seven days a week, but dropped its Monday edition in May 2012. Both the shift to outside printing and decrease in publication frequency triggered some layoffs.

American   Anacortes

Owner: Pioneer News Group
Address: 901 Sixth St., Anacortes, WA 98221
Phone: 360-293-3122
URL: www.goanacortes.com (subscription required for full access)
Established: 1890
Published: Wednesday
Market: Northern Skagit County
Circulation: 3,750
Publisher: Jack Darnton, jdarnton@goanacortes.com

Thanks to a naturally scouring deep-water port on Fidalgo Island, west of Mount Vernon, Anacortes developed into a significant a shipping, fishing and logging center. It underwent an initial boom that fizzled, then came back on the strength of docks, marinas, canneries and mills. In recent decades, tourism has entered the mix, enhanced by development of a substantial state ferry hub in Anacortes. So has industry, with development of major Shell and Texaco oil refineries that chose Anacortes over Bellingham.

A pair of papers emerged almost simultaneously with the emergence of the community itself – first the *Progress*, then the *American* hard on its heels. Both of them pre-dated Anacortes' formal incorporation as a city in 1891.

The *American* was launched by Douglass Allmond and F.H. Boynton on May 15, 1890, with this mission: "To publish an honest, independent, aggressive newspaper that shall tell the story of our marvelous city and its surroundings." They appealed for support from "all who have the welfare of our city at heart."

The *Progress* was already up and running by then, but the *American* gradually got the better of their competition and prevailed. Other papers also came and went in the community, including the *Citizen* from 1906 to 1927 and the *Mercury* and *Daily Mercury* briefly in the early 1950s.

John Webber and Wallie Funk acquired the *American* in 1950 and continued to publish it until 1964. They sold to the Pioneer News Group.

Skagit Publishing, owned by the Wood family, now holds a controlling interest in Pioneer. Skagit prints and exercises direct management control over all of Pioneer's Washington papers except Ellensburg.

The group includes weeklies in Burlington and Sedro-Woolley and the daily *Skagit Valley Herald* in Mount Vernon. Skagit also prints and manages the *Stanwood/Camano News*, in which Pioneer holds a minority interest in partnership with retired publisher David W. Pinkham.

The *American* features an innovative and unusual design on the web. Designed to serve as a community portal, it highlights the region more than it does the newspaper.

Times   Arlington

Owner: Sound Publishing.
Address: P.O. Box 145, Marysville, WA 98270
Phone: 360-659-1300
URL: www.arlingtontimes.com (unrestricted)
Established: 1879
Published: Wednesday
Market: Northern Snohomish County
Circulation: 5,475
Publisher: C. Paul Brown, pbrown@soundpublishing.com (joint with Marysville)
Editor: Scott Frank, editor@marysvilleglobe.com (joint with Marysville)
Deadline: 4 p.m. Monday

When settlement began in earnest in the Stillaguamish Valley, at the northern end of Snohomish County, part of what is now Arlington was platted as Haller City. As a result, the *Arlington Times* actually got its start, in 1879, as the *Haller City News*. That enables the paper to make a distinctive claim on its flag – "oldest continuously running newspaper in the state of Washington" – even though it did not acquire its current name until 1899.

Sound Publishing has largely merged operations of the *Arlington Times* with those of the nearby *Marysville Globe*. The two papers share an editor, a publisher and an office in Marysville. Sound employees three different distribution systems with its 40-odd general-circulation papers in Washington. Some are strictly paid, some are strictly free and some operate on a hybrid voluntary-pay basis.

The company operates both the Arlington and Marysville papers on a hybrid basis. It mails them to all households in their respective circulation areas, but actively solicits paid subscriptions in return and sells copies for 75 cents from a network of vending locations.

Review   Bainbridge Island

Owner: Sound Publishing
Address: P.O. Box 10817
Phone: 206-842-6613
URL: www.bainbridgereview.com (unrestricted)
Established: 1900
Published: Friday
Market: Bainbridge Island
Circulation: 6,800
Publisher: Donna Etchey, detchey@soundpublishing.com
Deadline: 4 p.m. Wednesday

The *Review* is based in a town known historically as Winslow, which is Bainbridge Island's lone population center, and which annexed all of the island's previously unincorporated territory in 1991. Having appropriated the rest of the island, it decided to appropriate the name as well. Goodbye Winslow, hello Bainbridge Island.

Once best known for its timber mills and shipyard industry, it is best known now for its exurban residential qualities, its scenic and pastoral setting and its magnetism for tourists. It's just a ferry ride away from downtown Seattle, which enhances its accessibility and its appeal.

The *Review*, which dates to 1928, has long kept a tight focus on the island community. Its web site declares it the only paper in the world "that cares about Bainbridge Island."

By way of history, it adds: "The Review has been there to cover it all, even making a little history of its own along the way as the only West Coast newspaper to defend the rights of Japanese-American citizens during the war."

In recent years, it has become part of Sound Publishing's Kitsap group. Unlike many of the company's more than three-dozen other publications in Western Washington, it operates on both a paid-circulation and carrier-delivered basis.

News-Tribune   **Ballard**

Owner: Robinson Newspapers
Address: 2208 N.W. Market St., Suite 202, Ballard, WA 98107
Phone: 206-708-1378
URL: www.ballardnewstribune.com (unrestricted)
Established: 1891
Published: Monday
Market: Ballard area of Northwest Seattle
Circulation: 7,500
Publisher: Jerry Robinson, jerryr@robinsonnews.com (joint with Burien, West Seattle)
Managing Editor: Ken Robinson, kenr@robinsonnews.com (joint with West Seattle)
Deadline: Noon Friday

Ballard is not truly a separate city – not these days anyway. It was once, but that was a long time ago. Rapacious Seattle swallowed it up in 1907. As a Northwest Seattle neighborhood, however, it has retained a strong – and strongly positive – identity.

Local newspapering is as old as the community itself. The *Ballard News Tribune* and its predecessors have been covering the community since 1891. Jerry Robinson bought the paper in 1993 and incorporated it into his suburban Robinson Newspapers group. It's still there.

Reflector   **Battle Ground**

Owner: Lafromboise Communications
Address: 20 N.W. 20th Ave., Battle Ground, WA 98604
Phone: 360-687-5151
URL: www.thereflector.com (unrestricted, including e-edition and archives)
Established: 1909
Published: Wednesday
Market: Northern Clark County
Circulation: 28,040
Publisher: Steve Walker, steve@thereflector.com
Managing Editor: Ken Vance, ken@thereflector.com

The *Reflector* actually got its start in Ridgefield rather than Battle Ground. It was founded by there by Kelley Loe on Oct. 8, 1909, and it remained there for the next 40 years. The move to Battle Ground came after Jack Dodge bought the paper in 1949. He evidently thought it would prove more fertile ground for his new endeavor.

Marvin Case maintained the *Reflector*'s unbroken chain of local ownership when he bought the paper in 1980 for something in the neighborhood of $100,000. Case, then 36, was working for the federal government at the time. He knew absolutely nothing about newspapering, and he had a wife and three small children to support.

But he was as long as confidence as he was short on experience. *The Washington Newspaper*, bulletin of the Washington Newspaper Publishers Association, quoted him as saying: "I thought, on a newspaper, I could live in one place and get involved in a community. I relish that."

And he did just that – for the next 30 years. In the process, he became the state's longest-tenured publisher.

On June 30, 2010, Case sold the paper to Lafromboise Communications, a family newspaper firm whose centerpiece is the *Centralia Chronicle* 80 miles to the north.

According to the Washington Newspaper, "He wrote stories, took photos, worked in the printing room. He repaired the toilets and rekeyed the lock boxes on the newspaper stands when they broke. He did it all. He always worked Sundays." It quoted Case as figuring, "The more I did, the more profitable we would be."

Herald   Belfair

See Mason County Journal, Shelton.

The Bellingham Herald building. (photo/Tom Harpel,, Wikipedia)

Herald   Bellingham

Owner: McClatchy Company
Address: 1155 N. State St., Bellingham WA 98225
Phone: 360-676-2660

URL: www.bellinghamherald.com (unrestricted)
Established: 1890
Published: Monday through Sunday AM
Market: Whatcom County
Circulation: 16,562 weekday, 19,923 Sunday (ABC)
Publisher: Mark Owings, mark.owings@bellinghamherald.com
Executive Editor: Julie Shirley, julie.shirley@bellinghamherald.com

The daily *Bellingham Herald* began life on March 10, 1890, as the tri-weekly Fairhaven Herald. At the time, Fairhaven was a boomtown on Bellingham Bay, eclipsing its bayfront rivals Whatcom and Sehome.

The first editor was William "Lightfoot" Visscher, which a company history describes as "a colorful outspoken character." Before managing to get himself fire after just 18 months on the job, it says, he oversaw the paper's conversion to a daily. Fairhaven, Whatcom and Sehome merged in 1903 and took the bay's name of Bellingham – a politic choice. With the merger, the paper that served them morphed from the *Fairhaven Herald* into the *Bellingham Herald*.

The *Herald* was forced to briefly suspend publication at one point early in its history, but has since achieved goodly measures of prosperity and stability. It settled into its present quarters in the Herald Building in 1926. It's not too hard to imagine it reaching the century mark there.

Sidney Albert "Sam" Perkins bought the *Herald* in 1911. He and his heirs continued to own and operate it until 1967, when they sold to Federated Publications, the first in a series of chain owners that remains unbroken today.

Gannett Co. Inc., then on an acquisition binge that would make it the nation's largest newspaper chain, scooped up Federated four years later. In 2005, Gannett traded the Herald and two other Northwest papers to another major national player, Knight-Ridder, for papers offering more synergy with other Gannett holdings. The following year, the California-based McClatchy Company swallowed up its larger rival.

The *Herald*'s switch from the afternoon to morning publication cycle in May 1997. It circulates everywhere in Whatcom County except Point Roberts, which is separated from the rest of the United States by a strip of Canada.

The paper is no longer being printed in Bellingham. It is now being printed at the *Skagit Valley Herald* plant in Mount Vernon to the south.

Courier-Herald

Bonney Lake/Sumner

See Courier-Herald, Enumclaw

Kitsap Sun   **Bremerton**

Owner: E.W. Scripps Co.
Address: 545 5th St., Bremerton, WA 98337
Phone: 360-377-3711
URL: www.kitsapsun.com (unrestricted)
Established: 1935
Published: Monday through Sunday AM
Market: Kitsap, Jefferson and Mason counties
Circulation: 28,262 weekday, 19,349 Saturday,
21,396 Sunday (ABC)
Publisher: Charles Horton, chorton@kitsapsun.com
Editor: David Nelson, dnelson@kitsapsun.com

Seattle had been under development for decades before much interest arose in the inlets on the Kitsap Peninsula, on the west side of the Puget Sound. But when interest did arise, it arose with a vengeance. The port district at Bremerton was founded in 1913. And military installations, notably the Puget Naval Shipyard, soon became central features of the Bremerton area. Bremerton has long been the largest city in Kitsap County. But at less than 40,000 population, it doesn't really dominate. The county seat is in Port Orchard, and the newspaper, the *Kitsap Sun*, presently is named for the county rather than the city.

The earliest consistent daily newspapers to serve the Kitsap Peninsula were the *Bremerton Evening Searchlight* and its morning counterpart, the *Bremerton Daily News*. They merged in 1922 to create the *Daily News Searchlight*.

The *Bremerton Sun*, forerunner of today's *Kitsap Sun*, didn't come along until 1935. Even then, it was aimed mainly at vanquishing the *Seattle Star*, which it succeeded in doing, rather than the lesser *Daily News Searchlight*.

In 1940, the John P. Scripps Newspaper Group, a California spinoff of the pioneer newspaper family's Scripps Group, ventured north to buy the *Sun*. It was one of the first purchases made in the region by a major outside operator. John P. Scripps was absorbed by E.W. Scripps, another Scripps family offshoot, in 1986. And E.W. Scripps still marks the *Sun* as its only Northwest holding.

Patriot   **Bremerton**

Owner: Sound Publishing
Address: 3888 N.W. Randall Way, Suite 100, Silverdale, WA 98383
Phone: 360-308-9161
URL: www.bremertonpartriot.com (unrestricted)
Established: 1999

Published: Friday
Market: Bremerton
Circulation: 12,983
Publisher: Sean McDonald, publisher@bremertonpatriot.com
Deadline: 4 p.m. Wednesday

The *Bremerton Patriot* – its name echoes the many military operations in the area, though it is not an official military paper – is an unusual though not unique creature. It's a general news weekly in a city also served by a long-running daily. Founded in 1999, the *Patriot* is owned by Sound Publishing, one of six papers Sound operates on the Kitsap peninsula. The daily at Bremerton – the *Kitsap Sun*, owned by E.W. Scripps – competes with all six of them for news, advertising and circulation reach.

On its website, the *Patriot* promises to give "comprehensive coverage to all aspects of life in Bremerton," including high school sports and community recreation programs in addition to staples like city government and the public school system.

Highline Times/Des Moines News/SeaTac News
Burien

Owner: Robinson Newspapers
Address: 14006 First Ave. S, Suite B, Burien, WA 98168
Phone: 206-708-1378
URL: www.highlinetimes.com (unrestricted)
Established: 1945
Published: Wednesday
Market: Burien, Des Moines and SeaTac, south of Seattle in King County
Circulation: 10,000
Publisher: Jerry Robinson, jerryr@robinsonnews.com (joint with Ballard, West Seattle)
Editor: Eric Mathison, ericm@robinsonnews.com
Deadline: Noon Monday

The *Highline Times*, *Des Moines News* and *SeaTac News* cover neighboring swatches of southwest King County south of Seattle in the SeaTac airport area. The papers burst on the scene in the boom that ensued when American soldiers returned home from World War II and, in many cases, headed West. The three papers feature separate nameplates and mixes of local news, but are all produced out of a central office in Burien.

They also share a common business and editorial staff. They also operate in close conjunction with other members of the Robinson Newspapers group, which itself is based in Burien.

News   Camano

See News, Stanwood/Camano

Post-Record   Camas/Washougal

Owner: Columbian Publishing Co.
Address: 425 N.E. 4th Ave., Camas, WA 98607
Phone: 360-834-2141
URL: www.camaspostrecord.com (subscription required for full access)
Established: 1908
Published: Tuesday
Market: Camas and Washougal in eastern Clark County
Circulation: 3,500
Publisher: Mike Gallagher, mike.gallagher@camaspostrecord.com
Editor: Heather Acheson, heather.acheson@camaspostrecord.com

The neighboring communities of Camas and Washougal in Southwest Washington may well owe their existence to a newspaper. But it wouldn't be a newspaper based in the area, or even the state. Rather, it would be *The Oregonian*, perched on the other side of the Columbia River in Portland. The first major commercial venture in the vicinity was a sawmill established in 1852. It burned down almost as soon as it was completed, though, and the site stood vacant for more than 30 years. Then came Henry Pittock, owner of the Portland Evening Telegram as well as its morning counterpart. The two big dailies consumed a lot of newsprint, and Pittock was in short supply. Seeing an opportunity, he built a paper mill in Camas. By 1884, work was underway.

The earliest predecessor paper was the *Washougal Record*, founded by Kelley Loe in 1900. It went through a series of owners, including J.A. Hart and Florence and Nina Charnley, before E.K. Curran moved it to Vancouver in 1913. The next year, D.L. McMillan launched the *Washougal Times* as a replacement. He subsequently sold it to Elmer Armstrong, who restored the old *Washougal Record* name.

The *Camas Post* got its start in 1908, by which time the town had developed a solid commercial advertising base. It eventually merged with the 1914 incarnation of the *Record* to create the *Camas-Washougal Post-Record*.

In its first foray across the Columbia River into Washington, Oregon-based Eagle Newspapers acquired the paper in 1979. After a 25-year turn at the helm, Eagle sold it to the Columbian Company in 2004. Long owned by the Campbell family, it takes its name from its flagship, the daily Vancouver *Columbian*.

Wahkiakum County Eagle   Cathlamet

Owner: Rick and Betsy Nelson
Address: P.O. Box 368, Cathlamet, WA 98612
Phone: 206-708-1378.
URL: www.waheagle.com (unrestricted)
Established: 1891
Published: Thursday
Market: Wahkiakum County
Circulation: 1,735
Publisher: Rick Nelson, ernelson@teleport.com
News Editor: Caroline Jennings, caroline@waheagle.com

When we refer here to the founding of various communities, we usually aim to mark the point when Americans of European ancestry began to arrive to claim land, carve out roads, clear fields and erect buildings. But long before European settlers began to pour west over the Oregon Trail, Native Americans had established a sizable permanent settlement at Cathlamet. Historylink.com calls it "the largest Native American settlement west of the Cascades, which could have numbered from 500 to 1,000 people and was clearly one of the main centers of Indian strength on the lower river." The site goes on to say, "The Cathlamet Indians, led by Chief Wahkiakum, were a Chinookan tribe. But today, the band is no longer a distinct group. In those days, the salmon, elk, deer and bear were plentiful, and they were very skilled in fishing and tracking game."

The European settlers, of course, took to Cathlamet for the same reasons – an expanse of flat space alongside the Columbia River that offered ready access to fish, game, furs, timber and other resources. And they soon displaced their native predecessors.

The earliest newspaper there probably was the *Cathlamet Gazette,* founded in 1889. But it lasted only about five years.

The *Skamokawa Eagle,* creation of Samuel Grant Williams, followed on May 14, 1891. And unlike the *Gazette,* it's still around and publishing.

Still in local hands, it's known these days as the *Wahkiakum County Eagle.* Owners Rick and Betsy Nelson boast on their website: "This is an age of mass media – daily newspapers, radio, the Internet and television. All are effective on a mass scale. Wahkiakum County, however, isn't the mass scale and the mass media don't always work here. The Eagle does."

Chronicle   Centralia

Owner: Lafromboise Communications
Address: 321 N. Pearl St., Centralia, WA 98531
Phone: 360-736-3311
URL: www.chronline.com (subscription required for full access)
Established: 1889
Published: Tuesday and Thursday PM, Saturday AM
Market: Lewis County, plus southern Thurston and northern Cowlitz counties
Circulation: 13,912
Publisher: Christine Fossett, cfossett@chronline.com
Editor in Chief: Brian Mittge, bmittge@chronline.com

Centralia, named for its central location between the communities on the Columbia River to the south and Puget Sound to the north, dates from the 1850s. But development was gradual.

The *Chronicle* was the first major paper to publish at Centralia, starting in 1889. For a couple of decades, it had competition from the *Evening News Examiner*, but absorbed its river in 1913. It traditionally published Monday through Saturday, but recently cut back to a tri-weekly schedule, publishing Tuesday, Thursday and Saturday.

The *Chronicle* maintained a free-access website until April 2013. The site remains free to print subscribers, but other users must pay a fee to gain unfettered access.

It has long served as the flagship for family-owned Lafromboise Communications. The company operates a contract printing operation in conjunction with the newspaper

Free Press   Cheney

Owner: Free Press Publishing
Address: 1616 W. First St., Cheney WA 99004
Phone: 509-235-6184
URL: www.cheneyfreepress.com (unrestricted)
Established: 1896
Published: Thursday
Market: Southwestern Spokane County
Circulation: 3,500
Publisher: Harlan Shellabarger, harlan@cheneyfreepress.com
Editor: John McCallum, mccallum@cheneyfreepress.com
Deadline: 10 a.m. Tuesday

The Washington town named for Benjamin P. Cheney, a director of the Northern Pacific, went through no less than four other names before settling on that one. It originally adopted the ungainly Section Thirteen.

Then it switched to the more picturesque Willow Springs. It became Depot Springs for a time, no doubt out of gratitude, after a railroad depot was established there. Then it was renamed Billings after the president of the Northern Pacific, presumably out of gratitude as well. In a final act of gratitude, it switched to Cheney after the railroad executive of that name chose it as the site of the Benjamin P. Cheney Academy, forerunner of Eastern Washington University, in 1882.

Cheney's newspaper history is, by comparison, a lot more linear. Since a trio of early newsmen came together to launch the Free Press Publishing Co. on April 4, 1896, it has been served by the *Cheney Free Press* and only the *Cheney Free Press*.

Cheney lies just 17 miles southwest of Spokane, which casts a big shadow. That has always limited its prospects to some extent. Though the smaller community has lost out to Spokane on a lot of things, including the county seat it once claimed, one thing it didn't lose out on was the university.

When the state Legislature set out to establish the Washington State Normal School in 1889, Cheney Academy was already turning out teachers, giving Cheney a leg up. Like Cheney, it went through various names, including Eastern Washington College of Education and Eastern Washington State College, before ending up with its present one.

The paper spent a number of years under the ownership of Journal-News Publishing. Jeff Fletcher, owner of the *Grant County Journal* in Ephrata, served as majority partner in the enterprise and Bill Ifft, scion of one of America's notable 20th century newspaper families, as junior partner. But in 2007, Ifft bought Fletcher out and recreated the Free Press Publishing Co. as his ownership vehicle. As Editor John McCallum said at the time, "A little over 111 years later, the paper is back to its roots."

Free Press Publishing also owns the *Spokane Valley News Herald* and *Davenport Times*, along with several specialty publications. It prints all of them out of a plant in Cheney, along with three other papers under contract – the *Adams County Journal*, *Wilbur Register* and *Newport Miner*. All are weeklies.

Independent   Chewelah

Owner: The Arnold family of Chewelah
Address: P.O. Box 5, Chewelah, WA 99109
Phone: 509-935-8422
URL: www.chewelahindependent.com (unrestricted)
Established: 1903
Published: Thursday

Market: Chewelah Valley in Stevens County
Circulation: 2,250
Publisher: Jared Arnold, theindependent@centurytel.net
Deadline: 10 a.m. Tuesday

The *Independent* is a locally owned and operated weekly serving the Chewelah Valley. Founded by William Hunter Brownlow, it has published continuously since June 19, 1903. Brownlow produced his eight-page weekly with the help of four sons: Truman, Ralph, Arthur, and Alex.

Half the pages, featuring national and international news, were printed elsewhere and shipped to Chewelah by stagecoach or rail. The other half, featuring local news, were assembled by the Brownlows at their office in Chewelah. It was a format the paper followed for decades.

In his initial issue, Brownlow called Chewelah "the future Butte of Washington", saying the newly incorporated town was "surrounded by mountains rich in mineral wealth, gold, silver, copper, iron, and marble of every known grain and color." Brownlow himself became involved in the local mining industry as president of the Chewelah Mining and Smelting Company. As such, he wrote several articles for East Coast publications extolling the mining industry and, not incidentally, recruiting investors.

The *Independent* is owned and operated these days by the Arnold family. It circulates in Chewelah, Colville, Addy, Bluecreek, Valley, Springdale and Suncrest.

After 109 years of print-only publication, it has now begun publishing on the web as well.

Northern Kittitas County Tribune   Cle Elum

Owner: Oahe Publishing Corp.
Address: 807 W. Davis St., Cle Elum, WA 98922
Phone: 509-674-2511
URL: www.nkctribune.com (unrestricted)
Established: 1953
Published: Thursday
Market: Northwestern Kittitas County
Circulation: 3,650
Owner & Publisher: Jana Stoner, jana@nkctribine.com
Deadline: Noon Tuesday

Newspapering in upper Kittitas County dates back to the 1896 founding of the *Cascade Miner* at Rosyln. The *Cle Elum Echo* followed in 1902, and they merged in 1922 to create the Miner-Echo, based in Cle

Elum. The *Miner-Echo* continued publishing until 1962, but was gradually eclipsed by the *Tribune* after its launch in 1953.

The paper is published by Oahe Publishing Corp., which is owned by Jack, Jerri and Jana Stoner. The paper's parent company also publishes an array of specialty publications, many of them tourist oriented. In addition, the company operates Tribune Office Supply & Printing, which touts itself as a "one-stop source for office supplies and quality custom printing."

On its website, the *Tribune* bills itself as a "community newspaper serving Cle Elum, Roslyn, Ronald, South Cle Elum, Easton, Thorp, Lake Cle Elum, Liberty, Mineral Springs, Hyak, Snoqualmie, Snoqualmie Pass and all of the surrounding upper Kittitas County."

Cle Elum experienced an early boom through the discovery of workable coal deposits. Coal mining played a major role in its early development. It also developed the first ski facility on the West Coast in 1922, and began to market itself as an outdoor recreation mecca.

Its early history is also marked by two great tragedies. On July 16, 1908, two carloads of blasting powder exploded while being unloaded at the Northwest Improvement Company. Felt for miles around, and likened to an earthquake, the blast claimed the lives of nine people, including members of a family living in a tent near the loading dock. It shattered windows throughout the downtown area, three-quarters of a mile away. An even greater disaster occurred on July 25, 1918, when a fast-moving fire swept 29 city blocks, causing half a million dollars worth of damage. It was blamed on a carelessly tossed cigarette. Thirty houses and 205 businesses were destroyed and 1,800 residents were displaced.

Whitman County Gazette   Colfax

Owner: Colfax Publishing
Address: 211 N. Main St., Colfax, WA 99111
Phone: 509-397-4333
URL: www.wcgazette.com (subscription required for full access)
Established: 1877
Published: Thursday
Market: Whitman County
Circulation: 4,200
Editor & Publisher: Gordon Forgey, gazette@colfax.com

Colfax is the seat of Whitman County, but dwarfed by one of its in-county neighbors – Pullman, home of Washington State University. What's more, Pullman and its Idaho twin Moscow, home of the University of Idaho, support a daily newspaper operation. That leaves the *Whitman County Gazette* with a highly local base mainly in the northern part of the county, which is more distant from the Pullman-Moscow axis.

The paper traces its history all the way back to the *Palouse Gazette*, founded in 1877. The *Palouse Gazette* morphed into the Colfax Gazette in 1893 and the Colfax Gazette-Commoner in 1932, following a merger with the *Colfax Commoner*. It did not become the *Whitman County Gazette* until 1989. The *Commoner* burst onto the scene in 1885. It's initial run lasted only seven years, but it was revived in 1911 and published continuously thereafter until the 1932 merger.

Colfax also had brief flirtations with the *Weekly Vidette* and the *Washington Democrat*.

Several newspapers gave it a go in other Whitman County communities over the years, but they have all departed the scene. The most recent to give it up was the *North Palouse Journal*, a 12-page tabloid based in Rockford. The *Journal* was founded in 2000 by Sally Edler and Dan Bothell, and achieved peak circulation of about 1,500. It shut down in January 2010, after Bothell died and Elder was unable to either sustain the paper on her own or find a suitable buyer.

Examiner   Colville

Owner: American Publishing Company
Address: 220 S. Main St., Colville, WA 99114
Phone: 509-684-4567
URL: www.statesmanexaminer.com (unrestricted)
Established: 1896
Published: Wednesday
Market: Stevens County and parts of Ferry and Pend Oreille counties
Circulation: 4,550
Editor & Publisher: Chris Cowbrough, publisher@statesmanexaminer.com
Deadline: 5 p.m. Thursday

Growing out of the old Fort Colville trading site and military post, Colville quickly became one of the largest logging, mining and manufacturing centers north of Spokane. Hudson's Bay agent John Work established Fort Colville in 1825. It was designed to replace Spokane House and the Flathead Post as the principal fur trading point on the Upper Columbia. After Britain and the United States got into a border dispute, the U.S. Army moved the post to a new site a few miles away in 1859 and built up its defenses. When the fort was abandoned in 1882, the current townsite was platted nearby, on the Colville River.

The weekly *Statesman-Index* was founded in 1896, just as Colville was beginning to emerge as a true commercial and governmental center.

It had the field largely to itself until Oct. 31, 1907, when the rival *Colville Examiner* emerged as a Saturday publication.

The two battled head to head until 1948, through the Great Depression and two world wars, then merged to form the *Statesman-Examiner*. Its website describes it as the largest community newspaper in Eastern Washington.

Three other papers made fleeting appearances in Colville over the years, the *Stevens County Reveille*, *Stevens County Republican* and *Stevens County Reporter*. But none of them displayed staying power.

News & Standard   Coulee City

Owners: ShirleyRae and Richard Maes
Address: 405 W. Main St., Coulee City WA 99115
Phone: 509-632-5402
URL: No website, but has free-access e-editions posted at www.smalltownpapers.com/newspapers/newspaper_pages.php?id=81
Established: 1890
Published: Wednesday
Market: Grant County
Circulation: Less than 1,000
Co-Publishers: ShirleyRae and Richard Maes, tns@accima.com

The *Coulee City News & Standard* is the product of a December 1945 merger between the *Coulee City News* and the *Hartline Standard*. The *Standard* was based in a community to the northeast that is even smaller (population 151 in the 2010 Census) than Coulee City (population 562). It has gone by a series of different names over the years, but all of them have combined the words "News" and "Standard" in some fashion, and always in that order.

Coulee City is actually the smallest of three Grant County communities appropriating the Coulee name in some way. The other two are *Grand Coulee*, population 988, and *Coulee Dam*, population 1098. To be fair, though, Coulee Dam slops over into two other counties, Douglas and Okanogan. It was, of course, named after the Grand Coulee Dam, a massive hydroelectric producer than spans the Columbia River at that point.

The *News & Standard* boasts on its flag that it was "Washington's first photo-offset newspaper." It serves Hartline and Almira as well as its home community. Its oldest antecedent was the *Coulee City News*, established in 1890. It has been owned and operated by ShirleyRae and Richard Maes since November 1998. The *News & Standard* is printed under contract at the Grant County Journal plant in Ephrata.

South Whidbey Record   Coupeville/Langley

Owner: Sound Publishing.
Address: 211 Second St, Langley, WA 98260
Phone: 360-221-5300
URL: www.southwhidbeyrecord.com (unrestricted)
Established: 1925
Published: Wednesday and Saturday
Market: South Whidbey Island
Circulation: 4,498
Publisher: Keven Graves, kgraves@soundpublishing.com
Deadline: 10 a.m. Tuesday for Wednesday, 10 a.m. Friday for Saturday

See Whidbey News-Times, below

Whidbey Examiner   Coupeville

Owner: Sound Publishing
Address: 6 N.W. Coveland St., Coupeville, WA 98239
Phone: 360-678-8060
URL: www.whidbeyexaminer.com (unrestricted)
Established: 1995
Published: Thursday
Market: Central Whidbey Island/Coupeville area
Circulation: 2,000
Publisher: Keven Graves, kgraves@soundpublishing.com
Deadline: 4 p.m. Tuesday

See Whidbey News-Times, below

Whidbey News-Times   Coupeville/Oak Harbor

Owner: Sound Publishing
Address: P.O. Box 1200, Coupeville, WA 98239
Phone: 360-675-6611
URL: www.whidbeynewstimes.com (unrestricted)
Established: 1891
Published: Wednesday and Saturday
Market: North Whidbey Island
Circulation: 6,983
Publisher: Keven Graves, kgraves@soundpublishing.com
Deadline: 10 a.m. Tuesday for Wednesday, 10 a.m. Friday for Saturday

The *Whidbey News-Times* was founded as the *Coupeville Examiner* in 1995. The aim was to create an independent community voice with a pronounced Coupeville focus. The founders included Keven Graves, Gretchen (Young) Somotmayor, Carlos Sotomayor, Bill Wilson, Mary Kay Doody and Kasie Pierzga, a group that had a deep reservoir of journalism experience. Initially, Doody served as publisher and Graves as editor.

Whidbey Island, which features more than 60,000 largely rural residents, boasts what has to be one of the strangest newspaper environments anywhere.

For starters, the island is served by not one, not two, but three separate newspapers. And despite a long history of competition, all are owned today by the same company – Sound Publishing – which has placed them all under the direction of a single publisher, Kasia Pierzga.

Though the island has several population centers dotting the 35-mile north-south arc it cuts in Puget Sound, including Oak Harbor, Langley, Greenbank, Clinton, and Freeland, the county seat of Coupeville serves as home base for all three these days, at least in most respects. What's more, two of them publish on identical Wednesday/Saturday cycles.

So how did this all come about? And how does it make sense?

The first paper to enter the publishing field on Whidbey Island, the largest of nine in Washington's Island County, was the *Island County Times in 1891*. The *Oak Harbor News* followed in 1911. After almost 50 years of fierce competition, they merged in 1959 to create the *Whidbey News-Times*, based north of Coupeville in the larger city of Oak Harbor.

The *Whidbey Island Record* launched in 1925 in Langley, down toward the southern end of the island, closer to Seattle. It became the *South Whidbey Record* in 1981.

That helps unlock the secret to their joint management out of Coupeville. Coupeville is the most centrally located of the island's population centers, which makes it a convenient base from which the *Whidbey News-Times* can serve the northern half and the *South Whidbey Record* the southern half. And indeed, the former maintains a strong presence in Oak Harbor and the latter maintains a strong presence in Langley, including an office. That reflects their respective orientations.

The *Examiner* has an interesting story to tell in its own right, though most of the founders have long since left the venture. Graves went on to become editor and publisher of the *Nisqually Valley News*. Coupeville native Gretchen Sotomayor and her husband, Carlos, moved to the East Coast. While he still makes his home on the island, Wilson retired. Doody retired some years ago and died in 2010. Only Pierzga persevered.

After ascending to the publisher's chair, she bought the paper in 2006 and renamed it the *Whidbey Island Examiner* the following year. She began to extend the reach of her Thursday weekly south to

Greenbank and Freeland, competing more strongly with Sound Publishing's pair of Wednesday/Saturday twice-weeklies.

That dynamic took a sharp turn on June 8, 2012, when Pierzga sold her paper to Sound. And in an unusual twist, Sound not only retained her as publisher of the *Examiner*, but also named her publisher of the other two papers in its Whidbey Island troika. She left the paper in 2013 to take a job in state government, and was replaced by Keven Graves.

Reporter
Covington/Maple Valley/Black Diamond

See Courier-Herald, Enumclaw

Times   Davenport

Owner: Free Press Publishing
Address: 506 Morgan St., Davenport, WA 99122
Phone: 509-725-0101
URL: No online presence
Established: 1884
Published: Thursday
Market: Lincoln County
Circulation: 2,200
Publisher: William Ifft, ifft@cheneyfreepress.com

Davenport's first paper was the *Davenport Tribune*, founded in 1884. Frank Gray launched the competing *Lincoln County Times* two years later, and the battle was on. Gray eventually sold the *Times* to a local syndicate, which took a fateful step in 1907 by bringing in a local high school student N. Russell (Russ) Hill to help. Within months, the syndicate had named Hill editor in chief, even though he had not yet completed his studies. The syndicate sold the *Times* to J.G. Hamlin in 1910, and he replaced Hill. Within a few months, Hamlin sold the paper to W.G. Newton. On May 11, 1911, only a year after his ouster, Hill returned and bought the paper from Newton. In the interim, he had been honing his editorial skills in Tacoma and Odessa.

The *Davenport Times* and *Lincoln County Tribune* continued their rivalry until World War I drained the area of both readership and labor, forcing a consolidation. Hill entered into a partnership with *Tribune* owner Jim Goodwin in 1918 to create the *Davenport Times-Tribune*.

Two years later, Hill bought Goodwin out and began a long run as one of Washington's best known and most respected newsmen. Known for the cigar he liked to keep clenched in his teeth, he held leadership positions in the Washington State Press Association for many years.

In 1957, the paper became simply the *Davenport Times*. It has published under that name ever since. Today, the *Times* is owned by Free Press Publishing, based in Cheney.

It also owns the *Cheney Free Press*, its flagship, and the *Spokane Valley News-Herald*. All three papers are printed on a press at the home office in Cheney.

Douglas County Empire Press   East Wenatchee

Owner: Donna Cassidy
Address: 2290 Grand Avenue, East Wenatchee, WA 98802
Phone: 509-886-8668
URL: www.empire-press.com (unrestricted)
Established: 1888
Published: Thursday
Market: Douglas County, parts of Chelan County
Circulation: 1,000
Publisher: Joe Pitt, weekly@empire-press.com
Editor: Linda Barta, weekly@empire-press.com
Deadline: Noon Tuesday

The *Douglas County Empire Press* is a weekly legal paper whose coverage area includes Waterville, Rock Island, Orondo, Bridgeport, Brewster, Mansfield, Douglas, Palisades, and East Wenatchee, as well as rural areas around and between. It is owned by Donna Cassidy, who also owns a monthly magazine based in Wenatchee, *The Good Life*, with her husband, Mike.

The paper is a descendent of the *Big Bend Empire*, founded in Waterville in February 1888 by Lucien Kellogg.

Kellogg had already founded papers in Cheney and Colfax when he hit on Waterville as the potential site for a third. Quite the entrepreneur, he shipped a press down from Spokane by rail, then hauled it from the depot in Ritzville to the newspaper office in Waterville by freight wagon – in a driving snowstorm. Sensing potential in the newly developing territory, the *Waterville Immigrant* and the *Douglas County Democrat* soon followed. But the *Douglas County Press* emerged as the *Empire*'s main contender.

They merged in 1921 to create the *Waterville Empire Press*. After almost 70 years of continuous operation under that name, it became the *Empire Press* in 1988 and *Douglas County Empire Press* in 1989, shedding its "Waterville" element in two stages.

Though its current business model is built around legal advertising, it also publishes news of its communities, both in print and online.

Islands' Sounder   Eastsound

Owner: Sound Publishing
Address: P.O. Box 758, Eastsound, WA 98245
Phone: 360-376-4500
URL: www.islandssounder.com (unrestricted)
Established: 1964
Published: Wednesday
Market: San Juan Islands
Circulation: 2,681
Publisher: Colleen Armstrong, carmstrong@islandssounder.com
Deadline: 2 p.m. Monday

Of the scattered islands making up the picturesque San Juans, Orcas is the largest in land area and second largest in population. But its 4,400 residents don't constitute much of a readership base and its tourist-oriented service economy doesn't provide much of an advertising base.

Al and Nickee Magnuson, refugees from a Bellingham-area paper called the *Mount Baker Experience*, founded the *Orcas Sounder* in 1964. They started out publishing just 15 issues a year, but gradually moved it to a weekly publication cycle. Along the way, they renamed it the *Islands' Sounder*, making it easier for them to extend their reach to neighboring islands. They were soon distributing it free of change to every mailing address in San Juan County.

In November 1985, they sold the *Sounder* to Ted and Kay Grossman, who put it on a paid circulation basis. The Grossmans sold it to Sound Publishing in 1994, and Sound, the dominant publisher in western Washington, added an edition focusing on Friday Harbor.

The company also publishes news on the web at islandssounder.com.

Dispatch   Eatonville

Owner: RIM Publications
Address: P.O. Box 248, Eatonville, WA 98328
Phone: 360-832-4411
URL: www.dispatchnews.com (unrestricted)
Established: 1893
Published: Wednesday
Market: Southern Pierce County
Circulation: 4,550
Publisher: Cliff Wright, cwright@rimpublications.com

Deadline:

The *Eatonville Dispatch* has been published in the sparsely populated southeastern corner of Pierce County since 1893, without ever facing apparent competition. It's about as distant from highly urbanized Tacoma as its possible to get and still share the same county.

One of Eatonville's biggest claims to fame is its service as a gateway to Mount Rainier, which lies due east. Another is Northwest Trek, a wildlife park opened in the 1970s. Both are the sources of significant tourism. Eatonville got its first significant boost in 1902, when the Tacoma Eastern Railroad provided a vital transportation link to populous and economically booming Puget Sound to the northwest. A few years later the Eatonville Lumber Company beefed up operations at its local mill. The mill expansion spurred Eatonville's incorporation on October 28, 1909. The mill's closure in 1954 struck a major blow, but growing tourism has served to at least partially fill the void.

The company continues to cover the news in the communities it serves and insists it is in the newspaper business for the long haul, regardless of what happens with highly variable legal notice traffic. The paper, which mostly relies on free distribution by mail, but does actively solicit paid subscriptions, is owned these days by RIM Publications, based in Bellevue. Rim is a subsidiary of Stephen Routh's privately held Northwest Trustee Service, a big, vertically integrated player in the foreclosure business.

The company employs lawyers, escrow officers, process servers, property managers and auctioneers – and legal advertising vehicles like the *Dispatch* – that collectively allow it to handle virtually every aspect of the process. To that end, it has been acquiring small but well established weeklies meeting statutory requirements to handle lucrative legal advertising.

Daily Record   **Ellensburg**

Owner: Pioneer News Group
Address: 401 N. Main St., Ellensburg, WA 98926
Phone: 509-925-1414
URL: www.dailyrecordnews.com (subscription required for full access)
Established: 1883
Published: Monday through Friday PM, Saturday AM
Market: Kittitas County, Kittitas Valley
Circulation: 6,000
Publisher: Tyler Miller, tmiller@kvnews.com
Managing Editor: Joanna Markell, jmarkell@kvnews.com

Ellensburg's first newspaper, the *Localizer*, debuted on July 12, 1883. Appearing just as the city was being formally organized, it predated the establishment of Kittitas County by several months and the admission of Washington to the union by several years. The *Localizer* was the forerunner of the *Daily Record*, which serves as the major media voice in Kittitas County today.

The first big step in the process came on July 1, 1909, when J.C. "Cliff" Kaynor and William Zimmerman acquired the paper, renamed it the *Evening Record* and began operating it as an evening daily. The paper marked the centennial of that development on July 1, 2009. Kaynor and Zimmerman, both 22, had been working for the Seattle *Post-Intelligencer* when they teamed up to buy the *Localizer*. Their partnership lasted three years, with Kaynor serving as publisher and Zimmerman as editor. Then Kaynor bought out his partner.

Kaynor went on to own and operate the paper – as the *Ellensburg Evening Record* until April 23, 1938, then as the *Ellensburg Daily Record* – for the next five decades. Along the way, he established an exemplary record of community and industry service. He was a leading spokesman for the development of Ellensburg and central Washington. He was a strong proponent of highway and dam construction. He not only championed the mighty Grand Coulee Dam on the Columbia River, but also all manner of U.S. Bureau of Reclamation and Kittitas Reclamation District irrigation projects in Kittitas County. When he changed the name of his paper in 1938, he called Ellensburg the "center of the Northwest's greatest irrigation development" – a claim he did much to make possible.

He retired in 1959 and died in 1979, but the paper, which eventually dropped the "Ellensburg" element from its flag, retained strong and progressive leadership.

It was the the second daily in Washington to computerize its newsroom. And in 1981, it became the first on the West Coast to augment its print operation with a cable TV outlet oriented to dissemination of community information: 24-hour Record TV-10.

McClatchy, a national chain based in Sacramento, bought the *Daily Record* in 1992. But just four years later, McClatchy sold it in turn to Seattle-based Pioneer Newspapers, now known as the Pioneer News Group.

The paper went morning with its Saturday edition in October 1999, but continues on the PM cycle with its weekday editions.

East County News   **Elma**

See Daily World, Aberdeen

Courier-Herald   **Enumclaw**

Owner: Sound Publishing
Address: 1627 Cole St., Enumclaw, WA 98022
Phone: 360-825-2555
URL: www.courierherald.com/enumclaw (unrestricted)
Established: 1900
Published: Wednesday
Market: Southern reaches of King County
Circulation: 13,536
Publisher: Scott Gray, sgray@soundpublishing.com
Deadline: 11 a.m. Monday

Enumclaw is perched atop the Enumclaw Plateau, formed by a volcanic mudflow from Mount Rainier about 5,700 years ago. Both the city and plateau take their name from the Salish Tribe's term for "place of evil spirits," an apparent reference to Enumclaw Mountain, about six miles north of town. Homesteaders Frank and Mary Stevenson put Enumclaw on the map in 1885, six years after they settled in, by offering the Northern Pacific Railroad a flat parcel of land well suited for development of a siding. That induced the railroad to run its transcontinental mainline through their holdings, and they quickly took advantage by platting a townsite, putting up a hotel and offering free sites for a general store and saloon.

The first local paper, the *Overland Evergreen*, was founded in 1891. But it lasted less than a year.

The first to make a real go of it was the *Courier*, which debuted in 1900. The *Herald* followed in 1908, and the race was on. Both papers capitalized on a fortuitous development – the founding of the White River Lumber and Shingle Company in 1897 by Charles M. Hanson, his three sons, and two outside partners. The six were bound by a Swedish heritage common to the area, and their venture flourished, providing the town with a solid base of employment that persists today.

The papers also benefited from the arrival in 1910 of a Chicago, Milwaukee, St. Paul, and Pacific branch line. That served to establish the community as a major supply and distribution center for logging, mining, and farming enterprises in the area. The *Courier* and *Herald* joined forces in the depression year of 1933, more out of necessity than anything else, as times were tough. Their union created the *Courier-Herald*, which has served the community continuously ever since.

The town of Buckley, lying to the southwest, just across the line in Pierce County, had a pair of papers of its own, the *News* and *Banner*, that merged in 1945 to create the *News-Banner*. The *Courier-Herald* absorbed the *News-Banner* and its coverage area in 1973.

Owner Sound Publishing also produces the *Bonney Lake/Sumner Courier-Herald* and *Covington/Maple Valley/Black Diamond Reporter* out of the *Courier-Herald* plant in Enumclaw. They share offices, staffing, leadership, and content, their chief distinction being nameplates and some of the content.

Grant County Journal   Ephrata

Owner: Journal-News Publishing
Address: 29 Alder St. SW, Ephrata, WA 98823
Phone: 509-754-4636
URL: No web presence
Established: 1908
Published: Monday and Thursday
Market: Grant County
Circulation: 4,550
Publisher: Jeffrey Fletcher, moser@gcjournal.net

Among Washington's rural newspaper communities, Ephrata is one of the youngest. It wasn't settled until around the time of statehood and not incorporated until 1909. The city didn't really become substantial until persistent lobbying, much of it originating locally, paid off with construction of the Grand Coulee Dam to the north. Federal activity associated with the construction and operation of the dam, and its massive hydroelectric plant, helped the town take off. So did irrigated agriculture, another byproduct of dam-building.

The Ephrata Journal was launched in 1907. Its original aim was simply to cover the small farm town serving as its home base. But its ambitions grew over time. After absorbing several rival papers, it began to position itself as a paper capable of serving all of Grant County, via an array of separate geographically targeted editions. The state trade publication, *Washington Newspaper*, described the intent this way in 1919, "*The Grant County Journal* of Ephrata, recently purchased by J.P. Simpson, will try a new plan for covering its field by combining several separate papers and issuing them as departments of the *Journal.*"

In the article, architects of the plan were quoted as saying: "Each town retains its own reporting editor responsible to this town for a fair amount of publicity and attention. It is apparent that under this arrangement the people will be served with the best combination of news possible. In regard to the makeup of the new county paper, the first or front page will be reserved for county news or events of general interest. It will be the only page edited by the head office as such. On this page we will ask our readers to make with us the transition from town mindedness to county mindedness. Through its medium we shall devote ourselves to the general good of Grant County."

The paper is one of relatively few to remain in local ownership on a consistent basis. For many years, it was operated under a partnership between Jeffrey Fletcher and William Ifft. Eventually, they decided to split their holdings. Fletcher took the *Grant County Journal*, which he continues to publish under the auspices of their former partnership vehicle, Journal-News Publishing, incorporated in 1981. Ifft took the *Cheney Free Press* and two small associated publications, the *Davenport Times* and *Spokane Valley Herald*, which he continues to operate under the auspices of Free Press Publishing.

The *Journal* also maintains a substantial commercial printing operation. It prints a number of other papers under contract.

Newsboys at the Everett Daily Herald, about 1929. (photo/photographer unknown; in Wikipedia commons)

The Daily Herald   Everett

Owner: Sound Publishing
Address: 1213 California St., Everett, WA
98206
Phone: 425-339-3000
URL: www.heraldnet.com (unrestricted)
Established: 1901
Published: Monday through Sunday AM
Market: Snohomish and Island counties
Circulation: 39,477 weekday, 38,589 Saturday,
46,526 Sunday (ABC)
Publisher: Josh O'Connor,
joconnor@heraldnet.com
Executive Editor: Neal Pattison, npattison@heraldnet.com

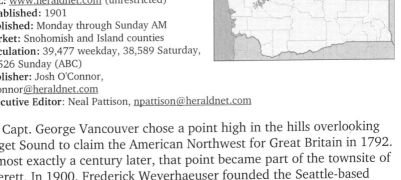

Capt. George Vancouver chose a point high in the hills overlooking
Puget Sound to claim the American Northwest for Great Britain in 1792.
Almost exactly a century later, that point became part of the townsite of
Everett. In 1900, Frederick Weyerhaeuser founded the Seattle-based
Weyerhaeuser Co., one of the largest timberland owners and lumber
manufacturers anywhere in the world. The company, which has more
than 20 million acres at its disposal today, started out with 900,000
acres in Washington that it acquired from railroad baron James J. Hill of
the Great Northern. Both Hill and Weyerhaeuser would inadvertently go
on to play major roles in the development of Everett, Hill by extending
the Great Northern main line to the city in 1893 and Weyerhaeuser by
subsequently choosing it as the site of what was then the world's largest
lumber mill and making it a focal point of his timber operations.

The city was platted in 1890 and incorporated in 1893, coincident
with the arrival of rail service. While its economy was originally built on
the timber trade, it is built on a major manufacturing endeavor of a very
different sort today – the production of planes for the airline industry.

Boeing produces the 747, 767, 777 and 787 at assembly plants in
Everett. Altogether, the company employs more than 32,000 workers at
those plants, dwarfing all other local employers.

Tacoma eventually developed into Seattle's No. 1 rival, and lesser
pretenders arose all around the Sound. For that reason, Everett never
managed to establish a truly distinctive media market.

The *Democrat*, emerging in 1890, was the first local paper to take the
field. *The Herald, News,* and *Times* followed in quick succession in 1891.
They were joined by the *Port Gardner News*, named for the inlet on
which the city is situated, at the mouth of the Snohomish River. But it
quickly flamed out.

The *Herald* swept the *Democrat* aside in 1897 and the *News* and *Times* in 1903. It also swallowed the rival *Independent*.

Known variously over the years as *The Everett Herald* (1891-1897), *The Everett Daily Herald* (1897-1963), the *Everett Herald* (1963-1981), and *The Herald* (1981-2009) before evolving into *The Daily Herald*, it also faced other competitors from time to time. They included *The Commonwealth* (1911-14) and the *Everett Morning Tribune/Everett Tribune* (1901-20). But the *Herald* prevailed. And until recently, it did so on the PM cycle, long abandoned by most other American dailies.

The paper remained in local ownership until 1978, when the Washington Post Company snatched it up from the Best family. At the time, the Post Company was planning on developing a national chain around its D.C. flagship. However, after acquiring the *Herald*, it abandoned the idea, leaving it (very nearly) with only two papers, one on the West Coast and the other on the East Coast.

Longtime company chairman Katherine Graham lamented the move in her 1997 autobiography, saying, "We paid a monopoly price for a paper that was in a somewhat competitive situation with Seattle and then proceeded not to run it well until recently, when it has been vastly improved."

However, the Post Company held onto the *Herald* until February 2013, when it sold to Canada's Black Press. Black proceeded to make the *Herald* the 39th and largest member of its Sound Publishing subsidiary, Washington's dominant newspaper publishing enterprise.

In a story on the sale, the *Washington Post* quoted company vice president Ann McDaniel as saying, "Over the years, as the newspaper business has changed, having it as our sole operation on the West Coast was not sound business strategy. Sound Publishing and Black Press expressed an interest; we saw an opportunity to preserve the company and most of the jobs, and we decided to move forward with this."

(Some real irony emerged in August 2013, when the *Washington Post* itself – though not the Post Company – was bought by Amazon.com founder Jeff Bezos, who lives and works only a few miles south of Everett.)

The Herald has undergone three rounds of cutbacks in recent years, leaving it with about 200 employees at the time of the sale. Sound was expected to reduce that further, as it already has a substantial corporate structure in place at its home office, making some of the *Herald* structure duplicative.

Sound was also planning to move the paper to new quarters at 41st and Colby streets, at the southern edge of the city's downtown core, early in 2014. The Washington Post Company opted to retain ownership of the building, forcing the *Herald* to seek new quarters.

Mirror   Federal Way

Owner: Sound Publishing
Address: 31919 First Ave., Suite 101, Federal Way, WA 98003
Phone: 253-925-5565
URL: www.fedwaymirror.com (unrestricted)
Established: 1997
Published: Friday
Market: Suburban area between Seattle and Tacoma
Circulation: 30,339
Publisher: Rudi Alcott, ralcott@fedwaymirror.com
Deadline: 4 p.m. Wednesday

Now the largest city between Seattle and Tacoma, Federal Way wasn't incorporated until 1990, making it one of Washington's newest. Before that, it was an unincorporated network of sprawling subdivisions, interspersed with retail outlets and a handful of manufacturing plants. Its largest employer was, and is, the Weyerhaeuser timber company.

Several small weeklies came and went over the years, including the *News, Review,* and *News-Review* in the early 1950s, the *Indian Voice* in the late 1950s and the *City Herald* in the early 1990s.

Robinson Communications, which owns and operates a string of weeklies to the south and west of Seattle, revived the *News* in 1998 and continued publishing it until 2009. It continues today, but only in a digital format online.

Sound Publishing launched the *Mirror* the same year, in the midst of the city's most intense boom period. Sound expanded the paper to twice-weekly for a time, then cut it back to weekly again in January 2012.

Record   Ferndale

Owner: Lewis Publishing
Address: 2044 Main St., Ferndale, WA 99999
Phone: 360-384-1411
URL: www.ferndalerecord.com (subscription required for full access)
Established: 1885
Published: Wednesday
Market: Northwest Whatcom County
Circulation: 2,000
Publisher: Michael Lewis, mdlewis@lyndentribune.com (joint with Lynden)
Editor: Mark Reimers, news@ferndalerecord.com
Deadline: Noon Monday

The little community of Blaine, located along Interstate 5 on the American side of the border between the U.S. and Canada, no longer has a newspaper it can truly call its own, though it had two of them for much of the early part of the 20th century, the *Journal* and the *Press*. And the product of their 1927 merger, the *Blaine Journal*, soldiered on for another 45 years before being swallowed by the *Record* of nearby Ferndale.

Ferndale, just north of daily-served Bellingham, is the larger of the two communities. It boasted a population of about 11,500 in the 2010 census. Ferndale had been served by the *Record*, and only the *Record*, since 1885. The paper reinvented itself as the *Record-Journal* after the 1972 merger, but reverted to its original name again in 2010.

It is owned by the Lewis family, doing business as Lewis Publishing. The family also owns and operates the *Lynden Tribune*, a neighboring Whatcom County weekly. Michael Lewis serves as publisher of both papers, which are printed on a company press in Lynden.

The Forum   **Forks**

Owner: Sound Publishing
Address: P.O. Box 300, Forks, WA 98331
Phone: 360-374-3311
URL: www.forksforum.com (unrestricted)
Established: 1930
Published: Thursday
Market: Clallam County
Circulation: 5,500
Publisher: John Brewer, editor@forksforum.com
Deadline: 4 p.m. Tuesday

Suddenly famous as the setting for the *Twilight* series of vampire novels, Forks is about as insulated from Washington's metropolitan areas as it's possible to get. Located on the lightly populated ocean side of the rugged Olympic Peninsula, its economic mainstays have long been timber on the one hand and outdoor recreation on the other. These days, they are augmented by the prison industry as well. Still, the area has not been experiencing the kind of growth much of the rest of the state has. In fact, it is barely maintaining its existing population.

Newspaper history along the coast side of the peninsula dates back to 1890; *The Forks Forum* didn't get its start until 1930, and still managed to pre-date the city it serves by a solid 15 years. Forks wasn't incorporated until August 28, 1945, just days before Japan's surrender brought World War II to a close.

The *Forum* is one of 39 papers in the Sound Publishing stable. Sound classifies it as "voluntary paid," a category typically reserved for papers it is in the process of trying to convert from free to paid distribution.

It is operated closely tied to other Sound papers. Its interim editor at this writing, Joe Smillie, said that "the Forum's been in a state of flux," and a search was underway for a part-time editor; in addition to Forks, he writes about Sequim for the *Peninsula Daily News*.

The *Forum* does not have an ad sales team of its own. That function is performed on its behalf by a neighboring Sound publication, the paid-distribution *Sequim Gazette*.

Journal of the San Juan Islands
Friday Harbor

Owner: Sound Publishing
Address: 640 Mullis St., #103, Friday Harbor, WA 98250
Phone: 360-378-5696
URL: www.sanjuanjournal.com (unrestricted)
Established: 1906
Published: Wednesday
Market: San Juan Islands
Circulation: 3,111
Publisher: Roxanne Angel, publisher@sanjuanjournal.com
Deadline: 2 p.m. Monday

The San Juan Islands, 172 in all, make up Washington's most unusual county. The archipelago is bordered by the Strait of Juan de Fuca on the south, Rosario Strait on the east, the Strait of Georgia on the north and Haro Strait on the west. Its boundaries are contiguous with those of San Juan County. The surrounding waters are all considered part of the Salish Sea. And they are home to three resident pods of orcas, commonly known as killer whales. The islands were heavily logged in the 1800s, but once again boast extensive stands of fir, alder, maple, madrone, cedar, and hemlock. In addition to the largest concentration of bald eagles in the continental U.S., they also support blue herons, trumpeter swans, peregrine falcons, barred owls, and many species of shorebirds.

There are no bridges connecting any of the islands to each other or to any part of the mainland, so all travel, internal and external, must be undertaken by air or sea. The islands are served by three of Washington's state ferry systems, which helps greatly with accessibility. The economy is almost exclusively tourist-driven, a thin base for newspaper endeavors.

The San Juans were served by *The Islander*, later known as *The San Juan Islander*, from 1898 to 1914. The *Friday Harbor Journal*, known since 1981 as the *Journal of the San Juan Islands*, joined the field in 1906.

Owned by Washington's dominant newspaper group, Sound Publishing, the *Journal* launched SanJuanJournal.com in 1998. It is now facing a competitive challenge from the online-only SanJuanIslander.com, which took its name from the print publication of the late 1800s and early 1900s.

Peninsula Gateway   Gig Harbor

Owner: McClatchy Company
Address: 3555 Erickson St., Gig Harbor, WA 98335
Phone: 253-851-9921
URL: www.thenewstribune.com/gigharbor (unrestricted)
Established: 1917
Published: Wednesday
Market: Northwestern Pierce County
Circulation: 10,000
Publisher: Christian Lee
Editor: Brian McClean, brian.mclean@puyallupherald.com

Isolated from the Seattle and Tacoma metropolitan areas until the second Tacoma Narrows bridge was completed in 1950 (The original collapsed shortly after its 1940 opening, and the resource demands of World War II delayed its replacement.), Gig Harbor didn't officially become a city until July 12, 1946. After 75 years as a rural enclave drawing sustenance from logging, fishing, and boat-building, it has morphed into a Tacoma bedroom community and Olympic National Park tourism gateway. It now is virtually devoid of industry, and its population is still a modest 7,500.

The community has preserved and protected its historic downtown and bayfront. The combination of its downtown, its sheltered bay frontage, the fishing opportunities it offers and the Olympic Peninsula access it provides has made tourism its economic mainstay. And the paper reflects that.

The *Peninsula Gateway* counts itself as a descendant of the Bay Island News, founded in 1917. The *News* eased into the *Gateway* in 1923.

Gig Harbor has only ever been served by one other paper, the *Business Examiner*, operated from 1985 to 1995.

Like the *Puyallup Herald*, the *Gateway* is now owned by the national McClatchy chain through its Olympic Cascade Publishing subsidiary. The McClatchy Company operates the two weeklies as adjuncts of the nearby *Tacoma News-Tribune*, its largest Washington holding.

Both of the smaller papers piggyback off the *News-Tribune*'s website, which unveiled a svelte new design in October 2012. They also depend on the mother paper for other kinds of support.

In keeping with the times, it maintains active Twitter and Facebook accounts.

Sentinel   Goldendale

Owner: American Publishing Company
Address: 117 W. Main St., Goldendale, WA 98620
Phone: 509-684-4567
URL: www.goldendalesentinel.com (unrestricted)
Established: 1879
Published: Wednesday
Market: Klickitat County
Circulation: 2,875
Editor, Publisher & Co-Owner: Lou Marzeles, lmarzeles@goldendalesentinel.com
General Manager: Karen Henslee, khenslee@goldendalesentinel.com
Deadline: 5 p.m. Monday

Goldendale, situated high up above and some miles back from the Columbia River Gorge, barely has enough of an economic base to support a newspaper. But thanks to its remote location, far from any larger communities, it has managed to support one continuously for more than 130 years.

The *Goldendale Sentinel* traces its history back to the debut of the *Klickitat Sentinel* in 1879. It has been publishing under its current name since 1884, when it absorbed the rival *Goldendale Gazette*.

Other early competitors included the *Klickitat County Agriculturalist*, founded in 1900; *Goldendale Independent*, founded in 1909; and *Klickitat County News*, founded in 1934. The *Independent* went under in 1915 and the *Sentinel* absorbed the other two papers on April 16, 1936.

Other weeklies were also published in Klickitat County over the years, including the *Sun* in Bingen, *Press* in Mabton, *Record* in Roosevelt, *News* in Bickleton, and the *Enterprise* in White Salmon. Only the *Sentinel* and *Enterprise* remain today. Of the others, the *Sun* held the field the longest, operating from 1936 to 1968, when it was absorbed by the *Enterprise*.

Oregon-based Eagle Newspapers crossed into Washington in 1974 to acquire the *Sentinel* and *Enterprise*. The company already owned the *Hood River News*, lying just across the river, making the new Klickitat County acquisitions a good fit.

Andy McNab purchased the *Sentinel* from Eagle in 1984. He ran it for 26 years before selling it to current owners Lou Marzeles and Leslie Geatches, who are operating it under the American Publishing Company umbrella.

The paper only had five ownerships between 1910 and the Marzeles-Geatches purchase in 2010. Irving Bath owned it from 1910 to 1936, Harold Fariello and Archie Radcliffe from 1936 to 1956 and Pete May from 1956 to 1974, the year of the Eagle purchase.

Papers have been known to run through that many owners in a decade or two. Goldendale's distinctive personality, well reflected in its local paper, probably helps account for its stability and staying power.

That's not to say it's always been easy. Marzeles, who spent a year as editor before buying out McNab, said in a 2010 edition of the *Washington Newspaper*, publication of the Washington Newspaper Publishers Association: "It's been an adventure. To come to *The Sentinel* last April, immediately face some extraordinarily challenging circumstances, feel so supported by the community, and then have the opportunity to become an owner and publisher of this newspaper – it's just amazing.

"Since 1879, *The Sentinel* has reflected the heart of this community. It's an honor to continue that role and service."

Marzeles held an editing position with *The Washington Times* in Washington, D.C., before heading out West. Geatches came to Goldendale from Sedona, Ariz. Previously, she spent many years in Saudi Arabia, working for Aramco, the world's largest oil producer.

Herald   Grandview

Owner: Valley Publishing
Address: 107 Division St., Grandview, WA 98930
Phone: 509-882-3712
URL: www.thegrandviewherald.com (subscription required for full access)
Established: 1909
Published: Wednesday
Market: Southeast Yakima County and parts of neighboring Benton
Circulation: 1,500
Publisher: Danielle Fournier, publisher@thegrandviewherald.com (joint with Prosser)
Editor: Richard Burger, editor@thegrandviewherald.com
Deadline: Noon Monday

According to the Grandview Library Collection, Grandview got its name in 1905 because it afforded a pair of passing horseback riders such a "grand view" of Snipes Mountain in the foreground and snow-capped Mount Rainier and Mount Adams in the background. They were traveling across the virtually unbroken grasslands of pre-irrigation Yakima County, when they stopped to rest their horses – and admire the view – at this halfway point between Prosser and Sunnyside. The new city, which now houses more than 10,000 residents, was incorporated September 21, 1909.

It got its first newspaper, whose name seems to have been lost to history, in the summer of 1908. Printed in Sunnyside, it was owned and operated by Fred Harris during its few short months of life.

The Herald followed on March 4, 1909. It was founded by S.J. Star, who sold it to Chapin D. Foster in July 1911. Six months later, the building housing the paper's offices and press burned to the ground, forcing Foster to contract for printing with the *Sunnyside Sun* while he set about rebuilding. But he never missed an issue.

Fires were common on the wind-swept prairie at the time, and Grandview lacked any semblance of fire protection. Also common were calamities like the typhoid epidemic that hit a few years later, counting the *Herald*'s editor among its victims. But both the paper and community persevered, thanks largely to the almost simultaneous advent of local canal and rail systems. The former fostered the planting of massive stretches of orchard and vineyard and the latter provided a means of getting all the resulting fruit to market – a potent combination.

Prospering with its community, the *Herald* moved into a handsome new building in 1922. That caught the eye of T.J. Brown, who assumed ownership at the end of 1924.

The *Herald* had the field all to itself during most of its first 100 years. However, it faced competition from the *Yakima County Record* from January 4, 1935, to May 27, 1943, a run of more than eight years. Later, the *Herald* was owned by John L. Fournier, Jr., member of a longtime Washington newspaper family, until his death in October 2012. It continues to be owned by his heirs through Valley Publishing Inc., based in Grandview.

Through Valley Publishing, the Fourniers also own the *Record-Bulletin* in Prosser, the county seat of neighboring Benton County. John's daughter, Danielle, serves as publisher of both papers.

Star   Grand Coulee

Owner: Star Publishing
Address: 3 Midway Ave., Grand Coulee, WA 99133
Phone: 509-633-1350
URL: www.grandcoulee.com (unrestricted)
Established: 1941
Published: Wednesday
Market: Northern Grant County and parts of neighboring counties
Circulation: 1,800
Editor, Publisher & Owner: Scott Hunter, scott@grandcoulee.com

Construction of Grand Coulee Dam, one of the largest concrete structures in the world and the largest power-producing facility in the

United States, led to the relocation of one city and birth of another in northeastern Washington. Flooding 21,000 acres of Columbia River bottomland, the dam forced relocation of the town of Kettle Falls. But it also sparked creation of Grand Coulee, which housed construction crews initially and has housed operating personnel ever since. A large proportion of the town's approximately 1,000 residents are associated with management of the dam, the reservoir it backed up, or the tourism it spawned.

A New Deal project designed to help lift America out of the Great Depression, it got underway in 1933. And almost immediately, long before the 12 million cubic yards of concrete were all poured and the 150 miles of reservoir were all backed up, the rush was on to provide the associated community with a newspaper of its own.

First to enter the field was the *News*, a weekly that would absorb the *Big Bend Outlook* along the way. It published from November 3, 1933, to August 12, 1937. Next came a six-day daily, the *Daily Booster*, which debuted on November 18, 1933. It morphed into the *Daily Times* in June 1934 and continued publishing under that name until March 25, 1937.

Another weekly, the *Times*, joined the fray on June 20, 1934. It merged with the *News* to create the *News-Times* in the fall of 1937, but the merged paper succumbed the following spring. Two more weeklies soon took brief turns upon the stage as well. The *Journal*, launched sometime in 1934 or 1935, lasted until July 17, 1936. *The Advertiser* published from December 2, 1937, to July 28, 1938, before succumbing as well.

The one that stuck, the *Star*, came along on April 11, 1941, debuting just months before the Japanese attack on Pearl Harbor catapulted the U.S. into World War II. It had one rival, the *Almira Herald*, that it absorbed in January 1972.

Grand Coulee was incorporated in November 1935 and the dam was completed in May 1942. That makes the town, the dam, and the newspaper close contemporaries.

Press   Issaquah

Owner: Issaquah Press Inc., a subsidiary of the Seattle Times Company
Address: 45 Front St. S, Issaquah, WA 98027
Phone: 425-392-6434
URL: www.issaquahpress.com (unrestricted)
Established: 1900
Published: Wednesday
Market: Eastern King County
Circulation: 15,066
Publisher: Deborah Berto, dberto@isspress.com (joint with SnoValley Star)

Managing Editor: Kathleen Merrill, editor@isspress.com
Deadline: 3 p.m. Monday

Tucked into a valley at the southern end of Lake Sammamish, Issaquah is surrounded by mountains. They long stood as something of a bulwark against encroachment from Seattle, just 17 miles to the west, but the city gradually has become fully integrated into Seattle's suburban fringe. Originally known as Gilman, Issaquah was founded in 1892 to serve the mining industry that had developed on Squak and Cougar mountains. When the mines played out, it transitioned from mining town into timber town. Timber reigned supreme for decades, but Issaquah's dominant employers now are Boeing and Microsoft, just like its neighboring suburbs.

The Issaquah Press is the oldest and best established of a group of neighboring eastside weeklies owned by Issaquah Press Inc. The group has been operating as a wholly owned subsidiary of the Seattle Times Company since July 1, 1995. *The Press* evolved out of the *Independent*, founded in 1900, when Issaquah was still a mining town. It got a brief challenge from the *King County Record* in 1906-07, but has otherwise had the market pretty much to itself – at least until recently.

The paper was founded by J.B. Edwards of Kent, but he soon turned the reins over to Walter Gillis, a typesetter from Bellingham.

It published as the *Independent* until 1916, when new owner David Peacock opted to call it the *Press* instead. He only retained ownership for three years, but the name stuck. M. A. Boyden bought the *Press* from Peacock in 1919 and served as its editor and publisher for the next 28 years. After an interim ownership, Al and Eleanor Whitney took over and operated the paper through the 50s and into the 60s.

In 1973, Deborah Berto joined the sales staff in the ad department. She went on to become business manager in 1975 and managing editor/publisher in 1976. She helped lead the company during a series of absentee ownerships, culminating with the Seattle Times Company acquisition in 1995, and has continued to play a leadership role with the Times Company ever since.

Explosive recent growth spawned the Press' sister papers – the weekly *Sammamish Review*, founded in 1992; monthly *Newcastle News*, founded in 1999; and weekly *SnoValley Star*, founded in 2008. The group, editorially autonomous from other Seattle Times holdings, also publishes *Issaquah Living* and *Sammamish Scene* magazines.

The four newspapers share space in historic downtown Issaquah. They also share advertising and administrative staffing, but maintain independent editorial staffing. They contract with Rotary Offset Press in Kent for printing services.

The *Press* is classified as voluntary pay publication, a hybrid of the paid subscription and free distribution models. Its sister papers are operated on a free-distribution basis. About 3,000 of the 15,000 households receiving the *Press* have taken out paid subscriptions.

Tri-City Herald Kennewick

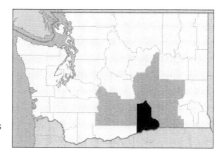

Owner: McClatchy Company
Address: 333 W. Canal Drive, Kennewick, WA 99336
Phone: 509-582-1500
URL: www.tri-cityherald.com (unrestricted)
Established: 1918
Published: Monday through Sunday AM
Market: Benton and Franklin counties, plus portions of surrounding counties
Circulation: 27,163 weekday, 26,652 Saturday, 32,244 Sunday
Publisher: Gregg McConnell, gmcconnell@tricityherald.com
Executive Editor: Laurie Williams, lwilliams@tricityherald.com

Among the tri-cities – actually, the quad-cities would be more accurate these days, as West Richland has come to rival Richland and Pasco for impact in the area – Kennewick is substantially the largest. It also serves as the home base for the newspaper they share, the *Tri-City Herald*. However, the *Herald* traces its ancestry back to Pasco, which got the earliest start. And all three of the tri-cities have supported newspapers of their own at some point.

The two key events in early development of the area were the laying of railroad tracks along a key stretch of the Columbia River in the 1880s, leading to the founding of Pasco and Kennewick, and the development of a federal nuclear facility at Hanford, leading to the transformation of Richland from a tiny farm hamlet to a substantial bedroom community.

The area hosted more than a dozen weeklies between 1891 and 1947, when the daily *Tri-City Herald* was born.

The first was the *Franklin Recorder*, launched in Pasco around 1891, followed in short order by the *Pasco News*. They merged in 1897 to create *The News-Recorder*. In 1902, *The News-Recorder* gave way to the *Pasco Express*, which gave way in turn to the *Pasco Herald* in 1918. The *Pasco Herald* continued until November 13, 1947, when it relocated to Kennewick, went daily and began publishing as the *Tri-City Herald*.

Across the river in Kennewick, newspapering got its start in 1902 with the advent of the weekly *Columbia Courier*, later known as the *Kennewick Courier*. The *White Bluffs Spokesman* followed in 1907 and the *Kennewick Reporter*, also known briefly as the *Twin City Reporter*, in 1908. The *Courier* and *Reporter* merged in 1914 to create the *Kennewick*

Courier-Reporter, which absorbed the *Spokesman* in 1938. It continued under that name until 1949, then published briefly as the *Courier-Herald*. In 1950, it surrendered the field to the ascendent *Tri-City Herald*, which had muscled its way in from Pasco three years earlier.

In Richland, the *Richland Advocate* entered the field in 1916 and morphed into the *Benton County Advocate* in 1925. When it went under in 1945, the *Richland Villager*, initially known simply as the *Villager*, emerged in its stead.

In neighboring Pasco, the old *Pasco News* was revived as a strike paper in 1949. Published as a morning daily, it absorbed the *Richland Villager* in 1950 and continued to publish out of Pasco as the *Columbia Basin News* until 1963.

The *Tri-City Herald* considers itself a direct descendant of the *Pasco Herald*, thus considers 1918 its year of founding. But it didn't take its dominant tri-city form until November 1947, when Glen C. Lee and Robert Philip bought the *Herald*, moved it across the river to Kennewick and turned it into an afternoon daily with a regional focus.

The paper's biggest challenge came when it locked out striking workers in 1950 and began publishing with replacements. With the backing of the International Typographers Union, the strikers combined a pair of weeklies – the *Pasco News*, revived in 1949, and *Richland Villager*, launched in 1945 – to create a morning daily strike paper in Pasco. Dubbed the *Columbia Basin News*, it continued to publish as a daily until 1963, long after the strike had ended. Howard Parrish, former publisher of the *Seattle Star*, which folded in 1947, served as publisher. He enlisted journalism students from Columbia Basin College, dubbed the Kiddie Corps, to supply much of the manpower. During that time, a story in Wikipedia notes, "The Tri-Cities was one of the smallest U.S. markets with two competing daily newspapers."

The *Tri-City Herald* has only had one other competitor in its six decades as a daily – the weekly *Richland Review*, published from the late 1960s to 1981.

Lee and Phillip, who probably are responsible for creating the region's Tri-Cities moniker, ran the paper for more than three decades before selling to the national McClatchy chain in 1979. Traditionally published in the afternoon, McClatchy switched it to morning in 1984.

Weekly News   **La Conner**

Owners: Sandy Stokes and Cindy Vest
Address: 313 Morris St., La Conner, WA 98257
Phone: 360-466-3315
URL: www.laconnerweeklynews.com (unrestricted)

Established: 1976
Published: Wednesday
Market: Southwestern Skagit County
Circulation: 1,600
Co-Publishers: Sandy Stokes, news@laconnernews.com, and Cindy Vest,
production@loconnernews.com
Editor: Sandy Stokes, news@laconnernews.com

Newspapering in La Conner got its start with the founding of the *Bellingham Bay Mail* in 1873. It became the *Puget Sound Mail* four years later and published continuously under that name until 1982, when it succumbed to a Johnny-come-lately rival, the *Channel Town Press*.

The *Press* was founded in 1976, more than a century after the *Mail* made its debut. It morphed into the *La Conner Weekly News* in 2008. That marked the first time a local paper had incorporated the community name. Maybe that's because La Conner still boasted fewer than 900 residents in the 2010 census – about the same as a century earlier.

The Skagit County community was founded by Alonzo Low in 1867 as Swinomish. J.S. Conner renamed it La Conner in honor of his wife, Louisa Ann Conner, after purchasing the local trading post in 1870. At one time, La Conner, situated at the mouth of the Skagit River, served as the county seat. However, it lost that distinction to Mount Vernon, the county's largest city, in November 1884. Traditionally known as a center for farming, logging and fishing, its quaint and historic waterfront has become a mecca for artists and writers in recent years.

The paper is locally owned and operated. It has the novel distinction of having two publishers, but only one reporter.

Chinook Observer Long Beach

Owner: EO Media Group
Address: 205 Bolstad Ave. E., Suite 2, Long Beach, WA 98631
Phone: 360-642-8181
URL: www.chinookobserver.com (subscription required for e-edition, full access)
Established: 1900
Published: Wednesday
Market: Long Beach Peninsula (Pacific County)
Circulation: 6,700
Editor & Publisher: Matt Winters, mwinters@chinookobserver.com

The Long Beach Peninsula's *Chinook Observer* was founded in 1900 by George Hibbert and a short-lived partner. Within weeks, Briton Charles Angus joined Hibbert in the enterprise. According to a history posted on the *Observer*'s website, they published the paper out of a "funny little shed" in Chinook, then moved into a two-story building now serving as an art gallery. They published the paper downstairs and lived upstairs.

About 1923, Hibbert sold to John and Margaret Durkee. They sold to Bill Clancey, who sold to James O'Neil in 1937, the posted account shows. The next year, O'Neil moved the paper to Long Beach, where it continues to call home today, more than 75 years later. However, he retained the *Chinook Observer* name. O'Neil's son, Wayne, and Wayne's wife, Frances, took over in 1963 and operated the paper for the next 20 years.

In 1984, they sold to Craig and Geri Dennis, whose family ran hardware stores in Raymond and Long Beach. The Dennises sold to the East Oregonian Publishing Co., now known as the EO Media Group, four years later, according to the online history. EO Media also owns *The Daily Astorian*, across the river where the *Observer* is now printed, along with several other media properties in Oregon.

As it proudly notes on its website, the *Observer* has a paid circulation of about 6,700, making it one of Washington's larger weekly newspapers. Matt Winters has served as its editor since 1991.

Daily News   Longview

Owner: Lee Enterprises
Address: 770 11th Ave., Longview, WA 98632
Phone: 360-577-2500
URL: www.tdn.com (subscription required for full access)
Established: 1923
Published: Monday through Sunday AM
Market: Cowlitz County
Circulation: 23,129 weekday, 18,274 Sunday (ABC)
Publisher: Rick Parrish, rparrish@tdn.com
Editor: John Markon, jmarkon@tdn.com

The Cowlitz County communities of Castle Rock, Kalama and Kelso each pre-date Longview. Each claims a longer, richer and more varied newspaper history, and Kelso boasts county seat status to boot. By comparison, Longview, founded in 1923 at the confluence of the Cowlitz and Columbia rivers, is a Johnny-come-lately. And except for a brief interlude from 1996-99, when Castle Rock's *Cowlitz County Advocate* shifted into the *Kelso-Longview Advocate*, it has only been served by one newspaper since the day of its founding – the Longview *Daily News*.

But Longview and its newspaper quickly came to dominate Cowlitz County commerce and politics.

Lots of early founders harbored grandiose visions of the futures of their communities. History proved most wrong, but it proved Missouri timber baron, Robert A. Long, dead right. He took the long view and it paid off. It seems Long's Long-Bell Lumber Company was running out of timber in the South, so he began to look out West for suitable acreage. Flush with cash, he was able to pick up a vast expanse of it in southwestern Washington in 1918.

He laid plans for a pair of massive mills in or near Kelso, founded by Scottish surveyor Peter Crawford, who established the area's first donation land claim in 1847. But to cut and mill all the timber he had just purchased, he figured he needed to assemble a workforce of 14,000. The workers would need places to live, and despite its long head start, Kelso's population stood at a mere 2,000. It wouldn't be nearly big enough. Long brought in a city planner from St. Louis and had him design a neighboring city to the west capable of supporting a population of 50,000. Then he set about building it.

An account in Wikipedia proclaims, "At the time of its conception, Longview was the only planned city of its magnitude to have ever been conceived of and built entirely with private funds."

Long thought of almost everything, including the R.A. Long High School, Longview Public Library, Monticello Hotel and Longview *Daily News*. He financed each of them with his own money. He launched the *Daily News* on January 26, 1923 as a six-day daily, publishing all but Sunday. That pre-dates Longview's official incorporation, which didn't come until February 14, 1924.

Kelso was platted in 1884 and incorporated in 1889. It soon became famous – infamous, actually – for an outsized quota of taverns and brothels catering to loggers from throughout the region. Kelso's first paper was the *Courier*, followed by the *Journal* and *Kelsonian* in 1906 and the *Tribune* in 1923. The *Courier* merged with the *Journal*, but folded in 1912. The *Kelsonian* merged with the *Tribune* and stuck around until 1954.

Castle Rock's first paper was the *Advocate*, which debuted in 1886. It published under various names through 1999, taking a Kelso/Longview orientation its final three years.

Several papers made brief appearances in Kalama, starting with the *Beacon* in 1871. The one with the most staying power was the *Bulletin*, published in Kalama from 1890 to 1977, when it moved to Woodland.

None of those papers ever put a dent in the supremacy of the *Daily News*. The credit should largely go to John McClelland Sr., who purchased the paper from Long early on, and his heirs, who continued to run it until 1999.

Ted and John Natt, sons of McClelland Jr. and grandsons of McClelland Sr., ended the decades-long family run by selling the paper to the regional chain, Howard Publications, but not before leading it to a Pulitzer Prize for coverage of the devastating 1980 eruption of Mount St.

Helens. The paper joined the national Lee Enterprises stable when Lee scooped up Howard's holdings in 2002.

Tribune   Lynden

Owner: Lewis Publishing
Address: 113 Sixth St., Lynden, WA 98264
Phone: 360-354-4444
URL: www.lyndentribune.com (subscription required for full access)
Established: 1888
Published: Wednesday
Market: Whatcom County
Circulation: 5,500
Publisher: Michael Lewis, mdlewis@lyndentribune.com (joint with Ferndale)
Editor: Calvin Bratt, editor@lyndentribune.com
Deadline: Noon Monday

Lynden, five miles south of the Canadian border in Whatcom County, is a secondary gateway to Canada, quieter than the Peace Arch border on Interstate 5, and open only from 8 a.m. to midnight. Early settlers Holden and Phoebe Judson established Lynden in 1874 near the site of the Nooksack Indian village of Squahalish. Phoebe plucked the name from the Thomas Campbell poem "Hohenlinden," but opted to alter the spelling. Lynden is virtually identical in size to Ferndale, lying to the southwest on Interstate 5. Both were hovering between 11,000 and 12,000 when the 2010 census was taken.

Lynden is home to the *Lynden Tribune*, published continuously since 1888. Neighboring Ferndale has the *Ferndale Record*, an equally venerable weekly. Both are owned by Lewis Publishing, headed by Michael Lewis, who serves as publisher of both papers.

Lynden's first paper was the *Pioneer Press*. Rivals included the *Pacific Pilot* and *Lynden Sun*, which merged in 1905. They all died out early on, but the *News* in neighboring Everson published until 1967. It also served the community of Sumas during the final two years of its run.

Lewis Publishing operates a press in Lynden that also prints papers from other points in northwestern Washington, including the *Whidbey Examiner*. When a fierce snowstorm struck in mid-January of 2012, Mike Lewis personally delivered the *Examiner*'s January 18 press run to a pickup point on South Fidalgo Island, traversing 50 miles in a four-wheel-drive truck.

Examiner Publisher Kasia Pierzga celebrated the feat by posting a photo of his arrival on her paper's Facebook page. She attached a note of thanks for four years of exceptional printing service.

Voice of the Valley   Maple Valley

Owner: Donna Hayes
Address: 23745 225th Way SE, Suite 203, Maple Valley, WA 98038
Phone: 425-432-9696
URL: www.voiceofthevalley.com (unrestrictedd)
Established: 1969
Published: Tuesday
Market: Maple Valley and vicinity (King County)
Circulation: 17,500
Editor & Publisher: Donna Hayes, voice9696@comcast.net

People began to settle in Maple Valley, which lies about 30 miles southeast of Seattle, in 1879. However, it didn't become a full-fledged city until 1997 – more than a century later. Originally known as Vine Maple Valley, then Maple Valley, the community began life as a supply center for miners digging coal out of Cedar Mountain and loggers hauling timber out of surrounding woods. Though coal mining continued until 1947, its economics began shifting long before that from mining and logging to farming and fishing. Tourism, which got its start in the 1920s, has also muscled its way into the mix over the years. Lake Wilderness, site of an airstrip, lodge, golf course and array of rental cabins, serves as the centerpiece.

The first local newspaper was the weekly *Maple Valley Messenger*, published by Chester Gibbon from 1921 to 1923. Affiliated with the Cedar Grange, its slogan was, "Smallest in size, but not in pep, punch and personality." In 1964, another community organization gave it a go – the Maple Valley Lions Club. It subsidized the *Maple Valley NEWS* for about a year, using it as a vehicle to support worthy community activities. The *VOICE of the Valley* got its start on August 21, 1969, launched by a pair of Tahoma School District teachers, Bill and Ruby Ziegner, who published it out an office in their home. In 1982, Bill hired Sandy Hipple to serve as the paper's bookkeeper because Ruby's health was failing. When Ruby died, Bill showed Hipple how to lay out the paper, and they became partners in 1985.

Hipple began to bring members of her family into the enterprise, including her husband, Bob, her sons Rob, Mike and Rick, and her daughter, Donna Hayes. Hayes worked in news, circulation and advertising by turns and eventually became advertising manager, a job her dad had once held. With the death of Bill Ziegner in 1992, Hipple took over, assisted by Hayes. They became full-fledged partners a few years later.

Hipple retired early in 2008 and died later that year, but the paper remains firmly in family hands. Hayes has a sister serving as advertising manager, a sister-in-law serving as office manager, a son serving as webmaster and a daughter-in-law serving as an ad designer. *The VOICE of the Valley* calls itself "a community-oriented paper that puts community first."

It operates on a voluntary-pay basis. It mails copies to 17,500 homes in Maple Valley, Black Diamond, Ravensdale, Hobart and parts of Covington free of charge, but has actively solicited paid subscriptions from its inception and sells individual copies from racks and shelves.

Globe   **Marysville**

Owner: Sound Publishing
Address: P.O. Box 145, Marysville, WA 98270
Phone: 360-659-1300
URL: www.marysvilleglobe.com (unrestricted)
Established: 1892
Published: Wednesday
Market: Marysville area (Snohomish County)
Circulation: 14,408
Publisher: C. Paul Brown, pbrown@soundpublishing.com (joint with Arlington)
Editor: Scott Frank, editor@marysvilleglobe.com (joint with Arlington)
Deadline: 4 p.m. Monday

The signing of the Point Elliott Treaty in 1855 opened the area to settlement, at first built around logging and trade with the Tulalip Indians, later the growing of strawberries and tulips. In 1872, a trading post was manned by James P. Comeford, who built a store with attached living quarters and a small dock. He ran that operation while his wife, Maria, ran the town school. Marysville didn't really take off, though, until the first sawmill was built in 1887, followed in quick succession by three more mills and a railroad to serve them. The community incorporated March 20, 1891. During the decades since, it has come to claim more than 60,000 residents, second only to Everett in Snohomish County.

Unlike many neighboring communities, which saw either a welter of papers come and go or didn't achieve enough size to support one until recent years, Marysville has been served throughout its history by the *Globe* and only the *Globe*. It was founded the year after the city and has published continuously ever since.

Both the *Globe* and the *Arlington Times*, serving Marysville's immediate neighbor to the north, are now part of Sound Publishing's growing stable of Washington newspapers, as is the daily *Everett Herald* to the south. The much-larger *Herald* operates independently, but the two weeklies share editors, publishers and offices.

Sound employees three different distribution systems with its 40-odd general-circulation papers in Washington. Some are strictly paid, some are strictly free and some operate on a hybrid voluntary-pay basis.

The company operates both the Arlington and Marysville papers on a hybrid basis. It mails them to all households in their respective circulation areas, but actively solicits paid subscriptions in return and sells copies for 75 cents from a network of vending locations.

Beachcomber Maury Island

See Beachcomber, Vashon/Maury Island

Reporter Mercer Island

Owner: Sound Publishing
Address: 7845 S.E. 30th St., Mercer Island, WA 98040
Phone: 206-232-1215
URL: www.mi-reporter.com (unrestricted)
Established: 1954
Published: Wednesday
Market: Mercer Island (western King County)
Circulation: 4,306
Editor & General Manager: Mary Grady, mgrady@mi-reporter.com
Deadline: 4 p.m. Monday

Mercer Island is a large but lightly populated land mass sitting in the middle of Lake Washington, east of Seattle. It was named for brothers Thomas and Asa Mercer, who settled in Seattle after making their way out from Virginia. It seems they enjoyed rowing over to hunt, fish and forage for berries. People began to carve out permanent homesteads on the island between 1870 and 1880, but having to travel by boat to reach Seattle to the west or Bellevue to the east was a serious limitation. It took people of no small means to cope, and the island has served as a haven for the affluent ever since. The East Channel Bridge to Bellevue opened in 1928 and the Lacey V. Murrow Memorial Bridge to Seattle followed in 1940. Eventually, their capacities would be greatly augmented and the Interstate 90 freeway would be routed across both of them on its way to Seattle.

Still, the island's population stood at just 22,699 in the 2010 census. The island not only has its own zip code – 98040 – but also its own city government. The city of Mercer Island was incorporated on July 5, 1960, encompassing all the island except its 70-acre business district, and it absorbed the final remnant 10 years later.

According to the Mercer Island Historical Society, the *Mercer Island Reporter*, founded in 1954, had several predecessors, all short-lived. Among them were the *Mercer Island News*, founding date uncertain; the *Live Wire News*, founded in 1919; the *Mercer Island Journal*, founded in 1927; and the *Mercer Islander*, founded in 1949.

The *Reporter*, whose circulation is all paid, was launched by Chicago newsman Fred Bassetti. It later came into the hands of Peter Horvitz. Horvitz is best known for merging two acquisitions, the *Bellevue Journal-American* and *Kent Valley Daily News*, a pair of dailies created through earlier mergers among weeklies, to create the *King County Journal*. It was designed to challenge the big Seattle papers, but did not, in the end, prove up to the challenge.

He also amassed a stable of nine weeklies or semi-weeklies under the King County Publications banner, including the *Mercer Island Reporter*. But failure of his flagship venture put him in such financial distress, he sold to Sound Publishing in 2006. Sound shuttered the *Journal* in January 2007, but immediately began beefing up the remaining papers.

The package included papers serving Auburn, Bellevue, Bothell, Kenmore, Kent, Redmond, Renton and the Snoqualmie Valley, and Sound was able to pick up the Kirkland paper from another publisher at the same time. The acquisitions served to triple the company's Puget Sound footprint and make it the largest publisher of community newspapers in the state.

Monitor & Valley News   Monroe

Owner: RIM Publications
Address: 125 E. Main St., Monroe, WA 98272
Phone: 360-794-7116
URL: www.monroemonitor.com (unrestricted)
Established: 1899
Published: Wednesday
Market: Skykomish Valley (Snohomish County)
Circulation: 4,000
Publisher: Cliff Wright, cwright@rimpublications.com
Editor: Polly Keary, editor@monremonitor.com
Deadline: Noon Monday

Monroe, a city of 17,000 situated about 30 miles northwest of Seattle, got its start as Park Place. When the Great Northern Railway began to snake its way over Stevens Pass and drop down into the Skykomish River Valley in the 1890s, it chose a route a mile distant. So the commercial district up and moved. In the new location, the general store christened itself Monroe at Park Place in honor of President James Monroe. The store incorporated the local post office, which shortened that to Monroe instead of Park Place, giving the community that built up around it a new identity. The principal economic focus was originally logging. When the timber supply began to dwindle, logging gave way to farming.

B.F. Smyth founded the community's first newspaper, the *Monroe Monitor*, in 1899. A.D. Gaisford soon followed with the Washington *Transcript*, later known as the *Monroe Transcript*. New owner H.D. Matthews merged the two papers in 1908, creating the *Monroe Monitor-Transcript*. It became simply the *Monroe Monitor* again eight years later, dropping the *Transcript* element.

Then-owner Voland Publications imposed the current name after its 1985 acquisition of the *Valley News*, a weekly serving the neighboring community of Sultan. The *Valley News* began life as the *Sultan Star* in 1905. It was renamed in 1923.

Seattle newsman Jerry Robinson, founder of Robinson Newspapers, purchased the *Monroe Monitor & Valley News* in 1993. He amassed a stable of Seattle-area papers now operated by his sons Ken and Tim, but the *Monitor*, a traditional paid-circulation paper, is no longer among them. It has been acquired by RIM Publications of Bellevue.

RIM's principal focus is publication of legal notices, but the company said it was staffing the *Monitor* with "a team of professionals who are dedicated to newspapering and to the local community."

The Vidette   Montesano

Owner: Stephens Media Group
Address: P.O. Box 671, Montesano, WA 98563
Phone: 360-249-3311
URL: www.thevidette.com (unrestricted)
Established: 1883
Published: Thursday
Market: Grays Harbor County, particularly east side
Circulation: 3,800
Editor & General Manager: Leif Nesheim, editor@thevidette.com
Deadline: Noon Tuesday

Montesano is Italian, *Vidette* is French and both are very distinctive on the American West Coast. Montesano is perched on the northern reaches of the Chehalis Valley, near the confluence of the Chehalis and Wynoochee rivers. It has served as the seat of local government since 1860, when the county, known as Grays Harbor since 1915, was still known as Chehalis.

Isaiah and Lorinda Scammons established the original homestead there in 1852. Lorinda Scammons wanted to call the fledgling community Mount Zion, but another early settler prevailed. He said Montesano, a combination of the Italian terms for mountain and health, meant essentially the same thing and sounded prettier.

The paper was founded as the *Chehalis Valley Vidette* by J.W. Walsh and J.E. Calder. They proclaimed in their first edition of February 1, 1883, "We are here. We mean business. And we mean to stay." And they were as good as their word.

According to an account in Wikipedia, it was the westernmost newspaper in the continental U.S. at the time – a sentinel, if you will. Asked to explain the choice of *Vidette*, that account has Walsh saying, "Because the name is a French term for the forward point, or outer perimeter guard, of the main body of troops."

Over the years, it was known by turns as the *Weekly Vidette*, the *Chehalis County Vidette*, *The Vidette*, the *Vidette and Washington Call*, the *Montesano Vidette*, the *Montesano/Grays Harbor County Vidette* and the *Montesano Vidette* again. It again returned to *The Vidette* in 1999 and has stuck with that ever since.

The Vidette faced one early competitor – the *Chehalis County Call*, later known as the *Washington Call*. It was founded in 1912 and folded into *The Vidette* in 1919. The only other paper published in Montesano was the *Grays Harbor Farmer*, later known as the *Farmer and Logger*, then as the *Suburbanite and Farmer-Logger*. Launched in 1952, it ceased publication in 1974.

The Vidette is printed on Wednesdays and delivered by mail on Thursdays to about 3,800 paid subscribers. It is owned by Stephens Media Group, based in Las Vegas.

Stephens publishes 11 dailies and 64 weeklies in nine states. Its holdings are concentrated in Nevada and Arkansas, but it also publishes three other Washington papers clustered near the *Vidette* – *The Daily News* in Aberdeen, the *South Beach Bulletin* in Westport and *The North Coast News* in Ocean Shores.

East County Journal   Morton

Owner: DeVaul Publishing
Address: 278 W. Main St., Morton, WA 98536
Phone: 360-496-6397
URL: www.devaulpublishing.com/eastcounty (unrestricted, but features no news content)
Established: 1936
Published: Wednesday
Market: Eastern Lewis County
Circulation: 7,000
Publisher: Frank DeVaul, fdevaul@devaulpublishing.com
Deadline: Noon Monday

Settlement began in Morton in the 1870s, but it wasn't incorporated until 1913 and still claims barely a thousand residents. It was named for Levi Morton, vice president in the administration of Benjamin Harrison. Like many communities in Washington's rugged interior, it began as a supply and processing center for the mining and logging industries. Nestled amid the Cascade Range's Mounts Rainier, Adams and St. Helens, it was blessed with rich deposits of cinnabar, the ore from which mercury is extracted, in addition to virtually unbroken stands of timber. It still serves as a wood processing center. In addition, it attracts a significant tourism trade with its fishing, hunting, camping, climbing and skiing opportunities. Good rail access helps facilitate the former and good highway access the latter.

The county as a whole is dominated by Centralia, its largest city, and Chehalis, its county seat, both located on the Interstate 5 corridor at the west end. But Morton reigns supreme in the county's rugged eastern half, served by Washington's Highway 12.

The first newspapers to emerge in Morton, both on the eve of its incorporation in 1912, were C.I. Kimples' *Lewis County American* and M.C. Hopkins' *Morton Mirror*. They did battle until 1935, when the *American* absorbed the *Mirror*.

The *East County Journal*, also known as the *Journal*, the *Morton Journal* and variations thereof at some points, got its start in 1936. It was owned for a number of years by H.M. and J.J. Rosin, then came into the possession of Frank DeVaul, principal in DeVaul Publishing. DeVaul Publishing is based in Chehalis. It also publishes the *Tenino Independent* and the *Rochester Sun News*.

The *Journal*, a paid-distribution publication, also serves Mossyrock, to the west between Riffe and Mayfield lakes, and seven other small East County communities. It maintains a static, single-page website listing contact information, but publishes no news online.

Columbia Basin Herald   Moses Lake

Owner: Hagadone Newspapers
Address: 813 W. Third Ave., Moses Lake, WA 98837
Phone: 509-765-4561
URL: www.columbiabasinherald.com (subscription required for e-edition, full access)
Established: 1941
Published: Monday through Friday AM
Market: Grant and Adams counties
Circulation: 8,500
Publisher: Harlan Beagley, hbeagley@columbiabasinherald.com
Managing Editor: Lynne Lynch, editor@columbiabasinherald.com

Moses Lake is the largest city in Grant County, claiming about 20,000 of the county's 90,000 residents. Known as Neppel until its incorporation in 1938, after one of its early settler's home town in Germany, it lies on the shores of an 18-mile-long body of water sharing the Moses Lake moniker. The area was barren and desolate until 1955, when irrigation water became available from Grand Coulee Dam via the Columbia Basin Project. Then farming took off, as the soil was rich. The community also owes dam-building to the state of the lake. It was so shallow and salty originally that early settlers dubbed it Salt Lake, but is a robust source of recreation and irrigation water today.

The first local newspaper was the *Neppel Record*, which published from 1912 to 1918. It had a brief rival, the *Pacific Farm Record*, which published for a few months in 1913.

The paper serving the area today debuted as the *Moses Lake Herald* in 1941. It was launched on July 31 by Glenn and Grace Arnold, a newspaper couple finding the competition too daunting in Grand Coulee, where the dam project was fueling a boom. In a history published in 2010, *Herald* staff writer Joel Martin in 2010 quoted them saying in their first edition, "...and here we are, bag and baggage, ready to become a part of the community... " But the following year, they sold the paper to Washougal transplant Archie Trenner, who renamed it the *Columbia Basin Herald*.

He was intent on the *Herald* also serving Ephrata, Othello, Quincy, Warden, Soap Lake, Coulee City, Ritzville, Lind and Crescent Bar, which it has continued to do to this day.

Trenner subsequently sold one-third shares to locals Bill Orthman and Ned Thomas for $2,150 each, Martin reports. Thomas bought the other two out a couple of years later, but took on another partner, Gib Kaynor, in 1952, the account goes. Previously a weekly, the *Herald* went twice-weekly in 1953 and daily in 1955. With the latter move, it renamed itself the *Columbia Basin Daily Herald*, which it continued to go by until 1988.

Duane Hagadone's newspaper division, Hagadone Newspapers, bought the *Herald* in 1967. It is now part of a group that includes nine papers in Montana, six in Idaho, two in Wisconsin and two in Washington.

Publishing aggressively on the web, the *Herald* boasts: "Our online presence dominates the Columbia Basin with the most page views and impressions available. If you want to reach the online community, www.columbiabasinherald.com is the number one choice for traffic. We also have full-video capabilities as well as blogs, online guides and local columnists." Like a growing number of news sites, particularly those maintained by dailies, the *Herald's* website is now paywall-protected.

Skagit Valley Herald   **Mount Vernon**

Owner: Pioneer News Group
Address: 1215 Anderson Road, Mount Vernon WA 98274
Phone: 360-424-3251
URL: www.goskagit.com (subscription required for e-edition, full access)
Established: 1884
Published: Monday through Sunday AM
Market: Skagit County
Circulation: 17,605
Publisher: Heather Hernandez, hhernandez@skgitpublishing.com
Managing Editor: Colette Weeks, cweeks@skagitpublishing.com

Now the largest city in Skagit County, Mount Vernon had humble origins. Settlement began in 1870, but 10 years later, its permanent population was fewer than 75. Its economy was driven initially by logging, with an assist from mining. Today, its economy is driven more by farming, with an assist from tourism. Tulips have come to outnumber trees by a wide margin in the surrounding countryside, making the Skagit Valley Tulip Festival the premier local event. It was named for George Washington's famous estate. It has a sister city, Anacortes, along the waterfront to the west.

Local newspapering began in 1884 with the launch of the weekly *Skagit News* by William C. Ewing. G.E. Harson merged the *News* with the *Herald* in 1896 to create the *Skagit News-Herald*.

The paper became the *Mount Vernon Herald* in 1912, the *Mount Vernon Daily Herald* in 1922, when it moved to a daily publication cycle, and the *Skagit Valley Herald* in 1956. It remained in local hands until 1964, when it was purchased by Scripps League Newspapers in one of the first chain acquisitions in the Northwest.

Scripps, which later morphed into Pioneer Newspapers, then the Pioneer News Group, named Leighton Wood publisher. And that turned out to have an unusual result.

In newspaper groups, top executives typically move about from paper to paper, working their way up the ladder over the years. But Wood dug in at Mount Vernon and remained publisher there for decades. In 1986, he formed Skagit Publishing and went into partnership with Scripps, eight years before that wing of Scripps morphed into Pioneer. Wood ended up with a majority interest in the company, which he exercises through Sagit Publishing, a limited liability partnership.

Skagit and Pioneer have an arrangement that gives Skagit direct oversight of all of Pioneer's Washington papers except the daily serving Ellensburg. In addition to the *Herald*, that group includes the *Anacortes American*, *Burlington Argus* and *Sedro-Woolley Courier-Times*. Skagit also exercises management control of the *Stanwood/Camano News*, in which Pioneer is a minority partner with retired publisher David W. Pinkham. It prints all of the papers in the group at a large new plant it has developed in Mount Vernon, along with outside clients like the daily *Bellingham Herald*.

The *Argus* evolved out of the *Mount Vernon Post* in 1898. It was published as the *Mount Vernon Argus* from 1898 to 1982, *Skagit Argus* from 1982 to 1996 and *Skagit Valley Argus* from 1996 to 2000, when it adopted nearby Burlington as its home base.

The *Argus* and *Courier-Post* are both free-distribution papers. The others are paid.

Miner   Newport

Owner: Willenbrock Publications
Address: 421 S. Spokane Ave., Newport, WA 99156
Phone: 509-447-2433
URL: www.pendoreillerivervalley.com (subscription required for full access)
Established: 1897
Published: Wednesday
Market: The Pend Oreille River Valley (Pend Oreille County in Washington and western Bonner County in Idaho)
Circulation: 6,000
Editor & Publisher: Fred J. Willenbrock, theminer@povn.com
Deadline: Noon Monday

Named for its role as a landing spot for steamboats on the Pend Oreille River, Newport is situated smack on the Idaho border. In fact, it actually spills over, and seamlessly so. Newport is the only city in the Northwest split between states in that fashion. Portland/Vancouver and Lewiston/Clarkston are adjacent, but separated by an expanse of river. The portion of Newport slopping over into Idaho is known as Oldtown.

The pre-1900 portion of Newport's newspaper history is not entirely clear, as copies of early newspapers and newspaper records are lacking. However, it appears the *Newport Pilot* was founded in 1897, the *Newport Miner* followed in 1899 and the *Miner* absorbed the *Pilot* in 1900.

One thing is clear: Since the *Pilot* departed the scene at some point in 1990, Newport has been served by the *Miner* and only the *Miner*. And thanks to the *Pilot*, it claims 1897 as its starting point.

Back then, Newport consisted of little more than a ferry landing, a trading post and a cluster of shacks. It didn't file incorporation papers and organize a government until some six years later, on April 16, 1903. And many more years passed before it earned county seat status, as Pend Oreille County, Washington's 39th and last, wasn't carved out of

Stevens County until March 1, 1911. Newport is Pend Oreille's largest city, but that's not saying a whole lot. As of the 2010 census, Newport claimed just over 2,000 of Pend Oreille's approximately 13,000 residents.

Owned by the Willenbrock family, the *Miner* is printed under contract by Free Press Publishing in Cheney. It circulates throughout the sparsely populated reaches of northern Pend Oreille County in Washington and western Bonner County in Idaho.

Early on, it was able to attain a status belying its small size and remote location. One indication of that came in a late 1918 edition of the *Washington Newspaper*, a Washington Newspaper Publishers Association publication: "Fred L Wolf, publisher of the Newport Miner, will sit in the Legislature for Pend Oreille County when it opens in January. It will be his first political venture. Mr Wolf was elected on the Republican ticket, made no campaign and had no platform. He announced that 'if the people wanted the same kind of service in the Legislature that they knew the *Miner* had been giving the county' he was at their call. They wanted it by a majority of 228."

By all appearances, the Willenbrock stewardship is upholding that tradition.

North Coast News   Ocean Shores

Owner: Stephens Media
Address: 668 Ocean Shores Blvd. NW, Ocean Shores, WA 98569
Phone: 360-289-2441
URL: www.northcoastnews.com (unrestricted)
Established: 1988
Published: Wednesday
Market: Southwestern Grays Harbor County
Circulation: 1,980
Editor: Angelo Bruscas, editor@northcoastnews.com

Bob Focht launched the *North Coast News* on August 17, 1988. Now owned by the Stephens Media Group it serves Ocean Shores and the outlying communities of Ocean City, Copalis, Iron Springs, Seabrook, Pacific Beach, Moclips, Taholah and Quinault, mostly strung along the beach to the north.

Ocean Shores occupies the tip of a pincer sheltering North Bay. Its counterpart on the other side of a relatively narrow ocean opening is Westport, which occupies the tip of a pincer sheltering South Bay. The two bays give way to Grays Harbor. Aberdeen, the largest city in Grays Harbor County, sprawls along the harbor shore to the east.

Stephens Media, publisher of the *Las Vegas Review-Journal*, 10 other dailies and 64 weeklies, also owns the daily serving Aberdeen, the weekly serving Westport and another weekly serving the county seat of Montesano, up the Chehalis River to the east. Stephens operates the three paid-distribution weeklies under the umbrella of Aberdeen's *Daily World*.

Virtually uninhabited through the first half of the 20th century, the peninsula served as a cattle ranch for several decades. But development took off after cattleman Ralph Minard sold it to the Ocean Shores Development Corporation for $1 million in 1960. The company drew up plans for 25 miles of canals, untold miles of road, hundreds of residential units of various types, a golf course, a shopping center, three restaurants, a 100-room motel, a marina, an airstrip and, subject to legislative approval, a casino. The casino never came off, but just about everything else did.

By the end of the decade, the former cattle ranch boasted 900 permanent residents and $35 million in assessed valuation. It achieved milestones in 1971 – incorporation and the opening of its first school.

The resort's Ocean Shores Community Club has had its own newspaper from the outset in 1960. It was known briefly as the *Vagabonder*, then the *Sandpiper*, before adopting its current *Ocean Observer* name in 1964.

The *North Coast News* and its *Daily World* parent have also faced – and vanquished – two general-circulation challengers. The *North Beach Beacon* emerged in 1973. It became the *Grays Harbor Beacon* in 1992 before ceasing publication in 1994.

The *Ocean Shores Journal* came along in 1994, followed by the *West Harbor Journal* in 1996. Published by A to Z Contacts, they merged into the *Journal* in 1997, and it went under before the year was out.

Record   Odessa

Owner: Terrie Schmidt-Crosby & Edward L. Crosby III
Address: 1 W. First Ave, Odessa, WA 99159
Phone: 509-982-2632
URL: www.odessarecord.com (subscription required for e-edition, full access)
Established: 1901
Published: Thursday
Market: Southwestern Lincoln, northwestern Adams and eastern Grant counties
Circulation: 1,250
Publisher: Terrie Schmidt-Crosby, therecord@odessaoffice.com

The *Odessa Record*, founded just after the 19th century deferred to the 20th, changed hands several times during the early years of its existence. Originally established by an itinerant printer, Mike Devlin, the paper was soon bought by R.S. Crowl. Crowl partnered on and off with L.C. Weik. At times, Crowl owned it outright; at times, Weik owned it outright; at times, they owned it in tandem.

Over the intervening years, it was owned by H.W. Brune, Charles Bragg, Ted Anderson, Walt Larson, Zane Crosby, Tom Bertsch and Donald E. Walter, in that order, before coming into the hands of current owners Terrie Schmidt-Crosby & Edward L. Crosby III.

The *Record*'s editorial office has also changed location from time to time. Originally housed in a small wood-frame building in the 200 block of First Avenue, it next moved to a former bank building of more substantial size and construction. Crowl eventually moved it further west on First Avenue, where it remained for 56 years. After a few years on North Division Street, it returned to the former bank building at 1 West First Avenue, where it has converted the old vault into a back-issues archive.

The *Record* is the only paper ever published in Odessa, a southern Lincoln County town of less than a thousand residents.

However, papers have been published – and in some cases, are still being published – in the Lincoln County communities of Almira, Creston, Davenport, Harrington, Reardan, Sprague and Wilbur. That's impressive for a dry, wheat-country county of less than 11,000 residents.

Surveyors employed by the Great Northern Railway chose George Finney's 1866 homestead as the site for a siding when the railroad laid tracks through the area in 1892. They dubbed it the Odessa Siding, in honor of the area's Russian wheat farmers, and the name stuck. Finney platted a townsite in 1899, the Great Northern erected a depot in 1900, the newspaper debuted in 1901 and the city incorporated in 1902. Within two years, the new town boasted 800 residents. But development in and around Odessa soon stalled out. The 2010 census pegged the community's population at 910 – about where it stood a century earlier.

Early publishers operated their own presses and set their own type. Later publishers adopted more advanced and automated methods, but at an ever-increasing cost. In the 1970s, then publisher Wal Larson decided to give up on-site printing and begin contracting with the *Grant County Journal* in Ephrata. And the paper is still being printed in Ephrata to this day.

Olympian   Olympia

Owner: McClatchy Company
Address: 111 Bethel St. NE, Olympia, WA 98506
Phone: 360-754-5400

URL: www.theolympian.com (unrestricted)
Established: 1860
Published: Monday through Sunday AM
Market: Thurston County
Circulation: 21,621 weekday, 21,088 Saturday, 30,143 Sunday (ABC)
Publisher: George Le Masurier, glemasurier@theolympian.com

The *Columbian*, founded in 1852, was the first newspaper published in what would later become the state of Washington. But it was not a forerunner of today's Vancouver *Columbian*, which has become one of the largest dailies in the state. No, this *Columbian* was published in Olympia, making it a forerunner of the *Olympian* instead.

Pockets of settlement began to appear in the Puget Sound area in the late 1840s, when Oregon Territory still ranged all the way north to the Canadian border. Olympia got a leg up on other emerging hamlets near the Puget Sound in 1851 when a customs house was established there, at the southern end of the Puget Sound, closest by land to the Oregon settlements near Portland.

In Portland, *Oregonian* Publisher Thomas Dryer thought the time ripe for someone to found a newspaper in the country to the north. He dispatched two men to establish one – editor James Wiley and pressman T.F. McElroy. They began printing the *Columbian* in September 1852 on a small press supplied by Dryer. According to a history produced in 2005 by the Washington Secretary of State's Office:

"Less than 4,000 people resided in the entire territory. Local farmers would pay for their subscriptions with produce or cords of wood. Wiley and McElroy had no staff of eager reporters, but depended on letters from residents of the widely scattered settlements to inform them of events and keep them abreast of local opinion. Editors of 1852 relied heavily on newspapers from the eastern states to supply them with national and international news."

Wiley and McElroy gave up on the venture in November 1853, after little more than a year. But by then, two other papers had taken up the cudgel – the *Washington Pioneer* and *Olympia Democrat*. They merged in 1854 into the *Pioneer and Democrat*, which in turn became the *Overland Press* in 1861, *Pacific Tribune* in 1864 and *Weekly Pacific Tribune* in 1868 and continued to publish until 1879.

Other early papers included the *Olympia Transcript* (1867-1885), *The Echo* (1868-1877), the *Territorial Republican* and its *Commercial Age* successor (1868-70), the *Puget Sound Daily Courier* (1872-1877), the *Olympia Chronicle* (1899-1929) and the *Anti-Imperialist* (1900).

A paper called *The Daily Olympian* was published in 1876-77 as a continuation of the *Puget Sound Daily Courier* and *Olympia Daily Courier*. However, today's *Olympian* claims entirely separate heritage, back to the founding of the weekly *Washington Standard* on November 17, 1860.

On its website, the *Olympian* describes its emergence this way:

"Early in 1889, it became apparent that if the territorial capital of Olympia were to be named the capital city when Washington was granted statehood, an all-out campaign would have to be organized. The editor of *The Washington Standard* realized his weekly newspaper would not be sufficient to carry out the campaign city officials had organized. Thus *The Evening Olympian* came into being to lead the fight to preserve Olympia's status as capital city." The *Olympia Tribune*, founded in 1890, was absorbed by the *Olympian* in 1893 to create the *Olympian-Tribune*, which was transformed into the *Daily Olympian* in 1895.

On a separate track, the *Washington Recorder*, founded in 1902, morphed into the *Olympia Daily Recorder* in 1903 and *Evening Recorder* in 1924. The *Olympian* absorbed its daily competitor in 1928 and the merged operation moved into spacious new quarters at the corner of State and Capitol Way. The paper remained under the control of the Perkins family until 1967, when it was sold to Federated Publications.

Federated owned several other Northwest newspapers at the time, including *The Idaho Statesman* in Boise. It was swallowed by the Gannett Company in 1971, and for the next 25 years, it continued to maintain ownership of all three of the Northwest's capital city dailies.

In 2005, Gannett swapped the *Olympian*, *Statesman* and the *Bellingham Herald* for Knight Ridder's *Tallahassee Democrat*. Just nine months later, the Sacramento-based McClatchy Company bought out much larger Knight Ridder in an epic, multi-billion-dollar deal.

The *Olympian*'s circulation base has never been very large, long exceeded by a number of suburban papers, in addition to the papers serving the major Washington cities of Seattle, Tacoma, Spokane and Vancouver. But the paper, which dropped "Daily" from its nameplate in February 1982 to become simply *The Olympian*, has long enjoyed unusual visibility due to its capital city location.

McClatchy's holdings in Washington include the much larger *Tacoma News Tribune*, just 30 miles to the north. In 2009, McClatchy took advantage of the proximity to merge much of the Olympia operation into that of its big brother in Tacoma. It left only skeleton news and advertising crews behind at the Olympia site, perched on a hill affording it expansive views of downtown, the Capitol and Puget Sound.

Okanogan County Chronicle   **Omak**

Owner: Eagle Newspapers
Address: 618 Okoma Drive, Omak, WA 98841
Phone: 509-826-1110
URL: www.omakchronicle.com (subscription required for e-edition, full access)
Established: 1910
Published: Wednesday
Market: Okanogan and Ferry counties
Circulation: 6,779
Editor & Publisher: Roger Harnack, rharnack@omakchronicle.com
Deadline: 10 a.m. Monday

Okanogan County is Washington's largest, but it is sparsely populated, home to a little more than 40,000 residents in the 2010 census, about a fifth of them living in or around Omak. The original county seat was Ruby, which was abandoned more than a century ago. Okanogan, Omak's smaller but older twin, now claims that honor. Okanogan, which is Salishan for rendezvous, was platted as Alma in 1886. It was later called Pogue, after orchardist J.I Pogue, before being dubbed Okanogan. Upset at the renaming, Pogue commissioned the platting of a rival town four miles to the north. He ended up losing out twice, as it came to be called Omak, Salishan for "good medicine."

The Okanogan Irrigation Project began delivering water to local orchardists in 1910, promising to spur the local farm-based economy. And C.P. Scates seized the opportunity to launch *The Omak Chronicle* on May 20 of that year.

The paper became the *Omak-Okanogan County Chronicle* in 1973, and except for a two-year reversion in the late 1990s, has stuck with that ever since. It not only covers Okanogan County, with a population density of eight people per square mile, but also neighboring Ferry County, with a population density of just three people per square mile.

The Chronicle was acquired by the Oregon-based Eagle Newspapers chain in the mid-90s. Eagle also publishes two other Washington papers, the *Daily Sun News* in Sunnyside and *The Enterprise* in White Salmon, a weekly.

Only one paper has ever been published in Omak, but neighboring Okanogan has had two, both pre-dating Omak's *Chronicle.* C.F. Rowell published the *Okanogan Outlook* – on wallpaper, no less – in 1888-89. And in 1905, O.H. Woody founded the *Okanogan Independent*, which continued publishing until 1975.

It's also worth noting the county's rich newspaper history, which belies its thin population base. In addition to Omak and Okanogan, papers have been published at Brewster, Chesaw, Grand Coulee,

Oroville, Twisp, Molson, Nespelem, Conconully, Tonasket, Loomis and Pateros – 13 different communities in all.

Okanogan Valley Gazette-Tribune   Oroville

Owner: Sound Publishing
Address: 1422 Main Street Oroville, WA 98844
Phone: 509-476-3602
URL: www.gazette-tribune.com (unrestricted)
Established: 1905
Published: Thursday
Market: Okanogan County
Circulation: 2,700
Managing Editor: Gary DeVon, gary@gazette-tribune.com
Deadline: 4 p.m. Tuesday

Oroville, four miles south of the Canadian border, is one of Washington's gateways to Canada. The crossing is at Osoyoos, Brtitish Columbia. First settled in the late 1850s, Oroville was known initially, and rather inelegantly, as Rag Town. It was dubbed Oro, Spanish for gold, in 1892. When the post office objected – because Washington already had a town named Oso, cause for confusion – it was renamed Oroville.

Oroville was a wild and wooly town in its mining heyday, full of saloons and such, but mining has long since given way to farming, supplemented by tourism. Thanks to irrigation, the area now supports a sea of orchards, interrupted here and there by vineyards and resort developments. The 2010 census tallied a population of less than 1,700, smaller than Okanogan and only about a third the size of Omak.

F.J. Fine founded the paper in June 1905 as *The Oroville Weekly Gazette*. Subsequent owners I.J and F.H Doerr shortened that to *The Oroville Gazette*, and it retained that name for several decades. In 1974, the *Gazette* merged with the *Tribune*, founded in 1951 in neighboring Tonasket, to create the *Gazette-Tribune*. It became the *North Okanogan County Gazette-Tribune* in 1984 and *Okanogan Valley Gazette-Tribune* in 1991.

It's the only newspaper ever published in Oroville, but has had plenty of company around far-ranging but lightly populated Okanogan County. In addition to Oroville and Tonasket, papers have popped up over the years in Omak, Okanogan, Brewster, Chesaw, Grand Coulee, Twisp, Molson, Nespelem, Conconully, Loomis and Pateros, and several of them remain in operation to this day.

The *Gazette-Tribune* had been owned by NCW Media, founded in 2000 by Bill and Carol Forhan of Leavenworth, Jeff and Audrey Walter of Brewster and Jeff and Liz Gauger of North Canton, Ohio. But on August 1, 2011, the company swapped it for Sound Publishing's *Wenatchee Business Journal*.

The *Business Journal* joined a stable including the *Leavenworth Echo*, *Cashmere Valley Record*, *Lake Chelan Mirror* and *Quad City Herald*. The *Gazette-Tribune* joined a stable including 57 publications fielding 500 employees at 36 locations, making it Washington's largest chain.

Outlook   Othello

Owner: Basin Publishing
Address: 125 S. First Ave., Othello, WA 99344
Phone: 509-488-3342
URL: www.othellooutlook.com (unrestricted)
Established: 1947
Published: Thursday
Market: Adams County
Circulation: 1,600
Publisher: Eric LaFontaine, publisher@othellooutlook.com
Editor: Briana Alzola, editor@othellooutlook.com

Othello's first newspaper was the *Othello Times*, founded by the Scofield family and actually published at the hamlet of Lind to the west. Though its actual starting and ending dates have apparently been lost to history, state library records suggest it remained in operation from late 1907 or early 1908 to at least 1938.

The paid-distribution *Outlook* is descended from the *Othello Progress News*, founded in 1947. Warren Baslee renamed it the *Othello Outlook* in 1951, according to state library records. An official paper of record for Adams County, it became *The Outlook* in 1977 and *The Othello Outlook* in 2000. It is one of several small media properties developed or acquired by Basin Publishing, headed by Greg Zaser and owned by members of the extended Zaser family.

The *Outlook* got a challenge from *The Othello Independent* and its *Independent Review* successor from August 2008 to April 2010. The *Independent* published until February 2010, when it merged with a pair of papers from neighboring Grant County – the *Review* out of Warden and *South County Sun* out of Royal City – to form the very short-lived *Independent Review*.

Elsewhere in Adams County, papers have been or are being published in Lind, Ritzville and Washtucna. While Othello is the county's largest city, Ritzville is its seat of government and has seen more publication activity over the years.

Tri-City Herald   Pasco

See Tri-City Herald, Kennewick

Peninsula Daily News   Port Angeles

Owner: Sound Publishing
Address: 305 W. First St., Port Angeles, WA 98362
Phone: 360-452-2345
URL: www.peninsuladailynews.com (unrestricted)
Established: 1916
Published: Monday through Friday and Sunday AM
Market: Clallam and Jefferson counties
Circulation: 12,444 Monday through Friday, 14,078 Sunday (ABC)
Editor & Publisher: John C. Brewer, john.brewer@peninsuladailynews.com
Executive Editor: Rex Wilson, rex.wilson@peninsuladailynews.com

Port Angeles is situated on a natural harbor – natural enough that two native Klallam villages were located there. The first European to encounter it was Spaniard Francisco de Eliza in 1791. He named it Port of Our Lady of the Angels, which ended up getting shortened to Port Angeles – Port of the Angels. It grew gradually as settlers moved in among the Klallam to engage in the timber and shipping businesses. Clallam County's largest city, it became county seat in 1890, the year of its incorporation. Clallam County, which includes the westernmost point in the continental U.S., was created in 1854. It has come to claim more than 70,000 residents, about 20,000 of whom live in Port Angeles. Port Angeles lies directly across the Strait of Juan de Fuca from Victoria, principal city of British Columbia's Victoria Island and a major Canadian tourist attraction. The two enjoy heavily-used ferry connections.

The *Peninsula Daily News* was preceded in Port Angeles by *The Model Commonwealth* in 1886, *The Port Crescent Leader* in 1890, *The Democrat*, *The Herald* and the *Port Angeles Tribune* in 1891, *The Beacon* in 1893, *Clallam County Courier* in 1895, *The Olympic* in 1904, the *Port Angeles Weekly Herald* in 1914 and *The Daily Leader* in 1915. But none of those survived and the *Daily News* did.

It was founded in 1916 as the *Port Angeles Evening News* and operated continuously under that name until 1972. It was then operated as the *Daily News* until 1987, when it became the *Peninsula Daily News*. After a series of ownership changes, the paper came into the hands of the Persis Corporation, founded in 1967 by Hawaiian Thurston Twigg-Smith after his sale of the *Honolulu Advertiser* to Gannett. Persis sold it in 1994 to Horvitz Newspapers, a family group based in Bellevue and managed by long-time newsman Peter Horvitz.

Horvitz published the paper for 17 years before selling to Sound Publishing, the largest owner and operator of community newspapers in Washington, both in terms of number of properties and total circulation. The transaction followed by five years Horvitz's sale to Sound of the *King County Journal* and weekly newspapers serving Auburn, Bellevue, Bothell, Kenmore, Kent, Redmond, Renton and the Snoqualmie Valley.

The Daily News has only had two competitors of any significance in the last 75 years – the *Olympic-Tribune* until around 1963 and *Chronicle* from 1961 until around 1983. The date of demise does not seem certain for either of them, but their origins are well-documented. The *Olympic-Tribune* traces its heritage back to the *Model Commonwealth*, founded in 1886, and the *Herald*, founded in 1891. The *Commonwealth* evolved into the *Port Angeles Times* in 1890, then merged with the *Port Angeles Tribune* in 1891 to create the *Tribune-Times*. Meanwhile, the *Herald* morphed into the *Democrat* in 1891 and merged with the *Port Crescent Leader* in 1893, then merged with the *Olympic* in 1905 to create the *Olympic-Leader*. The *Olympic-Leader* and *Tribune-Times* merged in 1918 to create the *Olympic-Tribune*, and it held on for another 45 years.

The *Chronicle* began life in 1961 as the *Shopping News*. It went through a series of early name changes before stabilizing under the *Chronicle* mantle in 1962 and continuing to publish until at least the end of 1983.

Elsewhere in Clallam County, papers have been published in East Clallam, Dungeness, Forks, Port Crescent and Sequim. They include the *Jimmy Come Lately Gazette*, later known as *Sequim's Jimmy Come Lately Gazette*. It is now owned by Sound Publishing and known simply as the *Sequim Gazette*, eliminating one of the truly striking names in Northwest newspaper annals.

Independent   Port Orchard

Owner: Sound Publishing
Address: 3888 N.W. Randall Way, Suite 100, Silverdale, WA 98383
Phone: 360-876-4414
URL: www.portorchardindependent.com (unrestricted)
Established: 1890
Published: Friday
Market: Kitsap County
Circulation: 18,254
Publisher: Sean McDonald, publisher@portorchardindependent.com
Deadline: 4 p.m. Wednesday

Port Orchard lies just 13 miles west of Seattle and only about a mile south of Bremerton. But Puget Sound separates it from Seattle, and Orchard Bay, its namesake, separates it from Bremerton. Though Bremerton boasts almost four times as many residents, Port Orchard, settled and incorporated earlier, serves as the county seat.

Settlement began in 1854, after Daniel Howard and William Renton decided to develop a sawmill on the bay's southern shore; the area was first called Sidney. In 1891, the local economy got a huge shot in the arm when the U.S. Navy chose Orchard Bay as the home of a naval station that would eventually grow into the massive Puget Sound Naval Shipyard, based in Bremerton. Known briefly as Slaughter County, Kitsap County was carved out of King and Jefferson counties in 1857. It encompasses 396 square miles of land and 170 of water, with more than 250,000 residents.

The paper at Port Orchard was launched by W.L. Wheeler in August 1890 as the *Sidney Independent*. It soon absorbed two older papers, the *People's Broadax* in 1891 and the *Kitsap County Pioneer* in 1893, putting it on the path to local dominance. Two other sheets mounted early challenges, but foundered. The *Pioneer-Sentinel* published from 1892 to 1895 and *The Record* from 1895 to 1897.

The paper morphed into the *Port Orchard Independent* on November 1, 1895, after Sidney underwent its name change. And it's been the *Port Orchard Independent* ever since.

The *Independent* hasn't had a competitor since – and it isn't likely to get one now that it has joined the fold of Sound Publishing, the largest community newspaper publisher in the state.

Not only does Sound count almost 60 titles all told, but six of them are on Kitsap Peninsula. In addition to the *Port Orchard Independent*, it publishes the *Bainbridge Island Review, North Kitsap Herald, Central Kitsap Reporter, Bremerton Patriot* and *Northwest Navigator*, the latter serving the naval base.

Sound not only centrally coordinates the printing and distribution of its Kitsap Peninsula group, but also offers a joint advertising buy, the better to compete with the daily *Kitsap Sun* out of Bremerton.

Leader   Port Townsend

Owner: Port Townsend Publishing Co.
Address: 226 Adams St., Port Townsend, WA 98368
Phone: 360-385-2900
URL: www.ptleader.com (unrestricted, including e-edition)
Established: 1889
Published: Wednesday

Market: Jefferson County
Circulation: 8,000
Editor & Publisher: Scott Wilson, scott@ptleader.com
Deadline: Noon Monday

Blessed with one of the best natural harbors in the state, Port Townsend was once known as the "City of Dreams" as a result of its extravagant aspirations. In the late 1800s, it was a contender with Seattle and Tacoma to become a major West Coast port and commercial center, and with Olympia to become the state capital. Its handsome private homes and grand commercial buildings from that era, largely preserved and restored and today a tourist magnet, still serve as a reminder of its period of glory – or at least glorious hope.

Alas, the rail line city leaders coveted never materialized. As a result, Seattle and Tacoma reaped the commercial spoils and Olympia the governmental spoils. The only incorporated community in all of Jefferson County, Port Townsend had to settle for county seat status.

The first European to visit the area, perched at the tip of the Olympic Peninsula, was Captain George Vancouver. He sailed into the bay in 1792 and named it for the Marquis of Townsend. When the first wave of settlers founded the city almost 60 years later, in 1851, they took the natural course and named it after the bay. Port Townsend quickly became one of the largest seaports on the American West Coast, a shipping point for timber and all kinds of finished goods. Expecting a big boost from the arrival of rail lines, ambitious residents erected magnificent Victorian showcases to house themselves and their businesses. But hard economic times left the railroads without the capital to push west from Seattle and Tacoma, which enjoyed prime water access.

By the time the *Leader* published its first issue on October 2, 1889, Port Townsend already had a 30-year history with six different papers, including two dailies. First on the scene, debuting in 1859, was the weekly *Port Townsend Register*. According to the Washington State Library, it was followed by *The North-West* in 1860, *The Weekly Message* in 1867, *The Weekly Argus* in 1870, *The Democratic Press* in 1877 and the *Port Townsend Call* in 1887, all founded as weeklies.

The *Argus* held on until 1888 and the *Call* until 1911. Both published on a daily basis for extended periods, but fell back to a weekly publication cycle again before going out of business entirely. The rest of the early papers all disappeared within four years, most lasting not even two.

One of the busiest of the early practitioners was Maine native Enoch S. Fowler, mate on a ship arriving with the first party of settlers in 1852. Fowler decided to stay on in the fledgling settlement, and went on to found a shipping company, a bakery and at least two newspapers, the *North-West* and *The Weekly Message*.

Fowler imported sandstone bricks for one of Port Townsend's classic downtown buildings, and it is now occupied by the *Leader*. Known as the Fowler Building, it is considered the oldest masonry structure in Washington. It served as the Jefferson County Courthouse from 1880 to 1892, when the current courthouse was erected.

W.L. Jones founded the *Leader* as a morning daily, dubbing it *The Morning Leader*. He launched his new enterprise the same year the *The Daily Argus* went out of business, enticing the weekly *Port Townsend Call* to seize the opportunity to begin publishing on a daily basis as *The Daily Call*. The *Leader* gave up daily publication in 1908 by which time it had the newspaper field in Port Townsend all to itself.

Two other papers mounted challenges – the *Key City Graphic* in 1890 and the *Jefferson County Journal* in 1906 – library records show, but neither lasted long. Local historian Tom Camfield, a former *Leader* newsman, also references three early papers not listed in library records – the *Puget Sound Express*, the *Cyclop* and the *Port of Entry Times*.

The *Leader* has published under at least 10 different names, all built around "Leader" in some fashion. It has passed through many hands along the way, but has remained in local ownership. Jones was followed at the helm by W.B. Jessup, Winslow McCurdy and, after McCurdy's death, a partnership of Fred Willoughby and Ray O. Scott, according to a history published on the paper's website. Eventually, control passed to Winslow McCurdy's son, Richard. The younger McCurdy sold to newcomers Frank and Pat Garred in 1967. They subsequently took in Scott Wilson and his wife, Jennifer James-Wilson, as partners, and the web account indicates the Wilsons became majority owners in 2001.

North Kitsap Herald   Poulsbo

Owner: Sound Publishing
Address: P.O. Box 278, Poulsbo, WA 98370
Phone: 360-779-4464
URL: www.northkitsapherald.com (unrestricted)
Established: 1901
Published: Friday
Market: Northern Kitsap County
Circulation: 12,701
Publisher: Donna Etchey, publisher@northkitsapherald.com
Editor: Richard Walker, editor@northkitsapherald.com
Deadline: 4 p.m. Wednesday

Poulsbo is a city of 10,000 that sits on Liberty Bay, at the north end of the Kitsap Peninsula in Kitsap County. The county's largest city is Bremerton and its seat of government Port Orchard, both of which lie well to the south. Poulsbo was founded in the early 1880s by Norwegian emigrant Jorgen Eliason. It drew a large number of Scandinavian emigrants, particularly Norwegians and Finns, because Liberty Bay's cold, rugged, storm-tossed shores reminded them of the coast they left behind. Its downtown displays a heavily Scandinavian look to this day, and that serves as a significant source of tourist appeal. Many tourists arrive by boat, as the peninsula is virtually surrounded by water and the city features a trio of marinas combined with excellent harbor anchorage.

Poulsbo was named by its first postmaster, Norwegian emigrant I.B. Moe, in 1886. He actually chose the name of his village back home – Paulsbo, Norwegian for Paul's Place – but postal authorities misread his submission. The city incorporated in 1907. It retained Norwegian as its primary language until World War II, when an influx of workers from the Puget Sound Naval Shipyard tripled – and thus anglicized – the population in just three years.

The paper was founded by Peter and Josephine Iverson in 1901 as the *Kitsap County Herald*. Renamed the *North Kitsap Herald* in 1995, better reflecting its orientation at the far northern end of the county, it has never had a direct competitor.

The *Herald* is owned by Sound Publishing, which also owns an array of other weeklies on the Kitsap Peninsula, including the *Bainbridge Island Review, Bremerton Patriot, Central Kitsap Reporter* and *Port Orchard Independent.* The largest publisher of community newspapers in the state, it markets them as a combination advertising buy in competition with the daily *Kitsap Sun* out of Bremerton.

Like a number of other Sound publications, the *Herald* is classified as a voluntary-pay publication. Sound mails free copies to local households, but actively solicits paid subscriptions and charges for copies picked up from racks or newsstands.

Sound publishes almost 60 Washington newspapers in all, a mix of dailies and weeklies, with weeklies predominating. All are printed at a state-of-the-art plant in Everett.

Record Bulletin   Prosser

Owner: Valley Publishing
Address: P.O. 750, Prosser, WA 99350
Phone: 509-786-1711
URL: www.recordbulletin.com (subscription required for e-edition)

Established: 1892
Published: Wednesday
Market: Benton County
Circulation: 2,300
Publisher: Danielle Fournier, publisher@recordbulletin.com (shared with Grandview)
Editor: Victoria Walker, editor@recordbulletin.com
Deadline: Noon Monday

The *Prosser Record-Bulletin* is descended from the *Prosser Falls Bulletin*, established in 1892; the *Prosser Record*, established in 1893; the *Prosser Republican*, established around 1905; and the *Benton Independent*, established in 1909. Those are the only four papers ever to serve the city.

The *Republican* and *Bulletin* merged in 1907 to create the *Republican-Bulletin* and the *Independent* and *Record* merged in 1918 to create the *Independent-Record*. Those two papers then merged to create the *Record-Bulletin*, which published its first edition on July 1, 1920.

Danielle Fournier is the third generation of Fourniers to head the paper. The *Record-Bulletin* was first acquired by John Louis Fournier Sr., who passed it down to his son, John Louis Fournier Jr. When Fournier Jr. died in late 2012, his daughter, Danielle, assumed the helm. Fournier Sr. launched the family newspaper business, immediately after his graduation from the University of Washington in 1932, by purchasing the *Oakville Cruiser*. Three years later he bought a half-interest in Valley Publishing, Kent-based owner of the *Kent Valley News*, and used that as a lifelong family vehicle.

The company went on to acquire papers first in Auburn, Renton and Issaquah in northwestern Washington, and later in the neighboring communities of Grandview and Prosser in southeastern Washington. Fournier Jr. served as publisher of various dailies and weeklies, including the *Valley Daily News* in Kent, before taking the helm now held by his daughter with the two eastern papers.

Kennewick, situated across the Columbia River from Richland and Pasco, its Tri-Cities siblings, is the largest city in Benton County. However, Prosser serves as the county seat. The county is bounded on the north, east and south by a giant loop of the Columbia River. It was carved out of Klickitat and Yakima counties in 1905.

Prosser is considerably older, having been surveyed in 1879, homesteaded in 1882, platted in 1885 and incorporated in 1899. It owes its existence, as well as its name, to its first resident – Col. William Prosser. The Northern Pacific ran a rail line through in 1884, furthering Prosser's prospects. However, it only counted 229 residents at the time of its incorporation some 15 years later.

Herald   **Puyallup**

Owner: McClatchy Company
Address: 103 W. Stewart St., Puyallup, WA 98371
Phone: 253-841-2481
URL: www.thenewstribune.com/puyallup (unrestricted)
Established: 1886
Published: Thursday
Market: Puyallup area in northern Pierce County
Circulation: 22,400
Publisher: Christian Lee, clee@theolympian.com (shared with Olympia)
Editor: Brian McLean, brian.mclean@puyallupherald.com

Puyallup has had two main lines of newspaper heritage.

The *Herald* can trace its lineage back to the *Puyallup Commerce*, founded in 1886 by J.W. Reddington and renamed the *Puyallup Independent* in 1898.

In 1903, the *Independent* merged with the *Sumner Herald*, founded in the nearby community of Sumner in 1889. The Washington State Library lists the three original principals in the merger as F. Franich, J. VanDevanter and W. Tupper. The result was the *Puyallup Valley Tribune*, which served the community under that name for more than 60 years. In 1967, a merger with the *Pierce County Herald* created the *Pierce County Herald and Puyallup Valley Tribune*. The name was subsequently compacted three times, to the *Pierce County Herald* in 1974, the *Puyallup Herald* in 1999 and *The Herald* in 2003.

The other local line originated with the *Puyallup Republican*, established by G.L. Townes in 1905. It became the *Mount Tacoma Herald* in 1911, the *Puyallup Herald* in 1911, the *Puyallup Press* in 1930 and the *Puyallup Press* and *Pierce County Shopper* in 1946, before fading.

Oddly, both local newspaper lines published for a period under the *Puyallup Herald* banner, one from 1911 to 1930, the other from 1999 to 2003. Both also published under variations, including *Mount Tacoma Herald* for one and *Pierce County Herald* for the other. It must have made it difficult, at times, for locals to tell their *Heralds* apart.

Puyallup takes its name from the Indian tribe that laid claim to the area earlier. The root is "poughallup," meaning "generous people." The community was platted, and named, by Ezra Meeker in 1890. He went on to become its first mayor and biggest champion. The surrounding Puyallup Valley is heavily agricultural, with hops, flowers and berries being the dominant crops. It lies at the base of Pierce County's most prominent feature – Mount Rainier. Tacoma, lying to the northwest on Puget Sound, is the county's dominant residential, commercial and industrial center. But Puyallup, now approaching 40,000 residents, continues to serve as the county seat from its inland niche.

In addition to Puyallup, *The Herald* serves Sumner, South Hill, Bonney Lake and Edgewood.

Tacoma's big daily, the *News Tribune*, could be considered a competitor in some senses. However, the papers are both owned by the national McClatchy chain, which serves to dampen the competitive fires considerably.

Valley Post-Register   Quincy

Owner: World Publishing Co.
Address: 202 G. St. SE, Quincy, WA 98848
Phone: 509-787-4511
URL: www.qvpr.com (unrestricted)
Established: 1948
Published: Thursday
Market: Grant County
Circulation: 2,050
Publisher: Joe Pitt, pitt@wenatcheeworld.com (shared with Wenatchee)
Editor: Rachal Pinkerton, editor@qvr.com

The *Post-Register* is owned by World Publishing Co. Based in Wenatchee, it is the publishing vehicle of the Woods family, longtime owner and publisher of the daily *Wenatchee World*. The *Post-Register* rode the boom that swept the country after the soldiers returned home from World War II, arriving on the scene in 1948. By then, three other papers had tried and failed to carve out a permanent niche in town.

The *Quincy Record*, established in 1903, was the first local paper. It was followed in 1904 by the S.G. Shaw's colorfully named *Quincy Quill*, which ran its course around 1919.

The *Quincy Valley Herald* filled the local newspaper void between 1919 and 1938. After a lapse, the *Post-Register* then entered the picture. Quincy is a community of about 6,750. It lies in the northwestern corner of lightly populated Grant County, west of Ephrata, the county seat, and Moses Lake, the largest city.

It got its start as a rail camp during construction of the Great Northern Railway's line from Chicago to Seattle in 1892. Named after Quincy, Ill., it was incorporated in 1907 – two years before Grant County was carved out of neighboring Douglas. Cattle ranching dominated the local economy in the early years. The balance later began to shift to dryland farming, then to irrigated farming when water from the massive federal Columbia Basin Project began to come on line in the late 1940s.

Ferry County View   Republic

Owner: Digital Documents (Gary Sheffield)
Address: 771 S. Keller St., Republic, WA 99166
Phone: 509-775-2425
URL: www.ferrycountyview.com (unrestricted)
Established: 2009
Published: Wednesday
Market: Ferry County
Circulation: 2,600
Publisher: Greg Sheffield
Deadline: 5 p.m. Friday

Except for two brief periods, Republic has been served from 1903 to 2009 by only one paper, the *News-Miner*. Today, it is again served by one paper, but a different paper, the *Ferry County View*. The *News-Miner* folded on May 16, 2013, ending a run that extended 110 years under that name and 117 years overall.

Until Greg Sheffield launched the *View* in 2009, the *News-Miner* had only faced competition twice – from the *Journal* from 1913 to 1917, after it moved to Republic from Kettle Falls, and the *Latah County Press* from 1955 to 1957, after it moved to Republic from Troy.

The *News-Miner* was the product of mergers among three early papers – the *News*, founded in 1896, the *Pioneer*, founded in 1898, and the *Miner*, founded in 1899. The *Pioneer* and *Miner* merged in 1901 to create the *Pioneer-Miner*, and it merged with the *News* in turn in 1903 to create the *News-Miner*.

Republic was founded by gold prospectors in the late 1800s. Gold was first struck on Eureka Creek in the early 1890s, leading Philip Creasor to plat a townsite under the name Eureka Gulch. In 1896, Creasor teamed with Thomas Ryan to begin developing an even bigger strike on nearby Granite Creek, known as the Great Republic Claim. When the Postal Service rejected Eureka, because Washington already had one, the settlement's townspeople chose Republic in honor of a claim they viewed as the key to local prosperity. That led to the community's incorporation on May 22, 1900, only the sixth on Washington's dry eastern reaches to that date.

The city's two biggest claims to fame today are the only Washington gold mine still in operation and one of the richest veins of scientifically significant fossils in the United States. It serves as seat of government for Ferry County, so designated largely because it was the county's only settlement of any size, which is still true today, as it accounts for more than 1,000 of the county's 7,500 residents.

Often described as one of the last frontiers of the American West, Ferry County combines a rugged mountain environment dominated by mining and logging with the breathtaking beauty of a wilderness retreat, serving to fuel tourism in recent years.

The *News-Miner* had been owned and operated by the Graham family since its purchase by family patriarch Dick Graham in 1968. Gina Graham was serving as publisher at the time of its demise, having taken the helm when Dick retired. A weekly coming out on Thursdays, it claimed a paid circulation of 900 as of June 2013. That compared to 2,600 for the Johnny-come-lately *View*, providing a pretty clear indication which paper was prevailing on the street.

The *News-Miner* never established a website of any kind, not even as a placeholder to provide names, addresses and contact information. In contrast, Sheffield quickly established a website for the *View* and began posting news regularly online.

"I'm old-fashioned," Dick Graham, then 75, said in a phone interview several months before his paper ceased publication. "I don't put nothing up for nothing." Asked if he would ever consider establishing an online presence, he said, "It's something that we've had some inquiries about. I'm just not too sure, in these small towns, how well that goes over."

Graham, who began working in the family newspaper business at the age of 12, continued, "People get their paper early Thursday morning and have their coffee." Then, after a pause, he noted, "Of course, they're all 80 years old now."

Sheffield is more comfortable operating in a digital world. In fact, Digital Documents serves as his ownership vehicle.

Tri-City Herald   Richland

See Tri-City Herald, Kennewick

Ritzville Adams County Journal   Ritzville

Owner: Stephen McFadden
Address: 216 W. Railroad Avenue, Ritzville WA 99169
Phone: 509-659-1020
URL: www.ritzvillejournal.com (unrestricted)
Established: 1886
Published: Thursday
Market: Adams County
Circulation: 2,100
Editor, Publisher & Owner: Stephen McFadden, mcfadden@ritzvillejournal.com
Deadline: Noon Tuesday.

Situated in wheat country between Spokane and the Tri-Cities on Washington's dry side, Ritzville was settled in 1880 and incorporated in 1890 as a shipping and farm supply center. It bills itself today, with some justification, as the world's largest rail shipping point for wheat.

It was named for its earliest homesteader, Philip Ritz. But it got its biggest early boosts from merchant William McKay, who built the first store in 1881, and the Northern Pacific Railway, which proceeded to put up a depot doubling as a hotel, theater and meeting hall. With a population of less than 1,700, it is small by comparison with Othello, the largest city in Adams County. However, it serves as county seat.

Local newspapering began in 1885, when G.F. Blankenship established the *Adams County Record*. The *Record* died the following year.

Better luck came with the subsequent founding of the *Adams County Times* as a replacement. It became the *Ritzville Times* in 1892, under the ownership of W.E. Blackmer. E.D. Gilson's *Adams County News* followed 1898, evolving through the unwieldy *Washington State Journal* and *Adams County News* in 1906, then the more concise *Washington State Journal* in 1907.

In 1910, the two lines merged to form the *Washington State Journal* and *Ritzville Times,* then the *Journal-Times* in 1918, *Ritzville Journal-Times* in 1928 and *Ritzville Adams County Journal* in 1973.

Kansas native Charles A. Sprague, who would become long-time owner of *The Oregon Statesman* in Salem and Oregon's 22nd governor, owned the paper for a time. But he gave up Washington newspapering for Oregon newspapering in 1925, when he acquired a part interest in the *Corvallis Gazette-Times*.

Now owned by Stephen McFadden, the *Journal* has managed to remain in local family hands throughout its long history.

Sun News   Rochester

See The Independent & Sun News, Tenino/Rochester

Capitol Hill Times   Seattle

Owner: RIM Publications
Address: P.O. Box 23356, Seattle, WA 98112
Phone: 425-213-5579
URL: www.capitolhilltimes.com (unrestricted)
Established: 1926
Published: Wednesday

Market: Central King County
Circulation: 5,000
Editor: Stephen Miller, smiller@rimpublications.com

Seattle's Capitol Hill neighborhood serves simultaneously as a center of nightlife and entertainment, of gay, lesbian and transgender culture, and of counterculture thinking and living. In the 1980s and 90s, it also served as the heart of Seattle's grunge music scene.

'Twasn't also so, of course. Neighborhoods change, and this one has changed plenty.

Pioneer settlers carved a wagon road up the hill's steep, heavily forested flanks to its 444-foot peak in 1872 and established Lake View Cemetery there. Ten years later, the hill was logged, opening it for residential and commercial development. Previously known as Broadway Hill, it got its current name from developer James Moore in 1901. Some accounts have it that he was hoping to lure the Washington State Capitol from Olympia, but the more likely story is that he named it after a high-end development he admired in his wife's native Denver. He started with a series of grand residences on a stretch of 14th Street known to this day as Millionaire's Row. Other landmarks include Volunteer Park, developed near the cemetery in 1887, and the park water tower, added in 1907.

Capitol Hill is roughly bounded by Interstate 5 to the west, Union and Madison streets to the south, State Route 520 to the to the north and 23rd and 24th avenues to the east. Its main arteries are Pike, Pine and Broadway.

After World War II, urban decay began to deter the affluent and draw the hip. Today, its commercial streets are dotted with coffee shops, music venues, art galleries, theaters, bookstores and boutiques, fueling gentrification in surrounding residential neighborhoods.

The *Capitol Hill Times* was launched in 1926, just before the onset of the Great Depression. It weathered that cataclysm, but could not, in the end, weather the radically changing nature of its clientele and industry. The publication combines news from the Capitol Hill neighborhood with coverage of art, food, music and culture. It was founded by Louis Magrini, who ran it for many years.

It subsequently came under the ownership of Pacific Publishing, which found the paper's finances posing growing challenges. Unable to find the key to righting the finances, Pacific laid off the staff, shut down the operation and sold the assets to RIM Publications in late 2011. RIM is an arm of Northwest Trustee Services, which handles foreclosures for mortgage-holders, It was created primarily as a cost-effective way to control its legal publication costs while also providing profitable service to others in the industry.

When RIM took the reins in January 2012, it told the Capitol Hill Seattle blog it planned to "revamp the paper and make it relevant again." It is currently promoting home delivery at the bargain price of $25 a year.

The Stranger   Seattle

Owner: Index Newspapers LLC
Address: 1535 11th Ave., Third Floor, Seattle, WA 98122
Phone: 206-323-7101
URL: www.thestranger.com (unrestricted)
Established: 1991
Published: Thursday
Market: Puget Sound
Circulation: 74,074
Editorial Director: Dan Savage, mail@savagelove.net
Editor: Christopher Frizzelle, editor@thestranger.com

The Stranger is an alternative weekly founded in 1991 by Tim Keck and James Sturm. Its principal competition is the *Seattle Weekly*. Both papers package probing and often irreverent political coverage with coverage of art, food, music, nightlife and, at least in the case of *The Stranger*, sex, romance and relationships. *The Stranger*, which has spun off a clone in Portland called the *Portland Mercury*, equally raw and profane, also publishes original comics, graphics and illustrations by notable cartoonists.

Keck had previously co-founded The Onion, a nationally and even internationally known publication whose specialty is satire – often misunderstood satire. Sturm's background was in cartooning, explaining the paper's strong artistic bent.

In addition to producing and circulating almost 75,000 copies of its free-distribution print publication, *The Stranger* maintains a richly featured website that includes a popular blog known as the Slog. Its online footprint, through the Slog and otherwise, is an increasingly important element of its overall presence and influence in Seattle.

Since its debut on Sept. 23, 1991, it has billed itself as "Seattle's Only Newspaper," which Wikipedia terms, aptly it would seem, "an expression of its disdain for Seattle's two dailies (the *Seattle Times* and the now-defunct print edition of the *Seattle Post-Intelligencer*) and *The Stranger*'s main rival, the *Seattle Weekly*."

Keck joined with a fellow undergraduate at the University of Wisconsin to found *The Onion*, borrowing $8,000 from his mother to help finance the venture. After 18 months, he sold out, dropped out and lit out for Brazil. He had never set foot in Seattle. When he returned to the U.S., he tapped it for his next publishing venture strictly by word of mouth. That made him a stranger in every sense of the word and gave him a title to work with.

Just 27 years old and still clinging to the college scene, he launched *The Stranger* as a localized University District publication. It had limited distribution and more classifieds and coupons than editorial content, but its editorial heft and reach have grown over the years, to the point it won a Pulitzer Prize in feature writing for a story published in June 2011.

Headlined "The Bravest Woman In Seattle," the winning entry was described by the Pulitzer jury as "a haunting story of a woman who survived a brutal attack that took the life of her partner, using the woman's brave courtroom testimony and the details of the crime to construct a moving narrative."

Dan Savage, author of *The Stranger*'s iconic Savage Love sex advice column since the paper's inaugural issue, served as Keck's editor for six years before awarding that job to Christopher Frizzelle in 2007. He now holds the title of editorial director, one of the two at the top of a masthead that does not list a publisher. The other top title is that of art director, filled by Aaron Huffman.

Currently held by Index Newspapers of Seattle, a limited liability corporation founded and headed by Keck, *The Stranger* has been locally owned from the outset. That serves as a point of contrast with its larger and older competitor on the alternative scene, as *Seattle Weekly* has been under chain ownership since 1997.

While largely free-distribution, *The Stranger* does offer home delivery at $40 for six months or $60 for 12, as an option.

Queen Anne & Magnolia News   Seattle

Owner: Pacific Publishing
Address: 636 S. Alaska St., Seattle, WA 98108
Phone: 206-461-1283
URL: www.queenannenews.com (unrestricted)
Established: 1919
Published: Wednesday
Market: Seattle's Queen Anne and Magnolia neighborhoods
Circulation: 11,000
Publisher: Mike Dillon, mdillon@nwlink.com
Deadline: 2 p.m. Friday

While unable to make a go of it in Seattle's Capitol Hill neighborhood, northeast of the city's central business district, Pacific Publishing has found firmer footing on Seattle's Queen Anne and

Magnolia neighborhoods to the northwest. They're among the oldest distinct neighborhoods in a city that takes neighborhood distinctions very seriously.

The first settler on what is now known as Queen Anne Hill was Thomas Mercer, who settled in 1853 on a donation land claim rising from a 320-acre meadow claimed by pioneer notables David and Louisa Denny. The steep slopes leading to the hill's 456-foot peak discouraged commercial and industrial development, but afforded spectacular views that encouraged high-end residential development. By the mid 1880s, wealthy merchants had begun to build residential showplaces in the popular Queen Anne style of the time, leading locals to dub the rapidly urbanizing settlement Queen Anne Town. A hurricane knocked down much of the timber in 1875, helping facilitate development. By 1902, the neighborhood had enough residents to justify running a street car line up its 18 percent grade, though it required use of counterweights installed underground.

By 1919, it had enough residents to support a newspaper – or two.

The first was the *Queen Anne News*, debuting in 1919. The *Magnolia News* followed in 1933. Eventually, both came under the ownership of Pacific Publishing, which merged them to create the *Queen Anne & Magnolia News* on March 27, 2013.

One competitor emerged along the way, the *Magnolia Journal* in 1965. It was absorbed by the *Magnolia News* in 1970.

Dominated by affluent, educated and opinionated residents, the Queen Anne and Magnolia neighborhoods have a long tradition of political activism. The paper reflects that.

Weekly   Seattle

Owner: Sound Publishing
Address: 307 Third Ave. S, Second Floor, Seattle, WA 98104
Phone: 206-623-0500
URL: www.seattleweekly.com (unrestricted)
Established: 1976
Published: Wednesday
Market: Puget Sound
Circulation: 109,000
Publisher: Wendy Geldien, wgeldien@seattleweekly.com
Editor: Mark Baumgarten, mbaumgarten@seattleweekly.com
Managing Editor: Daniel Person, dperson@seattleweekly.com

Seattle's first alternative newspaper was the *Helix*. Armed with $200 in borrowed startup money, Paul Dorpat launched it on March 23, 1967. Rejected by a commercial printer, Dorpat had *Helix* printed by

Democratic Party and International Association of Machinists activist Ken Monson on a press he managed to scrounge up. It went from 1,500 copies to 11,000 in its first four editions, and continued, though irregularly, through June 11, 1970.

A series of abortive attempts to replace the *Helix* followed under various names, including the *Puget Sound Partisan*, *Sabot*, the *Flag*, the *Sound* and *The Sun*.

Sabot, published from Sept. 11, 1970, to Jan. 13, 1971, was the most radical of the bunch and thus perhaps the more interesting. It was founded by the Seattle Liberation Front, a radical political collective marked by fierce in-fighting that eventually doomed the paper. Several members broke off to form a Weatherman unit that met its demise in a Tukwila bank robbery culminating in a fatal shootout.

The Sun enjoyed longer life than most, publishing from July 31, 1974, to January 6, 1982, and thus overlapping the *Seattle Weekly* for several years. It spun off *The Rocket* in October 1979 as a free music-oriented bi-weekly, and the *Rocket* hung on until October 2000, hitting a peak circulation of 55,000.

Seattle Weekly was founded by Darrell Oldham and David Brewster as *The Weekly of Metropolitan Seattle* on March 31, 1976. And they seemed to find the formula that had eluded others, combining the political fervor of the *Helix* with the musical fervor of the *Rocket*. Their ownership vehicle was Quickfish Media, which ran the paper for more than two decades. Brewster held both the editor and publisher titles until August 1993, when he relinquished the editorial reins.

In November 1995, the paper switched to free distribution, joining the trend among alternative weeklies. Portland's *Willamette Week* was among alternatives making the same move.

New York-based Stern Publishing, parent company of New York City's *Village Voice* and other alternative papers serving major American cities, bought the paper from Quickfish in April 1997. The company was reconfigured as Village Voice Media three years later. Stern was in the process of amassing a stable of alternative newspapers stretching from the East Coast to the West at the time of the purchase, with the *Village Voice* serving as its flagship. It felt *Seattle Weekly* would be a good fit.

The paper had long enjoyed alternative genre dominance in Seattle, but was facing growing competition at the time from *The Stranger*, an upstart that came on the scene in 1991 and was developing more muscle in the market.

After 16 years at the helm, Village Voice Media, coming under increasing financial pressure nationally, sold the paper to Sound Publishing.

Though new to the alternative market, Sound is Washington's largest publisher of traditional community newspapers, both weekly and daily, claiming almost 60 titles. It took over on January 1, 2013, installing Wendy Geldien as publisher and bringing it new editorial leadership.

Times Seattle

Owner: Seattle Times Publishing (majority stake, Blethen family; minority stake, McClatchy Company)
Address: 1000 Denny Way, Seattle, WA 98109
Phone: 206-464-2111
URL: www.seattletimes.com (subscription required for full access)
Established: 1891
Published: Monday-Sunday AM
Market: Western Washington from base in King County
Circulation: 229,764 weekday, 198,373 Saturday, 336,363 Sunday
Publisher: Frank Blethen, fblethen@seattletimes.com
Executive Editor: David Boardman, dboardman@seattletimes.com

Seattle is home to the most widely recognized and visual symbol of newspapering in the Northwest – the *Post-Intelligencer* Globe, a huge blue ball with an eagle atop and the slogan "It's in the P-I" proudly cast across the middle. Among Seattle images, the 30-foot, 13-ton, neon-festooned ball probably takes a back seat only to the Space Needle. The newspaper whose building it topped exists in paper form no longer. It continues only as a website, putting it outside the main scope of this book.

But its story is integral to Seattle journalism: Any discussion of Washington's largest newspaper, the *Seattle Times*, has to account for the *P-I* as well.

Seattle is the Northwest's largest city. It was being founded on Puget Sound about the same time as the region's second-largest city, Portland, on the Columbia River to the south. Both got their start in the mid-1850s, and both were located in Oregon Territory at the time, as Washington Territory wasn't carved out until later.

Like Portland, it started as a logging town and turned to shipping. It experienced its first boom as a supply point for gold rushes in Alaska and Canada's Yukon Territory. Only much later would airplane construction led by Boeing and computer technology led by Microsoft transform it into the thriving, bustling, cosmopolitan Seattle we know today.

As in so many frontier towns, a little bit of Main Street establishment led quickly to a newspaper, then to a gaggle of newspapers. The first was *The Washington Gazette*, which J.R. Watson launched on August 15, 1863. Though it carried a Seattle imprint, it actually was published in Olympia. When it met with early success, Watson moved it to Seattle and rechristened it the *Seattle Gazette* in December.

It expired on March 3, 1866, but was reborn as the *Weekly Intelligencer* on August 5, 1867 under the auspices of new owner Sam Maxwell. That iteration merged with the *Seattle Weekly Post* to create the *Seattle Weekly Post-Intelligencer*, forerunner of a daily that would dominate the market for decades before publishing its final print edition on March 17, 2009, and becoming a web-only presence.

In its early decades, it was a conservative, establishment-oriented paper, though its editorial page turned more liberal over the years, a reflection of its city.

By 1910, after a series of shutdowns, mergers and buyouts had winnowed Seattle's crowded newspaper field, the *P-I* was selling 18,000 papers a day on its morning publication cycle. The Hearst Corporation, one of the nation's largest newspaper chains at the time, bought the *P-I* in 1921 and stuck with it to the end. The paper went nearly a century without ever changing hands again. Its position seemed unassailable.

It wasn't.

The *Seattle Times*, a long-time underdog that turned top dog in the end, descends from a trio of papers, all publishing on a daily cycle from the outset. They were the *Daily Call*, later known as the *Seattle Daily Call*, founded in 1885; the *Seattle Daily Chronicle*, founded in 1881; and the *Seattle Daily Times*, later known as the *Daily Times*, then the *Seattle Times*, founded in 1883. The *Call* and *Chronicle* merged in 1886 to create the *Seattle Daily Press*, later known simply as the *Seattle Press*. The *Press* and *Times* then merged in 1891 to create the *Seattle Press-Times*, an afternoon daily that today's *Times* considers its forerunner.

It had a weak circulation of 3,500 in 1891, and soon fell into a slide leaving it on the verge of bankruptcy. Charles Fishback, a businessmen with no newspaper experience, bought the paper at a fire-sale price in 1895, restored the *Seattle Times* name and brought in a former newspaper executive as a partner in hopes he could effect a turnaround.

The man Fishback was counting on was Alden Blethen of Maine, who had succeeded spectacularly with one newspaper venture and failed spectacularly with another. Blethen came out West looking for redemption and felt Seattle might be the last shot he was going to get. A reporter who had worked for him at the *Minneapolis Tribune* said, "He couldn't write, he couldn't spell, he was more ignorant of grammar than Macauley's celebrated sixth-form boy, he never had any original ideas, he was coarse and intemperate and harsh and hasty." But he was a great newspaperman nonetheless, the reporter said.

Whsatever else he was, he was a larger-than-life personality.

Blethen faced a daunting task, as the *Times* was trailing several other dailies that were in turn trailing the *P-I*. It was a long way up from where he was looking. But he was broke, desperate and supremely confident, which turned out to be a winning combination. Drawing on lessons learned in other metro areas – despite his lack of editorial skills, he had plied the trade in Denver and Kansas City as well as Minneapolis – Blethen cut the per-copy price to raise circulation and adopted a stridently populist tone on the opinion pages.

Both moves struck the right notes in the mid-1890s, and Blethen followed up with one circulation-boosting stunt after another. Despite all that, the paper's fortunes slipped still further before finally gaining traction.

In a Blethen biography titled, "Raise Hell and Sell Newspapers," Sharon Boswell and Lorraine Mconaghy said that "during the quiet winter months of 1897, *Times* circulation and advertising declined," resulting in losses running $500 a month. They said: "The newspaper couldn't meet its payrolls, and family members and friends worked for free. Fishback's promissory notes … fell due and he was unable to pay, nor could Blethen afford to buy out his partner and their creditors. The cycle of indebtedness threatened to pull down this version of the Times as it had pulled down its predecessors – too many newspapers, too few readers, not enough money."

The authors said Blethen had taken aim at his big morning rival early on, but: "The *P-I* had maintained a dignified silence against the *Times*' gibes because its editors expected the evening paper's imminent collapse and Alden Blethen's hasty departure."

Then Blenthen got supremely lucky: Gold was discovered in Canada's Yukon Territory. By the end of 1897, the gold rush was raining money on Seattle, the biggest, best-equipped jumping-off point and supply center for the far Northwest. An ace promoter, Blethen knew how to take maximum advantage, and promptly did.

Ironically, he drew many of his yellow journalistic lessons from William Randolph Hearst, who assembled the national Hearst chain that would end up running the competing *P-I* after 1921.

As the 20th century dawned, the *Times* came to match the *P-I* in circulation. Then, over the next two decades, it nosed into a lead it would never relinquish. As time went on, the *Times* became the more conservative, Republican and establishment-oriented of the two papers. And hint of that early populism was left strictly to the *P-I*.

The *Times* has remained under Blethen family control, both financially and editorially, ever since. Today, the Blethens hold a 51% interest to the McClatchy Company's 49%, acquired from the national Knight-Ridder chain, and Frank Blethen sits in the publisher's chair. The family has always tried to marshal enough manpower, resources and leadership to produce excellence. And one way it has paid off is in the *Times*' bountiful harvest of Pulitzer prizes – a region-leading nine.

The *Times* and *P-I* co-existed for decades, albeit uneasily, having long since vanquished all other rivals of note from the field.

Experiencing financial stress in the later part of the 20th century, the Blethen family's *Times* and Hearst family's *Post-Intelligencer* entered into a joint operating agreement in 1983. The JOA gave the *Times* control of the advertising, circulation, production and accounting functions while keeping the *Times* and *P-I* news operations totally separate.

The *Times* remained on the PM publication cycle and the *P-I* on the AM, but that proved a source of increasing tension. Over time, afternoon papers began to increasingly give way to morning papers in major markets, including Portland to the south, where the *Journal* was closed, leaving the field to *The Oregonian*. Alden Blethen believed morning papers were playing a losing hand, but Frank Blethen came to learn it was actually the other way around. In 2000, the *Times* moved to the morning cycle, putting it in head-to-head competition with the *P-I* in the most direct way possible.

Three years later, the *Times* announced it was moving unilaterally to cancel the JOA, citing a clause giving it an out in the event it suffered three straight years of operating losses. Hearst bitterly disputed the accounting the *Times* used to support the claim, and the dispute went to court. In 2007, the parties struck an uneasy truce. In March 2009, it all became moot when Hearst announced the *Post-Intelligencer* was ceasing print publication and converting to online-only. It continues to post news online today, though with a drastically reduced staff.

Gazette   Sequim

Owner: Sound Publishing
Address: 147 W. Washington St., Sequim, WA 98382
Phone: 360-683-3311
URL: www.sequimgazette.com (unrestricted)
Established: 1974
Published: Wednesday
Market: Clallam County
Circulation: 6,432
Publisher: Sue Ellen Riesau, seriesau@sequimgazette.com
Editor: Mike Dashiell, mdashiell@sequimgazette.com
Deadline: 4 p.m. Monday

George W. O'Brien and his successors had the newspaper field in Sequim all to themselves from the founding of the *Clallam Bay Press* on August 20, 1909, until the founding of the *Jimmy Come Lately Gazette* on

July 10, 1974. That's a run of almost 65 years. Even then, the *Press*, which operated as the *Sequim Press* from 1911 on, hung on for 11 more years before succumbing. It published its last issue on May 15, 1985.

The newcomer began life in January 1974 as *The Sequim Shopper*. It was founded by Shirley Larmore. With the help of her husband, she transformed it into a traditional community weekly six months later under the unlikely name *Jimmy Come Lately Gazette* – doubly unlikely when you consider her husband's name was Bob. Larmore sold to Leonard and Linda Paulsen in 1978. Leonard served as publisher until his death in 1982, when Linda took over. Paulsen sold to Brown McClatchy Maloney in September 1988, and he tweaked the name slightly, making it *Sequim's Jimmy Come Lately Gazette*. By then, the *Press*, the only other paper ever published in Sequim, had folded.

Two years later, Maloney shortened the name to the more traditional *Sequim Gazette*. Long-time locals still call it "The Jimmy."

Maloney, who maintained his ownership through Olympic View Publishing, followed the lead of many other independent Washington publishers on November 1, 2011, selling to the state's overwhelmingly dominant chain owner, Sound Publishing. Another Olympic Peninsula weekly, the *Forks Forum*, was included in the deal.

Sound, which is based in Poulsbo but prints all of its 50-odd Washington papers at a central plant in Everett, also owns the *Peninsula Daily News* in Port Angeles. That gives it a near monopoly on Washington's wet, rugged, scenic and lightly populated Olympic Peninsula.

Lying across Puget Sound from Seattle, the peninsula is bounded on the east by the Hood Canal, north by the Strait of Juan de Fuca and west by the Pacific Ocean. It's most prominent features are Mount Olympus and the Olympic National Park. The interior was one of the last places in the continental U.S. to be explored, let alone settled. It wasn't even mapped until 1900.

Sequim's odd, one-syllable name is reportedly derived from the Klallam Indian term for "place to shoot," because elk were plentiful before the arrival of Anglo settlers. The city's population has been running neck and neck with the newspaper's circulation – around 6,500.

Mason County Journal   Shelton

Owner: Shelton-Mason County Journal Inc.
Address: 227 W. Cota St., Shelton, WA 98584
Phone: 360-426-4412
URL: www.masoncounty.com (unrestricted, but news is not posted online)
Established: 1886

Published: Thursday
Market: Shelton, Washington and Mason counties
Circulation: 8,300
Publisher: Kari Sleight, kari@masoncounty.com
Managing Editor: Adam Rudnick, adam@masoncounty.com

Mason County was cut from King on March 13, 1854. Originally known as Sawamish County, it was renamed in 1864 in honor of the first secretary of Washington Territory, Charles Mason. Though it has come to encompass 60,000 residents, it only has one incorporated community – the county seat of Shelton, the westernmost city on Puget Sound. Shelton was incorporated in 1890. Originally known as Sheltonville, it was named after David Shelton, the local delegate to the Territorial Legislature. It lies northwest of Olympia and southwest of the Olympic National Forest. The city's economy is resource-based, but diverse. It incorporates logging, farming, fishing, shipping, oyster ranching, lumber milling, dairy production and Christmas tree cultivation.

The *Mason County Journal* was established in 1886. It published its inaugural edition on Dec. 31 of that year, thus pre-dating the city it primarily serves.

The *Journal* drew two early challengers, The *Shelton Sentinel* in September 1890 and W.R. Lotz's *Shelton Weekly Tribune* in January 1894. The *Tribune* drove the *Sentinel* from the field almost immediately, but could not dislodge the *Journal* and called it quits in 1907.

The paper rechristened itself as the *Shelton-Mason County Journal* in March 1927, immediately prior to the April 3 launch of a new rival known as *The Shelton Independent*. The *Shelton Bulletin* joined the field as well in the fall of 1930, but quickly flamed out. When the *Journal* absorbed the *Independent* in 1937, a new contender rose to take its place – the *Shelton Daily Spokesman*, debuting March 25. However, the *Spokesman*, trying to make it as a daily, barely lasted two years.

The *Journal*, which dropped the Shelton reference in February 2013, has had the field all to itself ever since.

Along the way, it has made a pair of forays into the unincorporated community of Belfair, up in the county's northeast corner. After absorbing Belfair's two-year-old *Huckleberry Herald* in 1971, it continued publishing the *Herald* as a supplement through 1972. In 2010, it targeted Belfair with a new version called the *Belfair Herald*, which remains active.

Until recently, the Gay family had owned and operated the *Journal* since its purchase by family patriarch Henry Gay in 1966. Gay continued to hold the helm until falling to cancer in 1999, at the age of 72, at which point his son Charlie took over with assistance from other members of the family. Henry Gay was a firebrand editorialist and columnist who relished bucking journalistic tradition. He was a fearless figure with a mind of his own and a penchant for speaking it. His parents owned a paper in California when he was growing up and he learned the trade from them. He passed it on to sons Charlie and Stephen, and daughter Julie.

State corporation records list the current owners as Thomas and Ann Mullen in partnership with Robert and Jennifer Hicks through Shelton-Mason County Journal Inc., a corporation founded on January 24, 2008.

Central Kitsap Reporter   Silverdale

Owner: Sound Publishing
Address: 3888 N.W. Randall Way, Suite 100, Silverdale, WA 98383
Phone: 360-308-9161
URL: www.centralkitsapreporter.com (unrestricted)
Established: 1984
Published: Friday
Market: Central Kitsap County
Circulation: 18,268
Publisher: Sean McDonald, publisher@centralkitsapreporter.com
Editor: Greg Skinner, editor@centralkitsapreporter.com
Deadline: 4 p.m. Wednesday

Silverdale is a stubbornly unincorporated community of 20,000, about 10 miles northwest of Bremerton and nine south of Poulsbo on the Kitsap Peninsula. Poised at the northern tip of Dyes Inlet, it enjoys water connections to Bremerton via Sinclair Inlet and the Pacific Ocean via Puget Sound.

Newspapering here began late and proceeded fitfully. There were many short runs.

T. Hynes broke the ice with *The Silverdale Breeze*, which published from 1928 to 1938. G.T. Harrison revived it in 1945 for a reprise that ran until 1967. It was then merged with the *East Bremerton News* to create the *Reporter*, which held on for two more years.

The *Kitsap County Journal* published from 1929 to 1933, overlapping the original *Breeze*. It was revived in 1975, but went under again after a seven-year run. Meanwhile, Jack and Dorothy Rogers introduced the *Manette News* in 1944, but it died the following year.

The *Central County Press* debuted in 1981 and managed to drive the *Journal* under in short order. The *Silverdale Reporter* returned the favor when it debuted on June 20, 1984, putting the press out of business in a matter of months. The *Reporter* became the *Central Kitsap Reporter* in 1995, following a series of name changes. It shares no heritage with the *Reporter* published in Silverdale from 1967-69.

It addition to Silverdale, the *Reporter* circulates in the neighboring central Kitsap County communities of Keyport, Seabeck, Belfair, Allyn, Tracyton and Bangor, and the Bangor Naval Base.

The paper now is one of almost 60 titles in Sound Publishing's extensive Washington network, based in neighboring Poulsbo. Sound also owns and operates several other papers in Kitsap County.

Snohomish County Tribune Snohomish

Owner: Mach Publishing
Address: 27 Ave. C, Suite B, Snohomish, WA 98290
Phone: 360-568-4121
URL: www.snoho.com (unrestricted)
Established: 1888
Published: Wednesday
Market: Snohomish County
Circulation: 23,000
Publisher: Becky Reed, becky@snoho.com
Editor: Jessica Sparks, jessica@snoho.com

Snohomish was founded in 1858-59 as Cadyville. It was renamed for the dominant local Indian tribe in 1871. Snohomish has managed to preserve about two-dozen stately period homes, on display via a popular walking tour. Snohomish County was cleaved from Island County in 1861. Its dominant city is Everett, which also serves as the county seat.

Snohomish's first newspaper was *The Northern Star*, established by Eldridge Morse in January 1876. But it only last three years, printing its final edition in May 1879. *The Eye* followed in January 1882 and fared considerably better. Founded by H.F. Jackson and C.H. Packard, it held on until 1897, almost making the advent of the new century.

The Snohomish Sun, founded by George H. Head, joined the fray in the summer of 1888. Forerunner of today's *Tribune*, it went daily on July 5, 1889. The *Sun* fell on hard times after being sold to E.D. Warner, falling back to weekly in 1892 and suspending publication for six months in 1893. But it was revived in October 1893 by local civic and business leaders Charles "C.W." Gorham and Carl Clemans.

The paper underwent a pair of renamings in quick succession during that period, becoming the *Snohomish Tribune* on August 2, 1892, and *Snohomish County Tribune* two years later. It has published as the *Snohomish County Tribune* ever since.

In 1966, two smaller papers launched in neighboring towns, the *Lake Stevens News* and the *Granite Falls Press*. Four years later, they merged to create the *News-Press*, absorbed into the *Tribune* the following year.

The *Tribune* is privately held by Mach Publishing, founded by David Mach in January 1986. It also publishes editions serving Everett, Monroe and Mukilteo.

Valley Record   Snoqualmie

Owner: Sound Publishing
Address: P.O. Box 300, Snoqualmie, WA 98065
Phone: 425-888-2311
URL: www.valleyrecord.com (unrestricted)
Established: 1913
Published: Wednesday
Market: Snoqualmie area, east of Seattle (King County)
Circulation: 12,500
Publisher: William G.A. Shaw, wshaw@valleyrecord.com
Editor: Seth Truskott, struskott@valleyrecord.com
Deadline: 4 p.m. Monday

Tucked into the southeastern corner of King County, far from Seattle and the rest of its population centers, Snoqualmie barely topped 10,000 in the 2010 census. Lying in the foothills at the base of the Cascade Range, it is far removed from the madding crowd and likes it that way. It has a smaller sister community of North Bend, even further southeast. Originally, North Bend was known as Snoqualmie and Snoqualmie as Snoqualmie Falls. Despite the relative remoteness, they both enjoy easy access to the Seattle metropolitan area via Interstate 90.

The *Valley Record* traces its history back to a pair of papers founded in North Bend, the *Post* and the *Record*. B.N. Kennedy launched the *North Bend Post*, at a site east of town in the Tanner District, on October 16, 1913. It became the Snoqualmie Post in 1915. The *Post* morphed into the *Snoqualmie Valley Record* in 1924, apparently through some sort of alliance or merger with the *North Bend Record*. The *Record*'s origin is unclear, but it appears to date back almost as far as the *Post*.

The two papers continued to publish separate editions under the *Record* name until 1971, when they combined operations as the *Snoqualmie North Bend Valley Record*. It began publishing as the *Valley Record* in 1989, then the *Snoqualmie Valley Record* in 1998, serving Snoqualmie, North Bend, Preston, Fall City, Carnation, Novelty, Vincent and Duvall.

Ed and Charlotte Groshell published the paper in the 1950s, with the help of sons Johnny and Hi. The paper later came into the hands of Bob Scott. In 1996, Scott sold the *Record* to his daughter, Karen McKiernan, and her husband, Jim. They sold to Peter Horvitz's *King County Journal* Newspapers four years later, but continued at the helm. In 2006, Sound Publishing, Washington's largest owner and operator of community newspapers, with almost 60 titles, bought the King County Journal group.

Sound brought in Eastside native William Shaw as publisher two years later. He was working for the Journal chain when Sound acquired it for Horvitz, but had not been associated with the *Record*.

On March 6, 2008, the *Issaquah Press*, a wholly owned subsidiary of the *Seattle Times*, launched a free-distribution competitor in Snohomish under the *SnoValley Star* banner. It is mailed to 11,500 homes and businesses in Snoqualmie, North Bend and neighboring communities along the I-90 corridor. The company also publishes *The Issaquah Press*, *Sammamish Review* and *Newcastle News*, all either free-distribution or voluntary-pay. It is based in Issaquah, but has the papers printed in Kent.

Sound also publishes an array of other papers in King County. A mix of paid-circulation, voluntary-pay and free distribution, they serve Auburn, Bellevue, Bonney Lake, Bothell, Covington, Enumclaw, Federal Way, Issaquah, Kenmore, Kent, Kirkland, Maple Valley, Maury Island, Mercer Island, Redmond, Renton, Sammamish, Seattle, Sumner, Tukwila and Vashon.

Because it is operated on a free-distribution basis, the *Star* falls outside the scope of this guide. However, voluntary-pay publications have been included, and the *Valley Record* carries that designation.

Pacific NW Inlander   Spokane

Owner: Ted S. McGregor Jr..
Address: 9 S. Washington St., Spokane, WA 99021
Phone: 509-325-0634
URL: www.inlander.com (unrestricted)
Established: 1993
Published: Thursday
Market: Spokane County
Circulation: 49,768
Editor & Publisher: Ted S. McGregor Jr., tedm@inlander.com
Managing Editor: Jacob H. Fries, jacobf@inlander.com

The *Pacific NW Inlander*, an alternative weekly covering arts, culture, entertainment and politics, was founded on October 20, 1993, by Spokane native Ted S. McGregor, Jr. It is mostly free-distribution, but actively solicits subscriptions delivered by mail at $50 a year. Circulation hovers around 50,000.

After graduating from Gonzaga Prep and the University of Washington, McGregor pursued a master's degree in journalism at the University of Missouri. During the course of his studies, he developed a plan for the founding of a weekly newspaper back in his hometown of Spokane, and after receiving his degree, he went home to carry it out. Along the way, he enlisted his brother, Jeremy, as a partner. He also leaned on mom and dad, Jeanne and Ted Sr., making the venture truly a family affair. Both brothers remain involved today, Ted as editor and publisher, Jeremy as general manager. And they still retain ownership.

After 19 years in a series of rented spaces, the *Inlander* finally moved into a home of its own in 2012 in the Kendall Yards development. It circulates as far north as Sandpoint, Idaho, as far west as Cheney, as far south as Pullman, and as far east as Kellogg, Idaho – a bi-state expanse the dominant local daily calls the Inland Empire.

The Spokesman-Review tower in Spokane. (photo/Randy Stapilus)

Spokesman-Review   **Spokane**

Owner: Cowles Publishing Co.
Address: 999 W. Riverside Ave., Spokane, WA 99201
Phone: 509-459-5000
URL: www.spokesman.com (unrestricted)
Established: 1883
Published: Monday through Sunday AM
Market: Northeastern Washington and Idaho Panhandle

Circulation: 65,074 weekday, 72,329 Saturday, 106,611 Sunday (ABC)
Publisher: William Stacey Cowles
Editor: Gary Graham, garyg@spokesman.com

Spokane was privy to a pair of fierce newspaper wars. The first, and perhaps most intense, pitted a pair of morning dailies against one another – the longer-established *Review* and upstart *Spokesman*. The evening daily, the *Chronicle*, would have to wait its turn.

The gauntlet was laid down in the late 1880s, when the *Review* sought to strengthen its competitive position position by inviting in out-of-state investors from, horrors of horrors, *The Oregonian* in Portland. That led one of the *Review's* partners, Horace T. Brown, to bolt ranks and found the *Spokesman* as a morning rival in 1890.

The epithets were soon flying. The *Spokesman* branded the *Review* "The Morning Alien" and "The *Spokane Oregonian*." The *Review* shot back by dubbing its new rival "The *Squawksman*."

Despite blistering his former partners for inviting in outsiders, Brown turned to the *Chicago Tribune* and *Chicago Times* to help him underwrite his new venture. And one of the Chicago investors was a former *Tribune* police beat reporter named William Hutchinson Cowles.

Having put some of his personal money into play, Cowles decided to come out West and protect his investment by taking an active leadership role. And it's probably a good thing he did, as the battling papers were bleeding each other dry, putting both of them in a precarious position.

It didn't help matters that the *Chronicle*, launched in 1886 as the *Spokane Falls Evening Chronicle* and later known simply as the *Spokane Evening Chronicle*, was prospering mightily as the growing city's lone evening daily.

In 1893, the morning cycle combatants called a truce. Under the terms, the *Review* agreed to absorb the *Spokesman* just as the great financial panic of 1893 broke out. Cowles had money when no one else did and he took maximum advantage. He bought out his partners at low cost to became sole owner of the *Review*, which he renamed the *Spokesman-Review*.

Just 27 at the time, Cowles would run the paper for more than 50 years. In the process, he would take it from a publication of only about 4,000 to one of the largest in the state and region. Today, it ranks third in Washington, trailing only the *Seattle Times* and *Tacoma News Tribune*, and fourth in the Northwest, behind only those two and Portland's *Oregonian*.

The *Chronicle* got its start as a Democratic paper, the *Review* as a Republican paper. And while they were not nearly as partisan as many papers of the time, those lines tended to stick for a long time. When President Harry Truman was chugging around the country on his whistle-stop re-election campaign in 1948, U.S. Sen. Warren Magnuson, a fellow Democrat, joined him for the run across Washington. For some reason, Truman asked Magnuson what he thought of morning newspaper in Spokane, the *Spokesman-Review*. Magnuson recalled later, according to an essay in HistoryLink, "I told Truman it was the second-worst paper in the U.S., politically, after the *Chicago Tribune*."

Truman was evidently in one of his famous give-em-hell modes when he spotted a *Spokesman-Review* reporter in the audience during one of his speeches and stopped to deliver an admonishment. "The *Chicago Tribune* and this paper are the worst in the United States," he said, adding later, perhaps to ease the sting, "Nothing personal to you, young man." And he evidently meant it, because when returned to Spokane four years later, he delivered the barb again.

The city owes its name to the Spokane tribe and its location at the confluence of two rivers, the Spokane and the Little Spokane. A set of falls marked the spot, which first Native Americans and latter early trappers used as a place to trade and barter. The trappers created a fur trading venue known as Spokane House. It became the nucleus for the first longstanding settlement in what is now the state of Washington, being continuously occupied from 1810 to 1826, some two decades before the start of the great western migration by wagon train. Settlers migrating up from Washington established the townsite in the 1870s. A sawmill provided employment.

The fledgling community's first newspaper was the *Spokane Falls Review*, founded in 1883. The *Spokane Falls Evening Review* followed in 1884, creating name confusion that persisted for decades. The *Evening Review* became the *Morning Review* in 1885, the *Spokane Review* in 1891 and the *Spokesman-Review* in 1894, after absorbing the *Spokesman*. The *Spokane Falls Review* underwent a series of name changes of its own before becoming the *Spokane Daily Times* in 1929 and being absorbed by the *Spokesman-Review* as well in 1931.

Both *Reviews* were creations of a publisher named Frank Dallum, who arrived in Spokane more or less by accident. He was trying to answer the call for a Republican paper. The Democratic-leaning *Chronicle* followed on September 1, 1886. And benefiting from the morning in-fighting, it became Spokane's dominant daily.

Cowles took care of that in 1897 by buying the *Chronicle* as well. But instead of folding it into his *Spokesman-Review*, he continued to publish it separately. Cowles' heirs finally merged the two newsrooms in 1983 and closed the doors to the *Chronicle* in 1992. By then, the *Chronicle* had been publishing continuously in Spokane, dominant population center on Washington' dry east side, for more than a century.

Although competing papers have popped up occasionally in Spokane over the years, notably the Scripps chain's *Spokane Press* from 1910 to

1939, the *Spokesman-Review* would hold the dominance it gained by taking control first of the *Spokesman* and then the *Chronicle*.

Cowles died in 1946, but the paper remained in family hands, and remains there still.

Many successful newspaper families tried to expand their empires by buying newspapers in other parts of the country, but the Cowles family concentrated instead on investing in real estate and business ventures in Spokane, including radio and television stations. Members of the family control some of the most important tracts in downtown Spokane, leading occasionally to negative headlines in their own paper.

The *Spokesman-Review* has been one of the better-regarded papers in the region journalistically. It was a Pulitzer finalist for work on the Ruby Ridge shootout in 1992, and it conducted long-running, well-regarded investigations into Aryan Nations and Hanford Nuclear Reservation activities.

It sparked national controversy in journalism circles in 2004 when it revealed that Spokane Mayor Jim West had been using city computers to search for gay sex, developing the story through use of a computer consultant who posed as a high school student in online contact with the mayor. West was recalled by voters as a result.

The paper circulates most strongly in eastern Washington, but has long maintained a major presence in the Idaho Panhandle as well. In the 1980s and 1990s, it maintained a large Idaho news network and operated out of well-staffed offices in Coeur d'Alene, supplemented by smaller offices in other Idaho cities, including the capital city of Boise. That network has largely been shut down, but Dave Oliveria still hosts the popular Idaho-oriented Huckleberries blog for the paper, and reporter Betsy Russell continues to produce print stories and extensive blog posts from Boise.

Like many other papers, the *Spokesman-Review* has endured major cutbacks since the advent of the new millennium. From a one-time peak circulation of around 169,000 on Sundays in the 1960s, it fell to about 88,000 on Sundays in 2012. As a result, newsroom staff fell from more than 160 in the early 1990s to fewer than 100 by 2010.

News Herald   Spokane Valley

Owner: Free Press Publishing
Address: 525 N. Pines Road, Suite B, Spokane, WA, 99206
Phone: 509-924-2440
URL: www.spokanevalleyonline.com (unrestricted)
Established: 1919
Published: Friday

Market: Spokane County
Circulation: 5,174
Publisher: William Ifft, ifft@cheneyfreepress.com
Managing Editor: Mike Huffman, vnh@onemain.com

When the 2000 census was conducted, there was no city of Spokane Valley in Washington. When the 2010 census was conducted, almost 90,000 people were counted in Spokane Valley, a Spokane suburb incorporated in 2004. That made it the state's 10th largest city. And it had moved up two more notches by 2013, putting it within shouting distance of Everett.

Spokane Valley lies east of Spokane, toward the Idaho border. It is spilling out toward Coeur d'Alene, largest city in the Idaho Panhandle.

It has been served since 1919, the World War I era, most of a century before incorporation, by the paid-circulation *News Herald*. It was founded by Irving L. Smith as the *Spokane Valley Herald* and has been known by turns since as *The Valley Herald*, *The Valley News Herald* and, since 2002, the *Spokane Valley News Herald*.

During World War II, it typically consisted of four pages of intensely local news. It was gathered by correspondents from the communities of Veradale, Dishman and Opportunity, which would eventually combine to form Spokane Valley, nearly engulfing the incorporated community of Millwood.

John Vlahovich bought the paper in 1948 and moved into the publisher's chair. Twenty years later, his son, John Jr., joined the staff after earning a degree in journalism at Washington State University. The younger Vlahovich, who remained in journalism until his retirement, and continues to make his home in the area, said the paper was thriving in the 1960s and 70s. He said correspondents sent in reports from Otis Orchards, Greenacres and other points, as the paper's mission was to "cover the entire Valley."

According to a 2010 story by Craig Howard, John's brothers, Mike and Jerry, also worked at the *Herald*. He said Mike covered sports before moving on to the *Spokesman-Review* and Jerry worked on the commercial printing side of the business. By 1992, the paper was suffering severe financial stress. The family responded by selling to local businessman Clark Hager, who promised to keep it afloat.

Hager remained at the helm until 1996, a crucial period in Spokane Valley's march toward cityhood. He told Howard the *Herald* played a critical role, saying, "I don't think incorporation would have happened if we hadn't supported it."

News   **Stanwood/Camano**

Owner: Stanwood Camano Publishing, with Pioneer News Group
Address: 9005 271st St. NW, Stanwood, WA 98292
Phone: 360-629-2155
URL: www.scnews.com (subscription required for full access)
Established: 1905
Published: Tuesday
Market: Northwestern Snohomish County
Circulation: 4,500
Editor & General Manager: Kelly Ruhoff, kruhoff@scnews.com
Deadline: Noon Friday

Stanwood, a city of 6,000 in the northwest corner of Snohomish County, lies just across Davis Slough from Camano Island. Like larger and more heavily populated Whidbey Island to the west, Camano Island is part of Island County. Stanwood was first settled as Centerville in 1866. D.O. Pearson renamed it Stanwood in 1877, adopting his wife's maiden name. It lies at the mouth of the Stillaguamish River. It used to have a satellite settlement called East Stanwood, but absorbed it in 1922. A little over 13,000 people were counted on the large but lightly settled island immediately to the west in the 2010 census. They are dispersed, as Camano claims no there is no incorporated community.

Local newspapers began with founding of the weekly *Stanwood Tidings* in 1905. It became the *Stanwood News* in 1920, *Twin City News* in 1930, *Stanwood News* again in 1961 and *Stanwood/Camano News* in 1980. David W. Pinkham purchased the paper in 1985 and spent the next quarter of a century serving as its editor and publisher. He still holds a majority interest, through Stanwood Camano Publishing LLC. However, he sold a minority interest to the Pioneer News Group upon his retirement in 2009. Skagit Publishing LLC, privately held by members of the Wood family, has come to hold a majority interest in Seattle-based *Pioneer*. It exercises direct management control over all of Pioneer's Washington papers except Ellensburg, and has agreed to provide like services for the *News*, with Pinkham as a silent partner.

With the change in management came a change in printing. The *News* is now printed by Skagit at a large new plant it has opened in Mount Vernon to serve the daily *Skagit Valley Herald.* Skagit also prints the *Pioneer* weeklies serving Anacortes, Burlington and Sedro-Woolley there, along with the the daily *Bellingham Herald* and other contract clients.

Skamania County Pioneer   **Stevenson**

Owner: DeVaul Publishing
Address: 198 S.W. Second St., Stevenson, WA 98648
Phone: 509-427-8444
URL: Has not established a website, but maintains an active and extensive Facebook presence at www.facebook.com/pages/Skamania-County-Pioneer/106997649336776
Established: 1892
Published: Wednesday
Market: Skamania County
Circulation: 2,600
Co-Publishers: Frank and Judy DeVaul, fdevaul@devaulpublishing.com
News Editor: Joanna Grammon, scpioneer@gorge.net

The city of Stevenson, population 1,500, has only had one newspaper in a history extending back more than a century. The county of Skamania, population 11,000, has only had one newspaper in a history extending back more than a century and a half. In both cases, that would be the Skamania County Pioneer. It was founded in Stevenson, Skamania County's seat of government and largest city, in 1892.

The county ranks 39th out of Washington's 44 in population. It features a populations density of less than 7 per acre, a median age over 40 and a diversity index of barely 20. King county features a population of almost 2 million and a population density approaching 1,000 per acre. Its median age is 37 and its diversity index tops 40. There are counties in the state with median ages in the 20s and diversity indexes topping 50. That makes Skamania something of a throwback.

What Skamania does have is a set of the state's most prominent natural and man-made features, including the mighty Columbia River, the massive Bonneville Dam, volcanic Mount St. Helens. The dominant industry used to be logging. Today, it is tourism. Unfortunately, that's not sufficient to support the population, so more than half the county's residents commute to jobs in neighboring counties, including Oregon counties on the other side of the river.

Stevenson, so small it ranks second in local population to the unincorporated community of Carson River Valley, is named for a family that came to the Columbia River Gorge from Missouri in the late 1800s. Family patriarch George Stevenson purchased the townsite in 1893 for $24,000 – a princely sum at the time. It became the county seat that very first year, after someone spirited the county records out of Cascades, but didn't incorporate until 1907.

Eight of Washington's 97 general-circulation newspapers lack websites, and the Pioneer is one of them. However, it partially compensates by maintaining a very active presence on Facebook.

The paper was founded in 1892 as the *Skamania County Pioneer* and has published continuously under that name since. The lack of competitors, mergers or changes in frequency, cycle or name is unique in Northwest journalism. It is particularly remarkable for a paper past the century mark.

The paper is owned by DeVaul Publishing of Chehalis. It is headed by Frank DeVaul Jr., a native of Eugene, Oregon, but long-time resident of Chehalis.

The 25-year-old company, held in partnership with his wife, Judy, also owns the *East County Journal* in Morton, *Independent* in Tenino and *Sun News* in Rochester.

Daily Sun News   **Sunnyside**

Owner: Eagle Newspapers
Address: 600 S. Sixth St., Sunnyside, WA 98944
Phone: 509-837-4500
URL: www.dailysunnews.com (unrestricted)
Established: 1901
Published: Monday through Friday AM
Market: Eastern Yakima and western Benton counties
Circulation: 3,887
Publisher: Tim Graff, tgraff@eaglenewspapers.com

Lying midway between Yakima and the Tri-Cities on Interstate 82, Sunnyside seems an unlikely home for a daily newspaper, particularly given its relatively modest population of 15,000. Sunnyside falls within the overlapping circulation and coverage areas of the well-established dailies serving those larger population centers, to the point where both of them maintain full-fledged bureau operations there.

But Sunnyside has its own distinct character.

Minnesota entrepreneur Walter Granger founded the community in 1893 in conjunction with the Yakima Land and Canal Company's Sunnyside Canal Project, designed to bring in irrigation water from the Yakima River and ensure prosperity for all. Then the Panic of 1893 sapped all the momentum of both town and canal development and Granger's canal company went into foreclosure. Sunnyside appeared headed toward the 300-resident threshold required for incorporation earlier in the year. By year's end, it was back down to a mere handful of families.

Around that time, a group of German Baptist Progressive Brethren known as the Dunkards were on the move from South Dakota. Looking for a likely site for a Christian Cooperative Colony, they bought the townsite around 1900 and began moving in. They immediately took steps to ban drinking, dancing and gambling – three of the more popular pursuits in frontier towns of the day.

On the plus side, the Dunkards founded a bank, developed a phone system, erected the largest church in Yakima County and put Sunnyside back on the path to incorporation. When the population hit 314 in 1902, the colony's adult males voted 42 to 1 in favor of making Sunnyside a full-fledged city.

The *Sunnyside Sun* was founded in 1901, just as the Dunkards began arriving en masse. It has only had two competitors in all the years since, the *Sunnyside Times*, founded in 1915 and the *Sunnyside Daily News*, founded around 1962. The *Sun* was a weekly, as was the *Times*, which it absorbed in 1962. And it might have stayed that way had it not been scooped up in 1984 by Oregon's expansion-minded Eagle Newspapers chain.

Two years later, Eagle bought the *Daily News* from Sunnyside native Tom Lanctot, merged the two to create the *Daily Sun News*, and installed Lanctot as publisher. Lanctot, then just 39, went on to become executive vice president of Eagle in 2001. He has since become president and chief executive officer, so the company got a lot of bang for its buck with that acquisition.

News Tribune   Tacoma

Owner: McClatchy Company
Address: 1950 South State St., Tacoma, WA 98405
Phone: 253-597-8742
URL: www.thenewstribune.com (unrestricted)
Established: 1883
Published: Monday through Sunday AM
Market: Puget Sound from base in Pierce County
Circulation: 73,557 weekday, 68,200 Saturday, 102,080 Sunday (ABC)
Publisher: David Zeeck, david.zeeck@thenewstribune.com
Executive Editor: Karen Peterson, karen.peterson@thenewstribune.com

The so-called City of Destiny – it earned that moniker by being chosen as the western terminus of the Northern Pacific Railroad – was a close competitor to Seattle for much of the second half of the nineteenth century. They were rivals for social and political dominance as well as residential, commercial and industrial dominance. The events that finally solidified Seattle's role as Washington's leading urban center were the Alaskan and Yukon gold rushes of the late 1890s. Seattle became the main launch point for the northern exodus, and Tacoma, lying 30 miles to the southwest on Commencement Bay, could never catch up.

The fortunes of Washington's two most populous counties – King and Pierce – mirror those of the cities serving as their seats of government. Seattle's King surged ahead around 1900 and was never again seriously challenged.

There are more than 80 listings in Washington State Library records for Tacoma newspapers, but the three main lines merging into one another to create the *News Tribune* are the only ones that ever made a serious and lasting mark.

Tacoma's first newspapers were the *Daily Pacific Tribune*, which debuted on August 9, 1873, and *Weekly Pacific Tribune*, which debuted the following week. The weekly version was founded in Olympia in 1852 as the *Columbian*. It went through a series of name changes before coming under the ownership of Charles Prosch & Sons in 1864. The family partnership went on to launch the daily version, also in Olympia, three years later. One of the sons, Thomas W. Prosch, took them first to Tacoma, then to Seattle. The daily lasted less than a year in Tacoma and the weekly barely two. They fared little better in Seattle, the daily succumbing in 1878 and the weekly in 1879.

That was but a false start. The real start, the lasting one for Tacoma, came with the 1880 launch of R.R. Radebaugh's *Tacoma Ledger* and 1881 launch of H.C. Patrick's *The News*. They were both founded as weeklies, but were both taken daily in 1883, becoming the *Tacoma Daily Ledger* and *Daily Tacoma News*, respectively.

The *News* would not end up absorbing the *Ledger* until 1937, by which time it had already absorbed the *Tribune* to become the *News Tribune*. However, they first came under joint ownership back in 1898, when S.A. Perkins bought out Radebaugh and Patrick.

Radebaugh entered the market again in 1908 with the founding of the *Tacoma Daily Tribune*, but took his exit again four years later with its sale to Frank S. and Elbert H. Baker. The Bakers purchased the *News* and *Ledger* as well in 1918. They continued to operate the *Ledger* as a separate entity for almost 20 more years, but merged the *News* and *Tribune* to create the *News Tribune*. The paper went by the *Tacoma News Tribune*, *News Tribune & Sunday Ledger* and *Morning News Tribune* at various points before becoming simply the *News Tribune* again in 1993.

It was acquired by the McClatchy Company, a newspaper chain based in Sacramento, in 1986. McClatchy took the paper AM in 1987, introducing its *Morning News Tribune* phase.

The *News Tribune* office and production facilities occupy more than 250,000 square feet on a hill in the Tribune Business Park. Expanded and remodeled in 1997, the building overlooks downtown Tacoma from a vantage point in the city's South End neighborhood.

The News Tribune was also a major player at one time in Tacoma's broadcast market. The paper launched KTNT-Radio in 1948 and KTNT-TV in 1953, when broadcast television was still in its infancy. The radio station went on to become KIRO and the TV station KSTW.

It has become one of the big four in Washington newspapering, taking its place alongside the Seattle *Times*, Spokane *Spokesman-Review* and Vancouver *Columbian*.

McClatchy also owns the Tri-City Herald, Puyallup Herald and Peninsula Gateway in Washington, in addition to papers in Alaska, California, Minnesota, North Carolina and South Carolina. It publishes 32 dailies in 30 different markets in all, plus scores of weeklies.

Weekly   **Tacoma**

Owner: Pierce County Community Newspaper Group
Address: 2588 Pacific Highway E, Tacoma, WA 98424
Phone: 253-759-5773
URL: www.tacomaweekly.com (unrestricted)
Established: 1987
Published: Thursday
Market: Tacoma and vicinity
Circulation: 35,000
Publisher: John Weymer, jweymer@tacomaweekly.com
Managing Editor: Matt Nagle, mnagle@tacomaweekly.com

The *Tacoma Weekly* began life as the *Tacoma Monthly* in 1987. It acquired its current name seven years later, when it adopted a weekly publication cycle. It has been owned and operated from the outset by the Pierce County Community Newspaper Group, which also publishes the *Fife Free Press*, *Milton-Edgewood Signal* and *Puyallup Tribal News*.

The *Weekly* is mailed to homes and businesses in the greater Tacoma area, and distributed through stores and racks, at no charge. It is also available via paid subscription at $52 a year.

In 2001, it underwent the second biggest change in its more than 25-year-history, rivaling its switch from monthly to weekly in 1994. It converted from a tabloid format, strongly associated with free-distribution alternative weeklies, to a broadsheet format, more commonly associated with traditional community newspapers.

In fact, the *Weekly* has always combined elements of both. While it has a pronounced emphasis on politics, entertainment and the arts, a staple of alternatives, it also features a robust sports section and a rich menu of community news, reaching down to the neighborhood level. It would never be mistaken for *Seattle Weekly*, let along the *Seattle Stranger*. In Oregon terms, think *Portland Tribune*, not *Willamette Week*.

The Community Newspaper Group, headed by John Weymer, launched the *Fife Free Press* as a free-distribution twice-monthly in August 2003. The following year, it launched the *Milton-Edgewood Signal* on the same basis.

In a statement posted on each of its newspaper websites, the company says: "Our emphasis is on events that impact the lives of our readers – action taken by local governments, how local high school sports teams are faring, what's happening on local stages and where to go when readers have free time to enjoy."

In the statement, the company goes on to suggest additional community publishing ventures, saying: "As we grow, we look forward to becoming an even greater and more important resource for area residents. Other cities in Pierce County have the potential to support local newspapers, and we will keep this in mind as we make decisions on future expansion of our business."

Printing shop at the Tenino News, about 1900. (photo/Washington State Historical Society)

Independent & Sun News   Tenino/Rochester

Owner: DeVaul Publishing
Address: 297 Sussex Ave. W, Tenino, WA 98589
Phone: 360-264-2500
URL: No web presence

Established: 1922
Published: Wednesday
Market: Tenino and Rochester in southern Thurston County
Circulation: 1,300
Publisher: Frank DeVaul, fdevaul@devaulpublishing.com
Editor: Dan Fisher, unlisted

To say Thurston County pre-dates Washington's achievement of statehood would be an understatement. It actually pre-dates Washington's achievement of territorial status. Thurston was carved out of Lewis County by the Oregon Territorial Government in 1852, when its reign extended all the way north to Canada. Later the same year, King, Pierce, Island and Jefferson counties were split off from Thurston.

The county's largest city and seat of government is Olympia, which survived spirited challenges to also become Washington's state capital. Tenino, population 1,700, lies down in the lightly populated southern part of the county, on the other side of the Interstate 5 freeway from Rochester, population 1,850. Tenino's first settlers began to arrive in the 1850s and 1860s. They called in Coal Bank after a local coal outcrop, but Tenino later came into use, and the Northern Pacific formally adopted that name when it laid tracks through town in 1872 and established a station there. Tenino was a rich source of sandstone in its early years. Store from local quarries was used to build the state Capitol in Olympia, the Pittock Mansion and Pioneer Courthouse in Portland, and various courthouses, churches, college halls and post offices around the Northwest.

Rochester, named after Rochester, Minnesota, was founded in 1852 by Samuel James. It's economy revolved around timber until the timber ran out. Then the big local cash crop became strawberries.

The two towns now serve to a large extent as bedroom communities for the Olympia metropolitan area to the north.

Local newspapering began with the 1904 founding of *The Tenino News* by J.E. Zenner. M. McDonald followed in 1915 with *The Tenino Journal*, but it ran its course in three years.

G.E. Parks launched *The Tenino Independent* in 1922 and managed to drive the *News* under within two years, claiming the field for himself. The paper morphed into the *Thurston County Independent* in 1928, and continued under that name under 1968. Then it became *The Tenino Independent* again.

Rochester had no newspaper it could call its own until the *Independent* began distributing a Rochester edition as the *Rochester Sun News* in 1995. The *Independent's* staff produces that edition from its offices in Tenino.

Both the *Independent* and *Sun News* editions sell for 50 cents on newsstands – a bargain in today's world, where the Penny Press of yore has given way to the Dollar Press.

The operation is owned by the privately held DeVaul Publishing, based in Chehalis. Frank DeVaul Jr. heads the company and serves as publisher of its four papers – the *East County Journal* in Morton, the *Skamania County Pioneer* in Stevenson, *The Independent* in Tenino and the *Sun News* in Rochester.Only the East County Journal has a website, and it features no news, but is limited to a snippet of basic contact information.

DeVaul began his newspaper career delivering the *Spokane Spokesman-Review* at 5 a.m. He went on to earn a bachelor's degree in journalism at Iowa State University and go on to serve as the managing editor *The New Sharon Star* in Sharon, Iowa.

Returning to Washington, he worked for the *Newport Miner* and then the *Columbia Basin Herald* – where he met his future wife and business partner, Judy – before beginning to build his own company.

Review-Independent   **Toppenish**

Owner: Yakima Valley Publishing
Address: 218 W. First St., Toppenish, WA 98948
Phone: 509-314-6400
URL: http://www.reviewindependent.com (unrestricted but limited; still under construction)
Established: 1905
Published: Wednesday
Market: Southeastern Yakima County, Lower Yakima Valley
Circulation: 2,000
Publisher: Mike Lindsey, mike@yvnewspapers.com

Toppenish, a city of 9,000, lies just off Interstate 82 in southern Yakima County, about 20 miles southeast of the county seat and principal population center of Yakima. It was created on land ceded by the Yakama Nation in the Treaty of 1855, but remains wholly within current reservation boundaries. In fact, the reservation accounts for more than one-third of Yakima County's overall acreage. The first 40 acres of the townsite was platted by Josephine Bowser Lillie, whose half-Indian heritage earned her an 80-acre allotment. She is known to history as the "Mother of Toppenish." The settlement didn't get its first Anglo residents until the Northern Pacific ran a rail line through in 1883. Incorporated in 1907, it takes its name from Sahaptin word for "protrude" or "stick out," apparently referencing an old landslide feature.

Wapato, a city of 5,000 lying just up the highway to the northwest, was founded in 1885 as a rail stop. Platted by postmaster Alexander McCredy, it was originally known as Simcoe. The name was changed in 1903 to avoid confusion with Fort Simcoe. It incorporated as Wapato in 1908, after it reached the requisite population of 300.

Thanks to the wonders of irrigation, the Yakima Valley has become a huge producer of field and orchard crops. During World War II, those crops were tended largely either by Japanese from nearby internment camps or Germans from a large prisoner of war camp developed midway between the two towns. Afterward, the labor force turned heavily Hispanic and has remained so.

By the time the two communities achieved official city status shortly after the turn of the 20th century, they were already supporting newspapers.

The *Toppenish Review* and *Wapato Independent* both came into being in 1905, according to Washington State Library archives. They published separately in their neighboring communities for almost a century before merging in 2002 to create the *Review-Independent*, based in Toppenish. The *Review-Independent* went under on September 1, 2012. However, Yakima Valley Publishing bought the assets and resumed publication on Nov. 14, 2012.

Founded more than 25 years ago, Yakima Valley Publishing has long produced a pair of specialty publications based in Yakima – the *Yakima Valley Business Times* and the *Central Washington Senior Times*. Circulation of the business publication is limited to Yakima County, but the senior publication also serves neighboring Benton and Franklin counties.

The *Review-Independent* represents the company's first foray into general-circulation community newspaper publishing. As of July 2013, its website was still under construction.

The paper is direct-mailed to households in the two cities at no charge. In addition, it is offered for sale from stands and racks, making it a not-uncommon hybrid of paid and unpaid.

Methow Valley News   Twisp

Owner: Don Nelson
Address: 101 N. Glover St., Twisp, WA 98856
Phone: 509-997-7011
URL: www.methowvalleynews.com (unrestricted)
Established: 1903
Published: Wednesday
Market: Methow Valley in southwestern Okanogan County
Circulation: 3,400

Editor, Publisher & Owner: Don Nelson, editor@methowvalleynews.com
Deadline: Noon Monday

Tucked up into the heavily timbered Methow Valley, east of Lake Chelan, Twisp is small and remote even by the standards of Okanogan County. Sitting at the confluence of the Methow and Twisp rivers, virtually surrounded by the Okanogan National Forest, it has about 900 residents on just over 1 square mile. The county claims just over 40,000 residents, disproportionately arrayed around its largest city of Omak, over on Highway 97. Twisp is situated well to the west. It lacks any sort of direct access to the county's main locus of population, let alone the county's long northern border with Canada.

It has managed nonetheless continuously to support a local newspaper since July 10, 1903 – the *Methow Valley News*, currently owned by Don Nelson. The paper proudly proclaims, "Published every Wednesday since 1903."

Twisp has never given birth to any other paper, nor has the *News* ever gone by any other name or published on any other cycle – distinct rarities in Washington journalism.

The paid-distribution *News* recently introduced a website with a distinctly modern look and feel. On July 1, 2013, it got this review from local reader Rita Karro: "I'm impressed. Really like the news online, MVN, even though I subscribe and will continue to read it on hard copy. Thank you."

Columbian   Vancouver

Owner: Columbian Publishing Company
Address: 701 W. Eighth St., Vancouver, WA 98660
Phone: 360-694-3391
URL: www.columbian.com (unrestricted)
Established: 1890
Published: Monday through Sunday AM
Market: Clark County
Circulation: 45,816 weekday, 28,785 Saturday, 49,778 Sunday (ABC)
Publisher: Scott Campbell, scott.campbell@columbian.com
Editor: Lou Brancaccio, lou.brancaccio@columbian.com

In the effort to distinguish itself from the larger city of the same name on up north of the Canadian border, someone came up with this bit of doggerel: "Vancouver (not B.C.)/Washington (not D.C.)/Clark County (not NV)/by Portland (not ME). But Washington's fourth-largest city has enough history to distinguish it without the extra help.

The location, on the first large flat plain west of the Columbia River Gorge, was inviting for settlement early on. By 1845, an American had claimed much of what is now Vancouver and dubbed it Vancouver City. Some 12 years later, after a brief run as Columbia City, it was formally incorporated as Vancouver. Substantial Army barracks were established, at one point housing Captain Ulysses S. Grant, later the winning general in the Civil War and president of the United States. A substantial port was also developed, making Vancouver an important shipping center.

Early newspaper history is thinner than that of many other cities of the era. Perhaps the shadow cast by *The Oregonian*, ensconced directly across the Columbia River, dampened progress on the Washington side.

The city's first paper was *The Vancouver Register*, a weekly launched in 1865 by S.W. Brown and H.K. Hines. It lasted until 1876, when it fell victim to competition from a rival upstart, *The Vancouver Independent*. The *Independent*, a weekly founded on Sept. 4, 1875, by 27-year-old W. Byron Daniels, continued until 1905. It then merged with the *Chronicle* to form the *Independent Chronicle*. The *Register* was reincarnated by T. Daniels in 1881 as the *Clark County Register*. The same year, the Censor Publishing Co. introduced the oddly named *Pacific Weekly Censor*. The *Censor* only lasted one year, but the *Register* hung on until 1902.

The *Columbian* got its start in October 1890 as the weekly *Vancouver Columbian*. Its owners launched a six-day evening edition in 1908 as *The Daily Vancouver Columbian*, but continued to also publish the weekly version through 1927.

The *Columbian* has only had one daily competition once in its more than century long history, and then only briefly.

The *Clark County Sun*, launched as a weekly from 1907 to 1947, launched a companion daily edition, *The Morning Sun*, in 1935. Failing to dislodge its better established evening competitor, it ceased publication in 1938. The *Sun* continued to publish a weekly edition until 1947. The *Columbian* bought it out that year, but kept its memory alive for the next 10 years by incorporating a *Sun* reference into its flag.

Vancouver also hosted a pair of weeklies in the 1940s and 1950s. The *Clark County Review* debuted in 1948 and died in 1949. The *Clark County News* picked up the cudgel in 1949 and held on until 1959.

The *Columbian* was founded by a local printer named Tom Carolan. He was inspired in part by a desire to offer a Democratic counterbalance to Republican-oriented publishers he felt were dominating the field. But the paper underwent through a series of ownership changes that left it with a Republican orientation, matching that of its much larger morning counterpart on the other side of the river. Those changes culminated in the paper's purchase by Herbert J. Campbell in 1921. The Campbell family, currently headed by Scott Campbell, has remained in ownership and leadership ever since.

The *Columbian* published on a five-day basis for many years, after dispensing with its Saturday edition. It added a Sunday edition in 1972 and restored its Saturday edition in 1999.

Though historically an evening paper, it joined a growing trend by going morning in July 2000. And in 2004, it brought a small sister paper into the fold – the weekly *Camas-Washougal Post-Record*, acquired from Oregon-based Eagle Newspapers.

One of Herbert Campbell's early moves, in 1928, was construction of a new building designed from the ground up to house a newspaper. But when Scott Campbell tried to emulate Herbert in 2006, it blew up so badly it almost took the *Columbian* under. The staff moved into its new quarters in January 2008. Then the housing and mortgage industries crashed, triggering a massive recession for which the newly debt-burdened company was ill-equipped to cope. The hard times forced the *Columbian* to abandon its new digs and return to its old ones. The city eventually took the new building off the paper's hand s and converted it into a city hall.

The *Columbian* was forced into Chapter 11 bankruptcy in May 2009. It re-emerged in February 2010, after restructuring its debt. That had the community holding its collective breath for a time, but the *Columbian* appears to have regained sound footing.

Beachcomber   Vashon–Maury Island

Owner: Sound Publishing
Address: P.O. Box 447, Vashon, WA 98070
Phone: 206-463-9195
URL: www.vashonbeachcomber.com (unrestricted)
Established: 1957
Published: Wednesday
Market: Vashon-Maury Island in western King County
Circulation: 3,736
Publisher: Daralyn Anderson, publisher@vashonbeachcomber.com
Deadline: 4 p.m. Monday

Vashon-Maury Island, as they locals like to call it, or Vashon Island, shorthand commonly used by outsiders, is part of King County. But you would never know it. The island lies just a short ferry hop southwest of Seattle, the state's most populous city and seat of the state's most populous county. But it claims less than 11,000 residents spread across 37 square miles, making it a world all to its own. The island features not a single incorporated concentration of population, so is treated as one big census-designated place or CDP for census purposes. According to Wikipedia, it is 60% larger than New York City's Manhattan Island, but supports only about 60 one-hundredths of a percent of Manhattan's population.

It is flanked by the Kitsap Peninsula on the west, Bainbridge Island on the north, the Seattle-Tacoma Metropolitan Area on the east and Tacoma proper on the south, but isn't connected to any of them by bridge. That has helped preserve its relative isolation, despite multiple ferry connections. Once agricultural in nature, with strawberries serving as the dominant crop, it now serves largely as an affluent bedroom community for the Sound's major cities.

Local journalism got its start with establishment of the *Vashon Island News* in 1907. The *Vashon Island Record* followed in 1916 and the two merged in 1919 to create the *Vashon Island News-Record*.

Another flurry of activity followed in the 1940s and 1950s. In 1948, *Island Views* was launched. However, it failed to gain traction and went out of business the following year. In 1954, the *News-Record* absorbed an upstart rival called the *Island*.

Then it ran headlong into the *Vashon-Maury Island Beachcomber*, launched in 1957 by newsmen Carl Nelson and John VanDevanter. Nelson and VanDevanter were quickly able to achieve dominance in the market. Within a year, they bought the News-Record and absorbed its assets. Jay and Joan Becker purchased the paper in 1975 and ran it for the next 20 years. They then sold to Sound Publishing, the state's largest publisher of community newspapers.

The Beachcomber has reigned supreme on the island for more than 50 years now. Its alliance with Sound, which claims almost 60 titles in Washington, suggests that dominance may be destined to continue for some time.

The Times   **Waitsburg**

Owner: Imbert and Karen Matthee
Address: 139 Main St., Waitsburg, WA 99361
Phone: 509-337-6631
URL: www.waitsburgtimes.com (subscription required for full access)
Established: 1878
Published: Thursday
Market: Portions of Walla Walla and neighboring counties
Circulation: 1,482
Co-Owner & Publisher: Imbert Matthee, publisher@waitsburgtimes.com
Co-Owner & Editor: Karen Matthee, editor@waitsburgtimes.com
Deadline: Noon Tuesday

Waitsburg enjoys a unique distinction. It is the only city still operating under a territorial charter pre-dating Washington's statehood.

It was settled in 1859 by Robert Kennedy. It was named after Sylvester Wait, who opened a mill there in 1864. The community was incorporated on Nov. 25, 1881, some eight years before Oregon was admitted to the union. It claims about 1,250 residents in roughly one square mile.

Waitsburg lies just to the northeast of the much larger Walla Walla, which enjoys the dual distinction of being Walla Walla County's largest city and its seat of government. It lies almost due east of the also much larger Tri-Cities communities of Richland, Kennewick and Pasco, which occupy opposite sides of the Columbia River. The surrounding countryside is heavily agricultural. So like Walla Walla, it serves as a farm supply center.

Benjamin K. Land founded the first newspaper, *The Waitsburg Weekly Times*, on March 11, 1878. C.W. Wheeler bought it in 1883 and renamed it the *Waitsburg Times*. It published under that name until October 15, 1954, when it became simply *The Times*.

Wheeler also made an abortive effort to publish a daily in Waitsburg in 1889, but *The Daily Times* only held out from June 3 to December 28 before succumbing, according to state library records. The community only saw one other newspaper venture of note. J. E. Houtchens published *The Waitsburg Gazette* from 1901 to 1906 before giving it up.

Tom and Anita Baker became only the fifth set of owners in the paper's long history in 1964. After 35 years at the helm, they passed it down to the next generation of Bakers, Loyal and Kathy. Loyal and Kathy Baker ran it for 13 years before selling in 2012 to another husband-and-wife, publisher-and-editor team – Imbert and Karen Matthee.

The couple bought a home in Waitsburg in 2011. They made the move to the dry east-side community in August 2012 from decidedly wetter Bainbridge Island, with an 11-year-old son in tow. Imbert is a former *Seattle Post-Intelligencer* business writer and columnist. Karen is a veteran of the *Everett Herald*, the *Dallas Times-Herald* and a series of magazines, including *Seakayaker* and *Seattle's Child*. She co-founded *Seattle Woman*, a venture in which she remains part-owner and editor at large.

Union-Bulletin

Walla Walla

Owner: Seattle Times Company
Address: 112 S. First Ave., Walla Walla, WA 99362
Phone: 509-525-3300
URL: www.union-bulletin.com (subscription required for full access)
Established: 1869

Published: Monday through Friday PM, Sunday AM
Market: Walla Walla County and portions of neighboring counties
Circulation: 12,921 weekday, 12,241 Sunday (ABC)
Publisher: Rob Blethen, robblethen@wwub.com
Editor: Rick Doyle, rickdoyle@wwub.com

The North West Company, forerunner of the Hudson's Bay Company, established Fort Nez Perce in 1818 to trade with local Native American tribes it lumped under the Nez Perce label. The fort, later known as Fort Walla Walla, formed the nucleus for one of the Northwest earliest significant settlements. Northwest cities were typically welcoming their first settlers in the late 1800s and incorporating in the early 1900s. Walla Walla incorporated on Jan. 1, 1862, by which time it had already become a major hub of transportation, commerce and politics. At one point in the early 1860s, an Idaho gold rush turned Walla Walla into Washington's largest city. When Washington achieved statehood in 1889, Walla Walla was a serious contender for capital status, despite its location in the state's hot, dry and distinctly distant southeastern corner.

In its early decades, it was defined largely by trading posts, religious missions, Army encampments and a major trail nexus. But its economy soon came to be dominated by agriculture, the leading crop being sweet onions, augmented of late by wine grapes.

Newspapering started not long after the town did, with the founding of the weekly *Washington Statesman* by R.R. Rees and N. Northrup in 1861. It was a Democratic newspaper, in keeping with the Democratic tilt of mineworkers, who had turned Walla Walla into a major mining supply center. It underwent a pair of name tweaks before disappearing from the scene in 1906, capping a highly respectable 45-year run.

After the mining boom faded and the Civil War ended, R.M. Smith launched the *Walla Walla Union* in 1869 as a Republican counterweight. J.W. Ragsdale followed with the *Spirit of the West* in 1870, and it morphed into the *Walla Walla Watchman* in 1876.

The *Union* split into two branches. One merged merged with the Journal and Watchman in 1891 to create the *Weekly Union-Journal*, which continued publishing until 1904. The other underwent more than half a dozen name changes on its way to becoming the *Walla Walla Union* in 1911. The *Union* went daily in 1881. It subsequently absorbed the *Evening Statesman*, founded in 1880 as the *Daily Statesman*.

The *Union-Bulletin*'s other main branch boasts an only slightly less torturous history. It began with the founding of the *Evening Bulletin* in 1906. After absorbing the *Saturday Record*, descendant of the *Walla Walla Watchman*, it became the *Walla Walla Bulletin*, then *Walla Walla Daily Bulletin*. That makes the 1934 merger of the *Union* and *Bulletin* an amalgam of *Journal*, *Statesman*, *Spirit*, *Watchman* and *Record* as well.

The trigger for the merger was unusual. The Union fell into financial trouble and turned to William Cowles, owner of the *Spokane Spokesman-Review*, for help. But it wasn't enough, and the paper went into bankruptcy. Cowles foreclosed on the debt and ended up with the paper in 1931. Not wanting to run it himself, he sold it to John G. Kelly, who had come out west from Kansas in 1910 to purchase the *Bulletin*.

The Kelly family finally ended more than six decades of ownership in October 1971 by selling to the Seattle Times Company, in which the Blethen family holds a majority interest. The Times has since used it as something of a farm system for executives interested in rising in Times ranks, including members of the family.

The *Union-Bulletin*'s first new publisher under Times ownership was Frank Blethen, now president of the Seattle Times Company and publisher of the *Times*. Its current publisher is Rob Blethen, a member of the next generation, who took the helm in 2009.

The World   Wenatchee

Owner: World Publishing Co. (Rufus G. Woods and family)
Address: 14 N. Mission St., Wenatchee, WA 98801
Phone: 509-663-5161
URL: www.wenatcheeworld.com (unrestricted, including e-edition)
Established: 1905
Published: Monday through Friday and Sunday AM
Market: North-Central Washington
Circulation: 19,356
Publisher: Rufus G. Woods, rwoods@wenatcheeworld.com
Managing Editor: Cal Fitzsimmons, fitzsimmons@wenatcheeworld.com

Wenatchee, which regards itself as the apple capital of the world, is located in a deep valley at the confluence of the Wenatchee and Columbia rivers. It lies at the base of the Cascade Range's eastern foothills. It is the seat of government for Chelan County. It is also the county's largest city, accounting for about 32,000 of its 72,000 residents. And counting East Wenatchee, lying on the other side of the Columbia in Douglas County, its metro area encompasses 110,000 residents.

"Chelan" is a Native American term for deep water, presumably a reference to 55-mile-long Lake Chelan, which extends down almost 1,500 feet. The city derives its name from the dominant local tribe, the Wenatchi. In 1863, Father Respari founded a mission dedicated to converting members of local tribes to Christianity – specifically, Catholicism, and settlement followed. The city itself was platted in 1888 and incorporated in 1893.

When the Great Northern laid tracks through the area in the late 1880s and early 1890s – it completed its Minneapolis to Seattle line in 1893 – development got a big boost. Early newspapermen took note, leading to the founding of the *Wenatchee Advance* in 1891 and the *Republic* in 1898.

The *Advance*, founded by O.B. Fuller, continued publishing until 1927. The *Republic* had a shorter run, ceasing operations in 1914. The paper that drove them out of business was *The Wenatchee World*, founded on July 3, 1905, as the *Wenatchee Daily World*.

A daily from the outset, as the name suggests, it was the brainchild of a part of businessmen named C.A. Briggs and Nat Ament. However, they only stuck with it for two years before giving way to a pair of twin brothers, Ralph and Rufus Woods. The Woods family, currently headed by another Rufus, Rufus G., continues to own and operate the paper to this day. Its century-plus reign, overseen by Wilfred from 1950 to 1997, when Rufus G. took the helm, is one of the longest in the country.

The journalism practiced by the Woods family took a national scope in the 1930s, when debate arose over plans to build the Grand Coulee Dam and make it the centerpiece of a massive irrigation system. The World was strongly in favor, and its pages were flooded with stories about the proposed development. In fact, according to the newspaper, Rufus Woods himself wrote the paper's first article on the project in 1918.

When the project came to fruition, despite fierce opposition and the onset of the Great Depression, both the community and the newspaper were transformed.

The World was an early practitioner of online journalism and has not been afraid to introduce innovations. In recent years, it has created *Cashmere World* and *Leavenworth World* websites to serve neighboring communities. They are designed to serve partly as hyperlocal news sites and partly as sites designed to foster and promote citizen journalism. Most newspaper sites give readers the opportunity to post comments. Few also give them the opportunity to participate in the newsgathering process.

The paper instituted two other changes in 2011. In May of that year, it launched a joint weekend edition with the *Omak-Okanogan County Chronicle*, a weekly it owns in neighboring Okanogan County. The next month, it discontinued publication of a Saturday print edition.

South Beach Bulletin   Westport

Owner: Stephens Media
Address: P.O. Box 1395, Westport, WA 98595
Phone: 360-268-0736
URL: www.southbeachbulletin.com (unrestricted)
Established: 1993
Published: Thursday
Market: Southwest Grays Harbor County and northwest Pacific
Circulation: 5,400
Editor: Barb Aue, southbeachbulletin@comcast.net

The coastal community of Westport is situated at the tip of pincer sheltering South Bay. It is separated by a narrow opening from Ocean Shores, which occupies the tip of a like pincer to the north sheltering the somewhat larger North Bay. The two bays, called the Twin Bays locally, open into Grays Harbor. At the back of the harbor to the east, at the mouth of the Chehalis River, lies Aberdeen – largest city in Grays Harbor County. Grays Harbor was discovered by Boston fur trader Robert Gray on May 7, 1792. He dubbed it Bullfinch Harbor, but mapmakers opted for Grays Harbor instead.

Westport's first permanent settler was Thomas Barker Speake, who arrived with his family in 1857. The Army built Fort Chehalis, now home to a Coast Guard station, on the point's northernmost tip in 1860. Early on, the settlement was known variously as Fort Chehalis, Chehalis City and Peterson's Point. Lightly populated, it didn't incorporate as a city until 1914.

The first paper to serve South Beach, as the southern peninsula is known, was the *South Beach News-Review*. It published at Grayland from 1947 to 1953. *The Twin Harbors Press*, founded in Westport by Tom and Ilse Turnbull, former publishers of a weekly in Portola, California, followed in 1961. The state library only has copies through 1974, but other references suggest it published into the early 1980s.

From that point, South Beach went without a paper of its own until Barb Aue launched the *South Beach Bulletin* in Westport in 1993. It serves Westport, Grayland, North Cove, Tokeland, Ocosta and Markham. The paper is delivered each Thursday afternoon to more than 100 drops along an 18-mile stretch of ocean beachfront stretching down into Pacific County.

It is offered for pickup free of charge, but home delivery by mail requires a subscription. Subscriptions run $31 a year in the paper's two home counties and $46 a year outside.

While Aue continues to run the paper, she has sold her ownership interest to Stephens Media, publisher of the *Las Vegas Review-Journal*, 10 other dailies and 64 weeklies, owns Westport's South Beach Bulletin.

In August 2012, Stephens shifted printing of its Washington papers from *The Daily World* plant in Aberdeen to a plant in Centralia operated by the *Centralia Chronicle*'s Chronicle Printing Division. The company cited aging press equipment as a key consideration in making the move.

West Seattle Herald
White Center News   West Seattle

Owner: Robinson Newspapers
Address: 14006 First Ave. S, Suite B, Burien, WA 98168
Phone: 206-708-1378
URL: www.westseattleherald.com (unrestricted)
Established: 1923
Published: Wednesday
Market: West Seattle in King County
Circulation: 9,500
Publisher: Jerry Robinson, jerryr@robinsonnews.com (joint with Ballard, Burien)
Managing Editor: Ken Robinson, kenr@robinsonnews.com (joint with Ballard)
Deadline: Noon Monday

Captain George Vancouver first explored Puget Sound, dropping anchor between Bainbridge and Blake islands on May 19, 1792, in the British naval sloop Discovery. He dispatched Lieutenant Peter Puget and Master Joseph Whidbey to conduct a detailed survey of the lands and waters to the immediate south. However, the first permanent settlers didn't arrive until September 25, 1851, when the Denny Party entered the mouth of the Duwamish River with Captain Robert Fay and set up camp in what is now West Seattle. After conferred with Chief Seattle, they established homesteads three days later at Alki Point, site today of Seattle's most popular saltwater beach.

Though the ensuing flow of settlers largely chose to go on across Elliott Bay and establish claims in what is now downtown Seattle, West Seattle, the section lying west of the Duwamish River, encompasses two of the city's oldest, most historic districts in Delridge and Southwest.

West Seattle incorporated as a city in its own right in 1902. However, its independence was short-lived, as it was annexed by Seattle in 1907. White Center, the community lying immediately to the south, never underwent either incorporation or annexation. Encompassing about 14,000 residents, it remains simply a Census Designated Place.

On south of White Center sits Burien, which finally incorporated in 1993 after many decades as a CDP. The threat from expansion of the

SeaTac International Airport, lying along its eastern flank, had a lot to do with that.

G.S. Robinson established the *White Center News* in 1921, then the *West Seattle Herald* in 1923. The two papers published independently for more than 85 years before undergoing a merger on January 28, 2009 to create the *West Seattle Herald/White Center News*.

The paper is owned by Robinson Newspapers. A family firm, it was founded by Jerry Robinson, no relation to G.S., who began to amass a collection of suburban Seattle weeklies with his acquisition of the *White Center News* in 1952. Robinson added the *Federal Way News* in 1954 and *Highline Times* and *West Seattle Herald* in 1974. He expanded the *Federal Way News* into Des Moines along the way. He sold the papers in 1989, but reacquired them in 1998 after their new owner went under. By then, he had picked up the *Ballard News-Tribune* and *Monroe Monitor*, the latter since sold.

Run today by sons Ken and Tim, with help from sons Patrick and Scott, Robinson Newspapers serves Ballard, Burien, West Seattle, White Center, Highline, Des Moines, SeaTac and Federal Way. Though retired, Jerry continues to write a column carried by all of the family papers.

The *West Seattle Herald/White Center News*, *Ballard News-Tribune* and *Highline Times* are marketed together. New subscribers can get any one of the three delivered by mail for $20 a year.

The Enterprise   White Salmon

Owner: Eagle Newspapers
Address: 220 Jewett Blvd., White Salmon, WA 98672
Phone: 509-493-2112
URL: www.whitesalmonenterprise.com (unrestricted)
Established: 1903
Published: Thursday
Market: Southwestern Klickitat County
Circulation: 2,450
Associate Publisher: Elaine Bakke, ebakke@eaglenewspapers.com
Editor: Sverre Bakke, sbakke@eaglenewspapers.com
Deadline: Monday

White Salmon lies directly across the Columbia River from Hood River in the scenic Columbia River Gorge, which enjoys protection via a bi-state compact. It is accessible from its larger Oregon sister community by bridge. The Oregon side of the river is considerably more populated in that part of the Gorge, with The Dalles, which supports a daily, lying just a few miles on downstream; these communities are in effect a neighborhood. White Salmon was settled in 1852 by Erastus Joslyn, but not incorporated until 1907, some 55 years later. It claimed just under 2,200 residents in the 2010 census.

White Salmon is one of five cities in Klickitat County, the largest being Goldendale, which serves as county seat (and which also has its own newspaper). They are all relatively small, as the county only boasts 20,000 residents all told. Klickitat was sliced from Walla Walla in 1859. Its leading promoter was Samuel Hill, who built the the Maryhill Stonehenge and the mansion destined to become the Maryhill Museum of Art.

Despite the county's rural, lightly populated nature, it has hosted newspapers in Bickleton (the *News*), Mabton (the *Press*), Bingen (the *News* and *Sun*) and Roosevelt (the *Record*), in addition to White Salmon (the *Enterprise*) and Goldendale (the *Sentinel*, *Independent*, *Agriculturalist* and *News*).

Local newspapering got its start with the founding of the *White Salem Enterprise* by A. Meresse in 1903. The paper continued under that name until 1941, when it became simply *The Enterprise*.

The *West Klickitat News* was founded in Bingen in January 1936. Eleven months later, it morphed into the *Mt. Adams Sun* and relocated to White Salmon. It remained in the field until 1968, when it was absorbed by *The Enterprise*.

Eagle Newspapers, a regional newspaper group previously limited to Oregon, jumped the river to acquire the *White Salmon Enterprise* and *Goldendale Sentinel* in 1974. Eagle already owned the weekly *Hood River News*, positioned just across the river, and the tight geographical concentration had a lot of attraction. It has since sold the *Sentinel*, but acquired two other Columbia River papers – *The Dalles Chronicle* on the Oregon side and *Sunnyside Sun* on the Washington side, both small dailies.

The *Enterprise* engages in joint projects with its two Oregon neighbors from time to time, including an annual directory of Gorge healthcare providers.

The Register   Wilbur

Owner: Frank and Kristine Stedman
Address: 110 S.E. Main St., Wilbur, WA 99185
Phone: 509-647-5551
URL: No online presence
Established: 1889
Published: Thursday
Market: Northwestern Lincoln County
Circulation: 1,400
Editor & Publisher: Frank Stedman, wilburregister.@centurytel.net

Wilbur, population 884 in the 2010 census, is located in Lincoln County, population 10,570 in the 2010 census. The county features only eight communities all told, the largest being the county seat of Davenport and the next largest the farm town of Odessa. In 1883, the year Lincoln County was carved out of Whitman, it featured no settlement west of Davenport. And Davenport lies up toward its northeastern corner. Even today, the county is longer on wheat than people.

When the Central Washington Railroad proposed to run a line through the area in 1889, Samuel Wilbur Condin, owner and operator of Wild Goose Bill's Ranch, saw an opportunity. He quickly set about platting a town incorporating his middle name. For a site, he picked a former lakebed bisected by Goose Creek. The ranch was a longtime stage stop, and Condin succeeded in securing a post office. That soon led to development of a hotel, bank and mill.

A series of failed incorporation attempts gave way to a successful one in August 1890. The Panic of 1893 produced a run of lean years, but a record wheat harvest in 1897 pumped more than $1 million into the local economy. Smelling the sweet scent of returning prosperity, H.J. Hubler founded *The Wilbur Register* on April 20, 1889. The only paper ever to serve Wilbur, it has come out every Thursday since.

Every one of the county's eight communities has hosted a newspaper at some point. Three remain – those serving Wilbur, Davenport and Odessa. Their counterparts in Almira, Creston, Harrington, Reardan and Sprague are long gone.

State records show the *Register* as owned by Frank and Kristine Stedman, now in their 70s, since 1986. It has no online presence.

Herald-Republic   Yakima

Owner: Seattle Times Company
Address: 114 N. Fourth St., Yakima, WA 98901
Phone: 509-248-1251
URL: www.yakimaherald.com (unrestricted)
Established: 1903
Published: Monday through Sunday AM
Market: Yakima, Kittitas and Klickitat counties, plus northwestern Benton County
Circulation: 28,003 weekday, 30,738 Sunday (ABC)
Publisher: Sharon Prill, sprill@yakimaherald.com
Editor: Bob Crider, bcrider@yakimaherald.com

When Captain Meriwether Lewis and Lieutenant William Clark traveled up the Yakima Valley, during their Corps of Discovery expedition of 1804-05, they logged reports in their journals of rich soil and abundant game. And those reports were widely circulated in the press of the day upon their return. The Yakama people, who already occupied the valley, also thought highly of it, of course. And were not uniformly welcoming to settlers of European descent. That eventually triggered the Yakima War, which was put down by the Army. The natives were forced onto a reservation, and the Army established Fort Simcoe to make sure they stayed put. So it was open season on immigration, and the choicest spot was platted as the townsite of Yakima.

When the Northern Pacific bypassed the fledgling town in 1884, townsfolk took matters into their own hands. Unable to move the tracks, they moved the town. They lifted more than 100 buildings onto rollers and hauled them to a new trackside location by horse team, leaving only remnants behind. The new settlement was incorporated and designated the county seat in 1886 as North Yakima, a name it retained until 1918. When the new settlement reverted to Yakima, the old one adopted the name Union Gap. (It would later provide part of the name for the rock group Gary Puckett and the Union Gap.)

Today, the city accounts for more than 90,000 of the county's quarter of a million residents. Its suburbs account for a good share of the rest, as the Yakama Indian Reservation covers more than 35 percent of the county and the rest is largely in farm use. Yakima County produces 75 percent of the nation's hops. Hop production is so concentrated here that a warehouse fire in Yakima destroyed 4% of the nation's entire crop in 2006.

The city's first newspapers were *The Yakima Republic* and the *Yakima Record*, a pair of weeklies founded in 1879. The *Record* burned out in 1884, but the *Republic* continued until 1919. Next came two more weeklies, the *Yakima Signal*, published from 1883 to 1888, and *The Yakima Herald*, published from 1889 to 1914. They were followed in 1897 by *The Weekly Epigram*, which transformed itself into the *Democrat* and then the *Independent* before succumbing in 1939.

But the daily *Herald-Republic* traces its heritage back to a pair of dailies, *The Daily Yakima Republic*, which debuted on Oct. 12, 1903, and the Yakima Daily Herald, which launched somewhere in the 1903-04 range.

The Republic published for all of three days before tweaking the elements of its name to become *The Yakima Daily Republic*. The *Herald* played a round of the name game itself in 1905, becoming the *Yakima*

Morning Herald. And it remained that way until 1968, when the rivals of 65 years joined forces to create the *Yakima Herald-Republic.*

The Robertson family owned the paper until 1972, when it sold to the national Harte-Hanks chain. Harte-Hanks, which owned 29 dailies and 68 weeklies at the time, sold it to an arm of William Dean Singleton's MediaNews Group in 1986. MediaNews, which publishes 56 dailies with more than 2.5 million in total circulation, sold it to the Seattle Times Company 1991.

In addition to the *Seattle Times,* the company owns the *Walla Walla Union-Bulletin* in Washington's southeastern corner. The company has been using both of the smaller dailies as training grounds for future Times executives, particularly members of the Blethen family, which owns a controlling stake.

Nisqually Valley News   Yelm

Owner: Lafromboise Communications
Address: 106 Plaza Drive N.E., Yelm, WA 98597
Phone: 360-458-2681
URL: www.nisquallyvalleyonline.com (unrestricted)
Established: 1922
Published: Friday
Market: Communities of eastern Thurston County
Circulation: 4,300
Editor & Publisher: Michael Wagar, mwagar@yelmonline.com

Thurston County, anchored by Olympia, still claims more than a quarter of a million residents. But you'd never divine that from the vantage point of Yelm, tucked up into a bulge on the county's far eastern fringe, in the Nisqually Valley. It was one of the fastest growing cities in the state between 2000 and 2010, and still logged less than 7,000 residents in the 2010 census.

Yelm is Salish for "heat waves from the sun," a reference to heat mirages, according to an account published in Wikipedia. In occupies the Yelm Prairie, originally used by members of the Nisqually tribe pasture their horses. The first European settlers came in 1853 to assist with a Hudson Bay Company sheep operation. But settlement and accompanying commerce didn't really begin to pick up until the Northern Pacific laid track through the area 20 years later. The economy was built on logging and farming, the latter enhanced greatly with introduction of irrigation in 1916. Yelm soon became a major handling and processing center for beans, cucumbers and berries.

The *Nisqually Valley News* capitalized on the agricultural boom with its launch in February 1922, two years prior to Yelm's incorporation.

The only newspaper ever to serve Yelm, it has published continuously ever since. The paper circulates across a broad expanse of eastern Thursday County, reaching the communities of Rainier, Roy McKenna and Tenino, along with rural areas in between. In addition to serving about 4,300 paid subscribers, the paper mails a Wednesday shopper to another 23,500 households.

The *News* was founded by Elmer Fristoe with the help of a partner he bought out the following year. After passing through a series of hands over the ensuing decades, it was acquired by Centralia-based Lafromboise Communications on January 1, 1994.

The Lafromboise family got its start with newspapers in Bellevue and Enumclaw. It went on to acquire papers in Ellensburg, Aberdeen, Centralia and Redding, Calif. Richard Lafromboise, a member of the second generation, ran the company until his premature death in 1968. Then his wife, Jeraldine "Jeri" Loomis Lafromboise, took over. Jeri Lafromboise sold all of the dailies except the *Centralia Chronicle*. She also sold the weeklies over time, but acquired two others – the *Battle Ground Reflector* and the *Nisqually Valley News*.

She retired in 2011 and died the following year at the age of 79. The company is now being headed by a daughter, Jenifer Lafromboise Falcon, who was born shortly after her father's death.

Tomorrow's editions

Radio didn't make a dent in the newspaper industry. Television put some pressure on evening newspaper editions, but the print industry roared along regardless.

The Internet has been a different story, and its immense impact has thrown the newspaper industry for a loop.

Many people, especially outside the industry, point to the web's capability to deliver news essentially immediately, something many newspapers do on their own web sites. In some ways, the Internet has been (or at least can be) a wonderful journalistic tool, allowing for nearly unlimited loading of information and documents – no more limits to "eight column inches" or less for a complex news story – as well as links to other news reports and documents, pictures, artwork, audio and video. More than any other segment of news providers, newspapers have taken advantage of much of the technological assets the Internet allows. And many newspaper web sites get heavy readership traffic; they are hardly ignored by seekers after news.

The downside of the Internet for the industry has been less on the news side than on the advertising side, which is where most newspaper revenue has, over the last century, been concentrated.

Classified advertising, including personals, job announcements, and "for sale" notices, long has been a backbone for newspapers; Craigslist and other online services such as Monster.com for employment have eviscerated the field for newspapers. Auto advertising has traditionally been a big money-maker for newspapers; now, online sites such as cars.com and autotrader.com have eliminated much of that revenue.

Jeff Ackerman of the *Roseburg News-Review* outlined some of the challenges this way:

"There are some obvious land mines on the horizon that will further erode revenues. They include what we call "Legal Notices" and preprints, or inserts.

"Legals represent a good chunk of a typical newspaper's revenues and most state Legislatures are (and have been) considering statutes that would sidestep the requirements to publish them in newspapers. In Oregon, for example, the state bar would love to publish Legal Notices for a lot less than newspapers charge, giving money back in the form of

Legal Defense Funds, etc. For some smaller community papers, the loss of legal revenue would be catastrophic.

"Then there are the grocery inserts. Most supermarket chains would love nothing better than to find a way around printing, transporting and inserting hundreds of thousands of weekly newspaper grocery inserts. They are exploring digital options. Safeway, for example, has its own app. Preprints represent probably 20% of a newspaper's revenues.

"These revenue threats, compounded with the existing digital threats disrupting our business model, require us to diversify our revenue portfolio. Our goal, for example is to be generating 25% of our total revenue from Digital by 2015. We are currently at around 9%, so we have a ways to go."

The earliest papers jumping onto the Internet tended to be small or midsized and owned locally or in small groups, such as the McMinnville (OR) *News-Register* and the Lewiston (ID) *Morning Tribune*. Eventually, nearly all developed web sites – although some holdouts remain – and more recently, many have developed mobile apps as well. A number of them have turned into near wire-services, updating their local news reports regularly even on days when they do not publish.

But they still have had difficulty making money from the web. For many years only a few Northwest newspapers set up paywalls – or subscription requirements – for accessing their web sites' content. (Those early adopters included the dailies at Bend, Lewiston, Idaho Falls, and Spokane). But in the 2010s, a new move has developed toward pay requirements at nearly all daily newspapers, and many weeklies as well.

Papers are embracing paywalls because they have given up on online advertising as a meaningful source of revenue; they have concluded online page-view volume is no longer of any great significance. Papers have tried everything they could, year after year, to hawk online advertising, but with limited success. Volume and rates remain abysmal, as do click-through rates.

Still, newspapers are moving increasingly into the digital world. The Oregonian, perhaps most dramatically, is one of the leaders in that. As of October 2013, it reduced its print newspaper deliveries to four days a week (though smaller editions will continued to be printed and available at racks and stands the other three days). More of its effort will be directed toward online activities.

Oregonian Editor Peter Bhatia described in a column on September 7, 2013, what some of this will look like: "Traditionally, newspaper newsrooms have worked in a fairly factory-like manner. Reporters report, editors edit, photographers make pictures, stories are turned over to copy and design desks for final edits, pages are built and headlines written. It oversimplifies the creative process, but it is a straight throughput, to borrow a term from industry.

"When The Oregonian converts to a digitally focused company Oct. 1, that time-honored process will be no more. Instead, reporters will file straight to OregonLive.com, often from the field, often in relatively small pieces, as stories play out in real time. The emphasis won't be on initially crafting fully formed newspaper stories, but to get the news online as quickly as it can be reported and verified. Editors will still edit, and there will still be plenty of scrutiny of sensitive and complicated reporting, but the news cycle won't be chained to evening deadlines, as it has been for so long."

One of the more out-of-the-box thinkers among Northwest newspaper executives is Roger Plothow, publisher at the Idaho Falls *Post Register*. His paper has looked into everything from abandoning the Associated Press to experimenting with publication days.

He said that weeklies tend to be more profitable, as a percentage of revenue, than the daily papers like the *Post Register*. Many daily newspaper owners who buy weeklies, he said, are buying into successful operations but then change them, especially the local connections and control, that made them successful. (He said the Post Company has avoided doing that.)

"Salmon is not Shelley, and Aberdeen is not Kuna, and they each have different circumstances," he said. While some, for example, ought to have a strong online presence, "I think Salmon [the *Recorder-Herald*] is probably going to be just fine without a website for some time to come."

As for the *Post Register*, "We're profitable, and more people read our newspaper today than 10 years ago, when you combine print and online ... Our reach has never been greater. There is no denying there are two areas where we have been hurt: National advertising is significantly off from our peak days, and classified advertising – you just can't help but be affected ... But the best news probably has been that the bleeding has stopped. Revenues are no longer falling, profits are increasing. I would also add that the days of 28 percent margins will never return."

The effect of the Internet is widely, and debated. Some newspapers (mainly weeklies) have no Internet presence as this is written, and see no reason to go there.

Mark Steele, publisher of the *Caribou County Sun*, took a more traditionalist view. "I think in five years down the road most western rural weeklies will be doing exactly what they are, and have been doing, for the past 100 years – reporting on the important local happenings of their communities. I suspect the hoorah to become something we are not will have subsided and we will understand that we are not the Internet, never will be, and that it is not the threat or savior many thought. It, too, will pass for what it is, like the hysteria in my newspaper career of radio, TV, local cable TV, billboards, and advertising on buses. Certainly the New Wave will be with us, but blaring Yellow Journalism headlines with sensationalist stories will drown in numbers and content and community readers, leaders, and those with intelligent interest within their communities will continue to read newspapers. They are the ones who never left us and are the reason we have existed for the many decades we have.

"Dailies will be more challenged and will have spent millions chasing the illusive maiden called Digital Advertising Dollars, only to find she never really left them to begin – if they were doing their job of providing old-fashioned news and not screaming headlines and sensationalism, all provided with a reduced news staff forced upon them by some bean counter that the group newspaper board believes should be called publisher and who has never covered a city council meeting or wrote about the death of a puppy in his or her entire life. But they will have the latest electronic gadgets. And we in the business of providing news had better start paying attention to those who we are, and should be, mentoring as our replacements in hopes of instilling at least some of the same attributes those old hardline ethical news editors insisted on when we were starting out at college newspapers and on our first real journalism jobs. It is all about hard news and ethics – both of which are becoming as antiquated as the linotype and all of which I have had the pleasure of knowing in my lifetime."

A few miles away, Greg Madison of the *Preston Citizen* said that in the next few years "obviously the Internet will be a huge factor in our day to day operations. It has turned our weekly into a daily for little cost."

In Omak, Washington, *Omak-Okanogan County Chronicle* Publisher Roger Hamack said that "We are in the process of launching a full content management and marketplace system that will allow us to improve our website and develop a much more stable mobile news site. In terms of the marketplace, our new system will provide a new means of advertising revenue for us, essentially allowing our staff to market, create and maintain websites for businesses. We've also been experimenting with selling links into print ads. Those links seem to work very well in our e-edition. Speaking of our e-edition, it was recently upgraded to html 5 and are working on the next generation with our provider. In less than three years, our e-edition has about 400 subscribers."

Where does he expect that to lead? "In five years, I'd expect our weekly newspaper to be more of a 24-hour local news service for Okanogan and Ferry counties. We've already laid the groundwork for

Internet and mobile platforms. And our readership growth here has already led us to increase our main news cycle frequency to a Wednesday full newspaper and Sunday four-page extra, as well as different news stories for the web and mobile platforms. In five years, I'd expect about half of our revenue to be web or mobile based.

"Our future here lies more on the mobile and tablet platforms than it does on the web."

He is not alone in seeing a need to migrate into mobile devices – smartphones, tablets and other devices that come along. The *News-Register* in McMinnville, Oregon, for example, has partnered with an international firm in developing apps that may help move the paper in that direction.

Mike Patrick of the *Coeur d'Alene Press* saw significant growth potential in that area. He said that "our company purchased a WSI franchise (http://www.cdainternetmarketing.com/) several years ago. We were the first newspaper company to do so, and our success at helping businesses build and optimize their websites has given us a very different picture of how we might be operating five years from now. We're making money helping local businesses grow through their websites, and a positive consequence of that is they're looking increasingly for us to boost their marketing through our own print and online products. Five years from now I see us continuing to deliver a robust print edition – we produce more pages daily than does the *Spokesman-Review* – with paid circulation equal to or perhaps slightly less than it is today. On the online side, though, our digital marketing products, including a new multi-state tourism publication, should expand significantly. We do have a paywall now for our e-edition, and five years from now I expect that paid circulation to be much higher than it is today."

Other see a more gradual evolution.

Vicki Gowler, editor at the *Idaho Statesman*, said she didn't envision "significant changes. We have been diversifying more; we're finishing up a book on Boise's 150 Icons and have another one right behind it on gardening using our local columnist Margaret Lauterbach. We have been focusing on digital more: more apps, including tablet apps; more video, more interactivity. The newspaper itself seems to be working pretty well for readers (except they would love for it to be more robust!). Our goal is to stop the world once every 24 hours and help them understand the most important stories that are going on, catch them up on the breaking news we've had online and provide lots of useful information to help them save time and money. Our descriptive words for our website and smart phone apps are breaking news and interactive; our descriptive words for our newspaper and tablet app are depth, watchdog and storytelling."

Where will this leave the paper down the road? "In five years, I think we'll still have a newspaper product; it might be fewer days; it might be more robust (if the economy recovers and the Orange County Register experiment continues to work). I'm not sure of its circulation; I think older readers may continue to migrate to electronic editions online with their bigger type and ease of getting it no matter where they are; although there's a reported uptick in interest in newspapers among younger readers, I really don't see that it will offset the decline. I think we will finally find a smarter, more efficient way of sharing content across newspapers so we can provide more robust content with fewer production people; it will be an outcome of technology advances that we're already seeing in our company.

"I think our digital platforms will be more distinctive, i.e. with content more tailored to take advantage of each platform, and folks will be using multiple ones to get news and information in the best format for them – or for the content. In five years, we will be more visual, we will be using more reader-generated content that has value for all our readers/users (in print, too) and hopefully we will have found a way to re-invigorate our watchdog role."

Still others are looking in other inventive directions. Ken Engelman, co-owner and publisher of the *McKenzie River Reflection* weekly, said that in near term "We're planning on a crowd funding project like Kickstarter or Indiegogo to digitize our complete files from 35 years of newspaper publishing." Further out, he said, "We see a shift into other fields of publishing – using that digitized data to produce both print and ebooks on the history of our region. In addition, we're starting to produce some multi-media and have already located over 300 videos related to our area."

Ackerman of the *News-Review*, looking at some of the options ahead, said "We also hope to generate around $200k from Events (Home and Garden Show, Cooking School, etc.) in 2014. And most papers have gotten a lot more aggressive in what they are charging for their product. My average home delivery subscriber only pays 35 cents or so to have the paper delivered to his door each day. What can you have delivered to your door...in the rain...for 35 cents? The *Orange County Register*, for example, determined that their content is worth $1 per day, no matter how it's delivered (print, digital, etc.). As an industry, newspapers spend roughly $6 *billion* to generate content each year...which is why we can no longer just give it away."

Lyndon Zaitz of the *Keizertimes* (at Keizer, Oregon) suggested that "By 2018 it's anyone's guess as to what percentage of readers will never pick up a newspaper. We will very likely have a fully integrated tech program utilizing all aspects of electronic media. We will be watching Jeff Bezos very closely to see how his millions of dollars will change journalism on a big scale. Our mission will not change: we editorially focus on the city of Keizer (no state, regional, national or international news). Surprisingly, there is enough happening in our city of 40,000 to fill the paper and satisfy most reader's needs."

But the slog ahead will not be easy. Dennis Roler, editor of the *Grants Pass Daily Courier*, said that "We cut back from six editions a week to five in March. We now print Tuesday through Friday and Sunday. We used to print Monday through Saturday. Realistically, I see a good chance we will have to reduce staff in the next five years. We may also have to cut another day off the publication schedule. It's going to depend on where revenues meet expenditures, with a little left over for profit. That's what my cloudy crystal ball says now. I wish I could say things look brighter, but I can't."

But it may be most fitting, in reflecting on how newspapers have evolved over and over again, to wrap up with these words from Deborah Steele Hazen of the small weekly in Clatskanie, Oregon, the *Chief*:

"We do not anticipate any significant changes in our operations within the upcoming months, nor, as far as we can predict at this time, in five years. We just intend to keep on giving accurate and thorough coverage to the communities of Clatskanie and Rainier and the surrounding rural area in Northwest Oregon."

Publishing a newspaper is, in the end, just putting out a brand new product one day at a time.

Washington state newspapers, 100 years ago

This is from the Washington Newspaper periodical list in 1918 of newspapers publishing then in Washington.

Aberdeen New Era VC Evans ed
Aberdeen Grays Harbor Post JW Clark ed
Aberdeen Herald
Aberdeen World W A Rupp
Acme Prospector JW Kelly pub
Almira Outlook Fred A Pier pub
Anacortes American JM Post pub
Anacortes Citizen JO McNary pub
Arlington Times CL Marsh pub
Asotin Sentinel KL Thomson pub
Attalia News Tribune RC Julian pub
Auburn Globe Republican Brown & Leslie
    pubs
Bellingham American Reveille FI Sefrit pub
Bellingham Post
Bellingham Herald WC Carver pub
Bellingham Journal Progressive Arthur V
    Watts pub
Bellingham Journal EC Jones pub
Bellingham Sentinel
Blckelton News WF Fowler pub
Blaine Journal John W Sheets pub
Blaine Press Charles A Payne ed
Bothell Sentinel J C Gregory pub
Bremerton News HD Matthews ed
Bremerton Searchlight WB Jessup pub
Brewster Herald DL Gillespie pub
Bridgeport Republican HC Freeman pub
Buckley Banner
Burlington Journal
Burton Island News Ira H Case pub
Camas Post George W Hopp pub
Cashmere Valley Record JF Corselius pub
Castle Rock Independent
Cathlamet Sun Joseph Girard
Centervllle Times FW Johnson ed
Centralia Hub ME Cue ed
Centralla Chronicle HL Bras
Charleston American Hal Smith pub
Chehalis Bee Nugget Clarence Ellington ed
Chehalis Advocate JP Hurley pub
Chelan News Leader CE Goodsell pub
Cheney Free Press Willis Swank & Sons
    pubs
Chewelah Independent Elmer W Burrows
    pub
Clarkston Republic JC Peterson pub

Cle Elum Echo AA Batterson ed
Colfax Commoner Thomas Brown ed
Colfax Gazette Bramwell Bros pubs
Colville Examiner JC Harrigan pub
Colville Statesman Index AM Doty pub
Concrete Herald Leonard & Webster pubs
Connell Register EG Bonney pub
Cosmopolis Times JE Hutchinson pub
Coulee City Dispatch Stapleton & Brott
    pubs
Coupeville Times WT Howard pub
Creston News D Frank Peffley pub
Davenport Times Tribune Hill & Goodwin
    pubs
Dayton Chronicle RE Peabody
Dayton Dispatch RP Richardson pub
Dayton Courier Press AL Ricardo pub
Deer Park Union Carl S Evans ed
Eatonville Dispatch CC Biggs pub
Edmonds Review Oscar Grace pub
Ellensburg Record JC Kaynor pub
Elma Chronicle Frank Jacobs pub
Endicott Index BM Martin ed
Entiat Times EP Murphy pub
Enumclaw Courier V Van Buskirk ed
Enumclaw Herald George W Hamilton ed
Ephrata Journal
Everett Commonwealth HT Hazard ed
Everett Herald JB Best ed
Everett Labor Journal George Rigglns
Everett Tribune AR Fenwick ed
Everson Valley Home Clyde Reed pub
Fairfield Standard FW Montieth pub
Farmington Independent BEH Manning
    pub
Ferndale Record Ray V Claud
Friday Harbor Journal Frits & Ludwig pubs
Garfield Enterprise JK Buchanan pub
Georgetown Duwamlsh Valley News A
    Schraffenberger pub
Gig Harbor Bay Island News Case & Mohr
    pubs
Goldendale Agriculturalist WJ Story pub
Goldendale Sentinel Irving S Bath pub
Grandview Herald Chapln Foster pub
Granger Enterprise PR Johnson ed
Granite Falls Post John F Davis pub

Guemes Beachcomber Charles L Gant pub
Hlllyard News WW Simpson pub
Hoquiam Record OM Moore pub
Hoquiam Washingtonian HW Patton ed
Harrington Citizen Robert E Gay pub
Ilwaco Tribune
Index News JP Kelley ed RW Wilcox pub
Ione Record
Issaquah Press David Peacock pub
Kalama Bulletin WH Imus pub
Kalama News RH Mitchell ed
Keller Eagle JR Sovereign pub
Kelso Kelsonian GH Umbaugh ed
Kennewick Courier Reporter AR Gardner
ed
Kent Advertiser Journal AA Risedorph pub
Kirkland Journal
Klrkland News Independent William Ulraer
pub
LaConner Mail LB Adams pub
LaCrosse Clipper Ray C Irvine pub
Langley Islander AJ Benton pub
Lamont Union JB Price pub
Leavenworth Echo Mayar & Mayar pubs
Lincoln Herald OU Hawkins pub
Lind Leader JP Simpson pub
Lynden Tribune Sol H Lewis pub
Mabton Chronicle Fowler & Mansfield
News BC Ferguson pub
Maple Falls Leader HJ Strlckfaden pub
Marcus Messenger AD Hill pub
Marysville Globe DC Owen pub
Medical Lake Mirror Willis Swank ed
Milton Eagle Charles F Lake ed
Molson Leader HL Mooney pub
Monroe Independent AW Reardon pub
Monroe Monitor Arthur
Monroe Monrovlan
Montesano Call AE Veach pub
Montesano Vidette Dan Cloud ed
Mt Vernon Argus Fred Ornes pub
Mt Vernon Herald MJ Beaumont pub
Morton Mirror Valen Honeywell pub
Newport Miner Fred Wolfe oub
Nooksack Reporter HE Stuatt pub
North Bend Mall Calvin Goss ed
Northport News Wm P Hughes pub
Oakesdale Tribune BH Manning pub
Oak Harbor News HL Bowmer pub
Oakville Cruiser BE Williams pub
Odessa Record L C Weik pub
Okanogan Independent George Stewart ed
Olvmpla Chronicle MD Abbott pub
Olympla Record FF McKenna pub
Olympia Olympian SL Lester gen mgr
Olympia Standard Eagle Freshwater pub

Omak Chronicle FA DeVos pub
Orovllle Gazette Frank M Dallam pub
Orting Oracle BF Young pub
Palouse Republic Schick & Hetzel pubs
Pasco Herald Sprague & Olson pubs
Pateros Reporter Arthur Dodds pub
Pe Ell Tribune GE Simmons pub
Pomeroy Washingtonian Peter McClung
pub
Port Angeles News Smith & Webster pubs
Port Angeles Herald Arthur V Watts pub
Port Orchard Independent HR
Port Townsend Leader
Poulsbo Herald Peter Iverson
Prescot Spectator Charles H O Neil pub
Prosser Republican Bulletin Walter Tyler
ed
Prosser Independent Record WR Sproull
pub
Pullman Herald Carl P Allen ed
Pullman Tribune Lou E Wenham pub
Puyallup Herald JP Rawson pub
Puyallup Tribune Robt Montgomery pub
Quincy Quill AT Brownlow pub
Raymond Herald JM Tadlock pub
Reardan Gazette RW Safford pub
Renton Courier Hugo Kelly pub
Republic News Miner CE Blair pub
Richland Advocate Perry and Mable
Willoughby pubs
Ridgefleld Reflector AW McCormlck pub
Ritzville Journal Times CA Sprague pub
Riverside Tribune
Rochester Leader RA Perkins ed
Rockford Register WJ Taylor pub
Roslyn Cascade Miner
Rosalia Citizen Journal CA Lynch pub
Seattle Argus HA Chadwick ed
Seattle Union Record EB Ault ed
Seattle Post Intelligencer
Seattle Bulletin CJ David ed
Seattle Ballard Press Robert Farrar ed
Seattle Freemont Colleague Sam Collins ed
Seattle Churchman HH Gowan ed
Seattle Star
Seattle Railway and Marine News Kenneth
Kerr ed
Seattle Green Lake News Norah K Nash ed
Seattle Ballard News Ruffner & Ruftner
Seattle Business Chronicle Edwin Selvln ed
Seattle Times
Seattle Washington Posten
Seattle Rainier Valley Times Harrison W
Mason pub
Seattle North End Herald John H Reid ed
Seattle North End News Sam F Collins ed

Sedro Woolley Courier Frank Evans pub
Sedro Woolley Times Ragsdale & Stowers pubs
Selah Optimist JT Brown pub
Sequim Press Angus Hay pub
Shelton Journal Grant C Angle pub
Skamokawa Eagle SG Williams pub
Snohomish Tribune Stevens & Wilcox pubs
Snoqualmie Post WH Rodman pub
South Bend Journal FA Hazeltlne pub
South Bend Pilot Edwin M Connor pub
Spokane Chronicle
Spokane Spokesman Review
Spokane Press Sprague Advocate EF Hultgrenn pub
Sprlngdale Reformer EW Burrows pub
Stanwood Tidings
Starbuck Standard HG Rowe pub
Stevenson Pioneer JH Ginder pub
St John Advocate Manning & Sutton pubs
Sumas Advocate News AJ Hicks & Son
Sumner News Index CE Andrews & Son pubs
Sunnyside Sun AS Hillyer pub
Sunnyside Times AM Murfln pub
Tacoma News Herald
Tacoma Tribune
Tacoma News Ledger
Tacoma Times
Tenino Journal C Kibbe ed
Tekoa Blade HM Cole ed
Toledo Messenger George A Dew pub
Thornton News Ben Manning pub
Tonasket Times Frank Putnam pub

Toppenlah Review Geo Allen pub
Toppenlsh Tribune Clara C Hutchinson mgr
Twisp News HE Marble ed
Uniontown Press RM Cross pub
Vancouver Columbian George M Hyland ed
Vancouver Sun Edward Curran pub
Vashon Record Robt M Jones pub
Walla Walla Bulletin JG Kelly pub
Waitsburg Times EL Wheeler pub
Wallula News Tribune
Wapato Independent Wm Verran pub
Warden Herald JP Simpson pub
Washougal Times DL McMillan pub
Washtucna Enterprise MB Martin ed
Waterville Empire JM Stoddard pub
Watervllle Press Robert Hamel pub
Wenatchee World Ruf us Woods pub
Wheeler Citizen JP Simpson pub
White Bluffs Spokesman FG Dunnichiff ed
White Salmon Enterprise EJ O Leary pub
Wilbur Register SG Shaw ed
Wilkeson Record
Wilson Creek World JP Taylor pub
Winloek News OL Isbell pub
Winthrop Journal WE Brinkerhoff pub
Withrow Banner WH Murray pub
Yakima Freeman's Farmer
Yakima Herald
Yakima Independent FC Whitney & Son pubs
Yakima Republic WW Robertson pub
Zillah Bulletin
Zillah Free Press George McArthur

STEVE BAGWELL is managing editor of the *News-Register* at McMinnville, Oregon. Previously, he held newsroom positions at the *Bend Bulletin*, the *Salem Statesman Journal*, the *Idaho Statesman* and the *Daily Astorian*. He teaches journalism at Oregon State University and Linfield College. He lives in McMinnville, Oregon.

RANDY STAPILUS worked for daily newspapers, including the *Idaho Statesman*, the *Idaho State Journal* and (what is now) the *Idaho Press Tribune*, for 15 years, and has been a weekly columnist for a number of Northwest newspapers for many years. He is editor and publisher of Ridenbaugh Press, and edits the *Weekly Briefing* e-publications for Washington, Oregon and Idaho. He lives in Carlton, Oregon.

from
RIDENBAUGH PRESS
www.ridenbaughpress.com

A FREE OFFER

Mention your purchase of this book, and we'll send you the next three editions of any of our *Weekly Briefing*s for free.

Just send an email to stapilus@ridenbaugh.com

Order more copies of this book

of **New Editions** directly from the publisher.

You can order from us on our main page at www.ridenbaugh.com

Or, by e-mail at stapilus@ridenbaugh.com

Reach us by phone at (503) 852-0010; or by paper mail at Ridenbaugh Press, P.O. 834, Carlton OR 97111.

IDAHO WEEKLY BRIEFING

OREGON WEEKLY BRIEFING

WASHINGTON WEEKLY BRIEFING

Our weekly e-mailed report, every Monday morning, on the Northwest states and how they are changing. Since 1990.

Name _____

Address _____

City _____ State _____ Zip _____

Email _____

8157230R00174

Made in the USA
San Bernardino, CA
31 January 2014